Regenerative EMF Cells

A symposium co-sponsored by
the Division of Industrial
and Engineering Chemistry and
the Division of Fuel Chemistry
at the 149th Meeting of the
American Chemical Society,
Detroit, Mich., April 8-9, 1965

C. E. Crouthamel and H. L. Recht
Symposium Chairmen

ADVANCES IN CHEMISTRY SERIES **64**

AMERICAN CHEMICAL SOCIETY

WASHINGTON, D.C.   1967

Library of Congress Catalog Card 67–25567

PRINTED IN THE UNITED STATES OF AMERICA

Advances in Chemistry Series

Robert F. Gould, *Editor*

Advisory Board

AMERICAN CHEMICAL SOCIETY PUBLICATIONS

FOREWORD

ADVANCES IN CHEMISTRY SERIES was founded in 1949 by the American Chemical Society as an outlet for symposia and collections of data in special areas of topical interest that could not be accommodated in the Society's journals. It provides a medium for symposia that would otherwise be fragmented, their papers distributed among several journals or not published at all. Papers are refereed critically according to ACS editorial standards and receive the careful attention and processing characteristic of ACS publications. Papers published in ADVANCES IN CHEMISTRY SERIES are original contributions not published elsewhere in whole or major part and include reports of research as well as reviews since symposia may embrace both types of presentation.

CONTENTS

PREFACE

In our highly complex technical world, electricity is by far the most useful and clean form of energy. Yet, we have not been able fully to utilize electrical energy for our varied needs because of limitations in storing and generating it. Now the added spector of mass air pollution is an additional reason to find better ways of storing and generating electrical energy. The spontaneous combustion of coal and petroleum products is the major source of air pollution.

In the regenerative emf systems reviewed in this volume, emphasis is placed on the conversion of heat into electrical energy. These are the thermally regenerative systems. However, there are photochemical, chemical, and electrical regenerative emf systems of great interest. The latter are simply secondary batteries which could be used in electrical propulsion. The emf systems suitable to thermal regeneration are much more restricted in number than systems suitable to electrical regeneration. The bimetallic cells which occupy the largest number of pages in this volume show promise for both thermal and electrical regeneration.

Energy conversion systems which have received the most research and development attention in the past ten years are metal vapor turbines, thermionic diodes, magnetohydrodynamic generators, and thermoelectric devices. By comparison with any one of these four systems, regenerative electrochemical systems have received less support by several orders of magnitude. Nevertheless, conservative estimates of the practical cyclic efficiencies for several bimetallic systems and the lithium hydride system have been made in Chapter 6, and these efficiencies compare favorably with values estimated for the other systems. One outstanding difference exists, however, between the regenerative electrochemical converter and all the other systems—namely, the ability of the former to operate at high power densities in the temperature region below 1500°C. This is potentially an important advantage because a larger number of heat sources are available in this temperature region and also because the problems with materials of construction are markedly reduced.

The regenerative electrochemical converter can be virtually free of mechanical parts and, by comparison with the other systems, the flowing liquids or gases are low velocity streams. Nevertheless, liquid metal-fused salt static and dynamic corrosion data are needed; information in the literature is both poor and limited. In Chapter 10 the survey on corrosion of container materials by the liquid metals, bismuth, lead, and tin, and by fused alkali and alkaline earth fluorides, chlorides, and hydroxides indicates two major problems with this type of data. The first problem is that a great deal of the work was done with impure metals, wet salts, or under poorly controlled experimental conditions, so that the results do not represent the actual situation for clean systems and pure liquid salts or liquid metals. The second problem is that the scope of the data is too limited in many of the systems. This is especially true for the temperature variable; few results above a temperature of about 800°C. are known. Also, relatively few dynamic corrosion data obtained under temperature gradients such as would exist in a cyclic electrochemical converter have been published. Probably the most severe and limiting materials problem in these systems will be caused by mass transport of materials between the two temperature regions.

However, for the systems under study promising materials have been found which are not subject to corrosion in a dynamic system. The recent development of refractory metal vapor deposition techniques opens the door to relatively cheap fabrication of complex components—e.g., heat exchangers and boilers, which can be lined with metals such as tantalum, niobium, and tungsten.

Argonne, Ill.
March, 1967

C. E. CROUTHAMEL

Regenerative Electrochemical Systems: An Introduction

HERMAN A. LIEBHAFSKY

General Electric Research and Development Center, Schenectady, N. Y.

Among the increasingly complex and sophisticated methods of energy conversion needed today, regenerative electrochemical systems occupy an important place. In this introduction, the author attempts to mitigate the confusion that exists in the naming of these systems, to discuss their thermodynamics on the basis of simple examples, and to show that these systems may be regarded as foreshadowed by the work of Grove (1839). If experience with fuel batteries is a valid guide, the development of practical regenerative electrochemical systems will encounter many difficult engineering problems, and the difficulty of developing such systems will increase with the complexity of the transport problems involved.

The systems, terrestrial and extra-terrestrial, we need for energy conversion today grow increasingly complex and sophisticated. Describing these systems is difficult and entails a growing risk of confusion. Consider a patent (10) for fuel cells to fit between the axles of automobiles: these cells happen to be plastic fuel containers, and the story goes that electrochemical fuel cells benefited from mistaken identity when newspapers carried notices of a large contract for the fuel containers. Figure 1 shows the names used for some of the systems in the ACS symposium held on regenerative cells in 1965.

A short, general, and reasonably precise name for the systems under discussion is *regenerative electrochemical system*. All our complete systems seem to contain at least one electrochemical cell, a class in which "fuel cell" is included. The system regenerates a working substance to make a regenerated working substance; here we stretch a term associated with steam engines to include the two components fed separately to the anode and to the cathode of the fuel cell. For example, if AB is the working

Regenerative emf cells
Regenerative fuel cell system
Regenerative emf system
Thermally regenerative system
Regenerative bimetallic cell
Thermally regenerative galvanic system
Thermally regenerative emf cell systems

Figure 1. Partial list of names in symposium
programs
The term, Regenerative Electrochemical Systems, is
suggested to replace the above names

substance for a regenerative electrochemical system, then A and B make up the regenerated working substance.

The regenerative electrochemical system is thus a "black box" (Figure 2) into which only energy enters and from which only energy departs; it is an energy conversion system closed with respect to mass. Of course, the three-word name is too short to be completely descriptive and may need occasional amplification; for example, it might be taken to include black boxes (Figure 3), not closed with respect to mass—important in the field of fuel cells (7).

Thermodynamics, having no curiosity, finds black boxes to its liking. Given the input and the net useful output for a regenerative electrochemical system, one can calculate its efficiency without knowing what the black box contains. One must distinguish here between net useful output and total output, for the latter includes rejected energy that is degraded and heat attributable to irreversibility. The first two laws of thermodynamics must both be considered. To simplify this discussion, it will be assumed that the other energy inputs are converted either into heat or into electrical energy before they enter the black box. This simplification will include most systems near practical realization; it excludes, for example, the direct photochemical regeneration of the working substance.

Electrical energy (direct current) as input is the simpler case. As the output is energy of the same kind, one is entitled to ask what purpose the

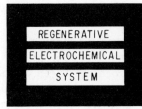

REPRESENTATIVE
INPUTS

ATOMIC ENERGY
HEAT ENERGY
LIGHT ENERGY
ELECTRICAL ENERGY

REGENERATIVE
ELECTROCHEMICAL
SYSTEM

OUTPUTS

ELECTRICAL ENERGY (USEFUL OUTPUT)
REJECTED ENERGY (USUALLY HEAT)
{ FROM REVERSIBLE OPERATION
ADD LOSSES CAUSED BY
IRREVERSIBILITY

Figure 2. Outputs of a regenerative electrochemical system with representative
inputs

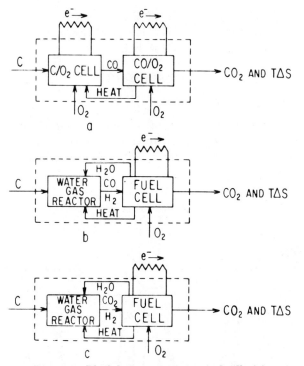

Figure 3. Black boxes containing fuel cells (7)

All boxes have the same ideal efficiency. Note that two of the
boxes are regenerative with respect to water

system serves. The answer is that it stores energy. If the regenerated working substance is A and B (dissociated AB), one may regenerate it from AB during time t_1; one may withdraw electrical energy during time t_2 by allowing A and B to be consumed in the electrochemical cell. Time t_1 could be night, the time of off-peak load in a terrestrial power plant; t_2 might then be the time of peak load. For a power plant on a satellite, t_1 could be orbital day with a silicon converter of solar energy in operation, and t_2 could be orbital night. In either case, the advantage gained by storing energy needs to be great enough to outweigh the disadvantages associated with the black box. To simplify further discussion, we shall take AB to be water and the electrochemical reactions to be as shown at the top of the following page.

This kind of regeneration was uppermost in Grove's mind when he invented the fuel cell. In a postscript dated January 1839 to his paper of a month earlier (5), Grove says of an experiment with a hydrogen/oxygen cell: "I hope by repeating this experiment in series to effect *decomposition*

Electrochemical Reactions

Anode: $H_2 = 2H^+ + 2$ electrons   (1)
Cathode: $\frac{1}{2}O_2 + 2H^+ + 2$ electrons $= H_2O$ (2)
Sum: $H_2 + \frac{1}{2}O_2 = H_2O$ (3)

Regenerative Reaction

Reverse of (3): $H_2O = H_2 + \frac{1}{2}O_2$ (4)

of water by means of its *composition*"—i.e., to electrolyze water with electrical energy from a hydrogen/oxygen battery (italics supplied). He did this with a battery of 26 cells in series; four of these cells are shown in Figure 4.

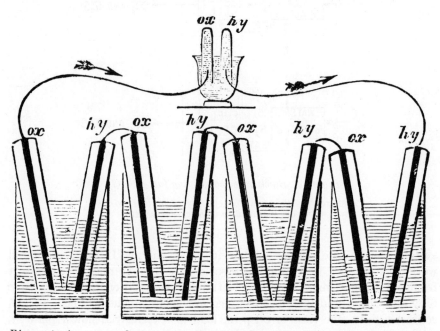

Figure 4. An approach to regenerative electrochemical systems; the work of Grove (1839)—showing only four cells of fuel battery

To change Grove's system into our black box, we supply electrical energy for electrolysis from the outside, remove from the box the electrical energy produced, and arrange for the necessary mass transport within. We then have a regenerative electrochemical system (Figure 5) with water as the working substance. It is easy to imagine a simplification (Figure 6) in which the same device functions part-time as an electrolysis cell or battery, and part-time as a fuel cell or battery. Hereafter we shall use "cell" to include "battery," unless a distinction must be made.

In principle, the cell of Figure 6 could be operated reversibly and isothermally without having heat rejected by the system. There would, of course, have to be provision for storing and exchanging within the system the small amounts of heat TdS associated with reversible isothermal operation. The ideal cycle efficiency would be unity: the fuel cell and the electrolyzer would each operate at $E^0 = 1.23$ volts under standard conditions and 298.1°K., and the current efficiency would be 100%. A current efficiency of less than 100% means that side reactions are occurring. These will almost never be reversible. When they are not, the system cannot be returned to its original state; the state of the system then depends upon its history so that the system cannot qualify as an invariant regenerative system. Side reactions include corrosion reactions, and these are often the greatest threat to invariance.

The cycle efficiency includes the efficiency of the fuel cell and of the electrolyzers, and each of these individual efficiencies is the product of a voltage efficiency and a current efficiency. With water as working fluid, it is usually possible to find conditions where the current efficiencies are virtually 100%. Consequently, we shall use only the voltage efficiencies here. At useful current densities optimistic values for these voltage efficiencies are:

$$\text{Fuel Cell: } \eta_{FC} = \frac{0.8}{1.23} \qquad \text{Electrolyzer: } \eta_E = \frac{1.23}{1.6} \tag{5}$$

whence the cycle efficiency (the product) is:

$$\eta_C = \frac{0.8}{1.6} = 0.5 \tag{6}$$

Actual efficiencies will be lower—partly because actual systems will contain auxiliary equipment with parasitic power requirements.

An account of early work (*1*) on the system of Figure 6 with an ion-exchange membrane as electrolyte contains the opinion: "it is likely that a more stable membrane can be found that will be suitable for regenerative operation." At the Direct Energy Conversion Operation, General Electric Co., Lynn, Mass., new membranes have been found that appear suitable.

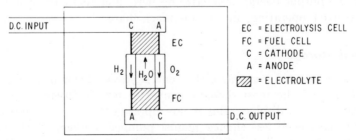

Figure 5. Grove's system (Figure 4) rearranged to make a regenerative electrochemical system

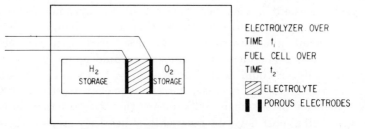

Figure 6. A regenerative electrochemical system in which the anode (cathode) during electrolysis (overtime t_1) becomes the cathode (anode) over the fuel-cell period (overtime t_2)

Note: More than a year after this manuscript was prepared, M. Klein, Xerox Corp., described the substantial progress that has been made on a system identical in principle with that of Figure 6 (9).

A successful, regenerative, electrochemical storage system with water as the working substance can probably be built for a specialty application. A useful classification of devices to produce electrical energy can be based upon an arbitrary separation of expected advantages into "low energy cost" and "convenience," the latter term including such attributes as low weight, small vol./kw., and silent and clean operation. We then have the following:

Type Device	Importance of Low Energy Cost	Importance of Convenience
Specialty	Minor	Overriding
Industrial	Comparable	Comparable
Central Station	Overriding	Minor

In the development of specialty devices, reduced emphasis on cost enlarges freedom of choice, and this advantage will usually outweigh the effect of the stringent requirements these devices must meet.

Can devices modeled on Figure 6 compete in the storage of electrical energy on a central-station scale? Not under ordinary conditions. Low cost of the output energy is overriding here, and this cost includes such items as fixed, operating, and maintenance charges.

Pumped Storage

Until about ten years ago, the central station generating alternating current seemed the most difficult converter for electrochemical devices (fuel batteries) to displace. But it now appears that systems modeled on Figure 6 have even less chance against pumped storage, which relies on pumping water uphill. Friedlander (4) points out that pumped storage in the United States has grown rapidly from a small beginning in 1950, and that about 10,000 Mw. of pumped-storage capacity is projected or being constructed.

Originally, in our language, pumped storage was envisioned as a way of storing low-cost, off-peak energy during time t_1 and releasing it as higher-cost peak energy during time t_2. Now it is expected (4) that this method of storage will be even more valuable as a "spinning reserve"—a reserve from which energy can be drawn instantly and at low cost to satisfy at any time an increase in demand beyond the capacity of the stations then operating. Friedlander cites convincing data to show that pumped storage can provide stored energy at lower cost than even a conventional steam reheat plant. The better steam plants offer formidable competition to fuel batteries because they achieve comparative thermal efficiencies of about 40%, are highly reliable, and call for capital investment as low as $100/kw. installed. Pumped storage has higher efficiency than such a central station, reliability at least equal, and a capital investment requirement that can be lower even when the cost of transmission line is included (4). (According to a rough but reliable guideline, pumped storage delivers 2 kwh. for each 3 kwh. input. This *actual* efficiency of $\frac{2}{3}$ significantly exceeds the 0.5 of Equation 6.)

The coming-of-age of the nuclear reactor is sometimes believed to offer an unusual opportunity to fuel batteries and to regenerative electrochemical systems. The argument advanced is that such reactors will provide off-peak electrical energy in large amounts at low cost, and that this energy can be used profitably to generate hydrogen and oxygen for fuel batteries or stored profitably by an electrochemical system. It seems more realistic to assume that there will be keen competition for this energy and that competing alternatives, such as pumped storage, will not lose their advantages. The generation of potential energy by pumping water uphill seems inherently more attractive on a large scale than the electrochemical regeneration of a working substance.

The principal problem discussed in the papers to follow is the electrochemical conversion of heat into electrical energy. The thermodynamics of these systems is conveniently approached on the basis of the rearranged Grove system (Figure 5). We have seen that this system can store energy isothermally, provided it operates reversibly. It becomes a heat engine if the working substance absorbs heat during reversible regeneration at the temperature, T_1, and rejects heat during the reversible generation of electrical energy at the lower temperature, T_2. As thermodynamic conclusions are independent of the means for carrying out a reversible process, electrochemical regeneration of the working substance, as in Figure 5, may properly serve for a general discussion of all methods for reversible regeneration. This kind of system has the great advantage of providing the regenerated working substance as separated components: here, hydrogen and oxygen. It is thus unnecessary to envision and discuss separation processes.

To emphasize that a regenerative electrochemical system of this kind is subject to the Carnot-cycle limitation, the following cycle was postulated for AB as working substance (2, 6, 8).

Dissociation in Reactor: AB = A + B at T_1 (I)

Recombination in Fuel Cell: A + B = AB at T_2 (II)

Heat Exchange (connecting link) between A and B

       initially at T_1 and AB initially at T_2 (III)

Figure 7 shows that Grove's system can be further changed to accommodate this cycle. Note that dissociation has been assumed to occur at T_1 and recombination only at T_2.

As the following quotation shows, the possibility of dissociation was considered in the earlier treatment and dismissed: "Instead of behaving like water, AB might be stable in State 2 but unstable in State 1. One might then assume that AB does not dissociate until it is passed over a catalyst at T_1, when it dissociates spontaneously to regenerate A and B" (6).

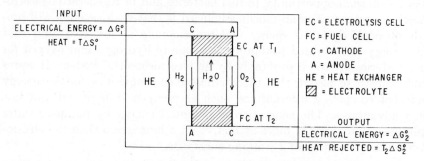

Figure 7. Grove's system made thermally regenerative (6)

The ideal efficiency for the postulated cycle is $\dfrac{G_1^0 - G_2^0}{T_1 S_1^0}$, and the system has become an electrochemical heat engine.

To make Reference 6 realistic, calculations were made for water as AB. At $T_1 = 2000°K.$, water vapor at 1 atm. is in equilibrium with about 0.0056 atm. hydrogen and half that of oxygen. Within the framework of Reference 6, it seemed logical to ignore the possibility that water might dissociate in the heat exchanger (3).

With $T_1 = 2000°K.$, and $T_2 = 500°K.$, the Carnot efficiency of this cycle is 75%. With water as working substance, it was shown that only 71.7% could be realized in the system of Figure 7 (*see* Equation 11). The reason for this decrease of 3.3% is that the heat transfer process (III) necessarily had to be irreversible under the conditions assumed because the combined heat capacities of the hydrogen and oxygen regenerated at T_1 exceeded the heat capacity of the water consumed in the regeneration.

It seems worthwhile to establish whether or not the 3.3% can be easily accounted for by driving reversible heat engines with the rejected heat that gave rise to the 3.3% deficit. This heat is rejected from A and B to AB during heat transfer, the transfer beginning at T_1 and stopping at T_2. The total heat rejected is:

$$\Delta H_2 - \Delta H_1 = \int_{T_1}^{T_2} \Delta Cp dT \text{ (for 1 mole of AB through the cycle)} \quad (7)$$

If the entire heat transfer is to be reversible, the heat must be rejected at a temperature, T, that decreases continuously from T_1 to T_2. We postulate an infinite number of reversible heat engines operating on this rejected heat, the inlet temperature of each engine differing by dT from that of its neighbor, and the outlet temperature being T_2 for all engines. We make the unrealistic assumption that ΔCp is constant, and we continue to neglect the changing dissociation of water between T_1 and T_2.

The reversible work then available from these engines is:

$$w = -\int_{T_1}^{T_2} \Delta Cp \frac{(T - T_2)}{T} dT \quad (8)$$

which becomes

$$w = -\int_{T_1}^{T_2} \Delta Cp dT + \int_{T_1}^{T_2} \Delta Cp T_2 \, d \ln T \quad (9)$$

or

$$w = -[\Delta H_2 - \Delta H_1] + \left[\frac{\Delta H_2 - \Delta H_1}{T_1 - T_2} \times T_2 \times \ln \frac{T_1}{T_2} \right] \quad (10)$$

$$= -1990 + \left[\frac{1900}{3} \times 1.3791 \right], (T_1 = 2000°K.; T_2 = 500°K.)$$

$$= -1075 \text{ cal.}$$

From Reference *6*, the efficiency with everything but heat transfer reversible was:

$$\text{Efficiency} = \frac{\Delta G_2^0 - \Delta G_1^0}{T_1 \Delta S_1^0} = \frac{-20{,}050}{-27{,}950} = 0.717 \quad (11)$$

The work done by the system with the reversible heat engines added is larger than $-20{,}050$ by -1075 calories; therefore, with the system completely reversible (III reversible, as well as I and II),

$$\text{Efficiency} = \frac{-21{,}125}{-27{,}950} = 0.756 \quad (12)$$

The approximations made in the calculation are probably responsible for the difference between 0.756 and 0.750, the Carnot efficiency. An exact calculation, which it does not seem worthwhile to make, would have to consider both the variation in ΔCp and the changing dissociation of water between 500°K. and 2000°K.

To end this introduction, let us look briefly at the recent history of fuel batteries. Although the field is active, programs going toward successful batteries have been moving more slowly than most of us would have predicted a decade ago. Among the reasons for slow progress have been the difficulty of going from cell to battery and the further difficulty of going from battery to complete system. The electrochemist in his laboratory is likely to be optimistic in evaluating how much he has done when he has found a fuel cell in which the proper reactions occur under conditions that make for good performance. Consider as just one example that difficult transport problems remain to be solved before the transport of mass, electricity, and heat can proceed so as to maintain the uniformity required in a system for satisfactory performance and long life.

In regenerative electrochemical systems, the problems will surely be no simpler. A black box is simple only on the outside, and long life is needed for energy converters on satellites. But it does seem certain that satisfactory regenerative electrochemical systems can be developed for specialty applications if the need is great enough.

Literature Cited

(1) Bone, J. S., Gilman, S., Niedrach, L. W., Read, M. D., *Proc. 15th Annual Power Sources Conference*, Atlantic City, 1961.
(2) deBethune, A. J., *J. Electrochem. Soc.* **107,** 937 (1960).
(3) Friauf, B., *J. Applied Phys.* **32,** 616 (1961).
(4) Friedlander, G. D., *IEEE Spectrum* **1,** 58 (1964).
(5) Grove, N. R., *Phil. Mag. 5.3* **14,** 127 (1839).
(6) Liebhafsky, H. A., *J. Electrochem. Soc.* **106,** 1068 (1959).
(7) Liebhafsky, H. A., Cairns, E. J. *Chem. Eng. Progr.* **59,** 35 (1963).
(8) Matsen, J. M., Liebhafsky, H. A., *J. Electrochem. Soc.* **108,** 601 (1961).
(9) P. S. C. Publications Committee, *Proc. 20th Annual Power Sources Conference.* Red Bank, N. J., 1966.
(10) U. S. Patent **3, 129, 014** (October 6, 1960).

RECEIVED November 10, 1965.

Continuous Gas Concentration Cells as Thermally Regenerative, Galvanic Cells

JOHN C. ANGUS

Case Institute of Technology, Cleveland, Ohio

The use of a gas concentration cell as a means of converting thermal to electrical energy is described. This cell, which is in the early stages of development, shows promise because of the absence of any chemical regeneration and separation steps. Initial results on cells using I_2 vapor and a PbI_2 electrolyte are given, as well as estimated characteristics of more advanced cells using alkali metal vapors and alkali metal halide electrolytes.

Thermal energy may be converted into electrical energy by means of a continuous gas concentration cell (hereafter denoted CGCC). This device has received very little attention but offers some unique advantages compared with other schemes.

Principle of Operation

The electrochemical nature of the CGCC is identical to that of the well-known gas concentration cell. In the CGCC, however, the pressure difference across the isothermal electrolyte is maintained by using the change in vapor pressure with temperature of the electrochemically active, gas phase species (working fluid). As in all gas concentration cells, work is done by electrochemical expansion of the working fluid through the electrolyte. After the expansion, the working fluid is condensed in a cold reservoir and, if desired, can be recycled to the high temperature-high pressure side of the cell by means of a pump.

The system is thermodynamically very similar to a conventional power cycle in which a working fluid is vaporized at a high temperature and pressure, expanded through a turbine, condensed at a low temperature and pressure, and then pumped back to the high pressure side. In the

CGCC, expansion is through the electrolyte rather than through the turbine.

Nomenclature

The abbreviations used in this paper are: E = cell potential; F = Faraday's constant; f = fugacity of working fluid at high pressure electrode; f_1 = fugacity of working fluid at low pressure electrode, taken as a constant; ΔH = enthalpy of gaseous working fluid minus enthalpy of condensed working fluid; n = electron number of electrode reaction; P = vapor pressure of working fluid at high pressure electrode; P_1 = vapor pressure of working fluid at low pressure electrode, taken as a constant; R = universal gas constant; T = vaporization temperature; and T_1 = condensation temperature, taken as a constant.

Operating Characteristics

The theoretical operating voltage is given by the Nernst equation:

$$E = -\frac{RT}{nF} \ln\left(\frac{f}{f_1}\right) \qquad (1)$$

The fugacities of the working fluid may be approximated by the partial pressures which may be estimated from the Clausius-Clapeyron equation:

$$\frac{d(\ln P)}{d\,T} = \frac{\Delta H}{RT^2} \qquad (2)$$

Differentiating Equation 1 and using Equations 1 and 2, one has:

$$\frac{d\,E}{d\,T} = \frac{E}{T} - \frac{\Delta H}{nFT} \qquad (3)$$

If ΔH is constant with T, Equation 2 may be integrated:

$$\ln\left(\frac{P}{P_1}\right) = -\frac{\Delta H}{R}\left[\frac{1}{T} - \frac{1}{T_1}\right] \qquad (4)$$

Combining Equations 1, 3, and 4, we have the simplified expression:

$$\frac{d\,E}{d\,T} = -\frac{\Delta H}{nF}\left(\frac{1}{T_1}\right) \qquad (5)$$

Using Equation 2, this becomes:

$$\frac{d\,E}{d(\ln P)} = -\frac{RT^2}{nFT_1} \qquad (6)$$

Numerous, small-scale laboratory versions of the CGCC have been constructed and operated (see Figure 1). Two different, working fluid/electrolyte combinations were used—one with I_2 as the working fluid and PbI_2 as the electrolyte, and another with Hg as the working fluid and an

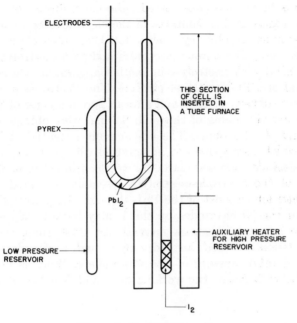

Figure 1. Early Pyrex cell

$Hg_2Cl_2/HgCl_2$ electrolyte. Both Ni and Pt wire electrodes were used with the I_2 cell; W and Pt wire electrodes were used with the Hg cell.

Typical results for the I_2/PbI_2 cell are shown in Table I. The voltage agrees with Equation 1; however, the agreement was not always this good. For example, when the PbI_2 electrolyte was held just above its melting point (402°C.), the voltage was approximately double the predicted value. This may be caused by a change in the electron number for the electrode reaction. The predicted voltages were calculated with $n = 2$ in accordance with the simple electrode reaction $I_2 + 2e = 2I^-$.

Regeneration of the cells was accomplished by cooling the original hot end and vaporizing the I_2 from the original cold end. The cell voltage reversed as expected.

It was not possible to reduce the internal resistance to acceptable

Table I. Voltage Characteristics of I_2/PbI_2 CGCC with Ni Electrodes

Vaporization temperature, T_2, °C.	177	193
Condensation temperature, T_1, °C.	24	24
Electrolyte temperature, °C.	538	538
Voltage (low pressure side is negative)	0.22	0.28
Predicted voltage from Equation 1	0.207	0.22

levels using the small glass cells. For this reason, several more advanced
types of cells have been constructed. The most successful configuration
is shown in Figure 2. The contacts to the electrodes are made secure by
screwing the inner, graphite cylinder in until the entire electrode assembly
is in compression. The porous electrodes and thin electrolyte cavity are
completely filled with electrolyte in another apparatus. I_2 was used as the
working fluid and PbI_2 as the electrolyte. The electrodes were porous Ni
with a relative density of 40% and a mean pore diameter of 22 μ.

In the initial running of this cell, 6.2 ma. were obtained through an
external load of 24.5 ohms. The open-circuit potential of the cell was
0.17 volt, which corresponds to an internal cell resistance of 2.9 ohms.
The cell resistance increased markedly with continued running of the cell.
Inspection of the electrode-electrolyte assembly indicated the pressure
difference had forced most of the PbI_2 through the porous Ni electrodes.
Corrosion of the Ni electrodes by the I_2 may have been responsible for
part of the internal resistance increase. In these runs, the full vapor
pressure of I_2 was not used; instead, only enough I_2 was placed in the cell
to produce a total pressure of one atmosphere. Work is under way on
similar cells, with Na as the working fluid and NaCl as the electrolyte.

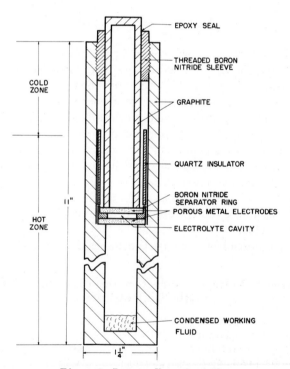

Figure 2. Latest cell configuration

Comparison with Existing Methods

The principal advantage of the CGCC is the absence of any chemical regeneration step. Because the working fluid undergoes no chemical change, no regeneration and separation steps are necessary. The ultimate values of power/mass and power/volume for the CGCC would therefore appear to be quite favorable.

The CGCC appears similar to the thermocell—which is simply a thermocouple in which one leg of the couple is an electrolyte (*1, 4, 5*). In the CGCC, however, the temperature gradient does not appear across the electrolyte, thus minimizing one major source of irreversibility (heat leak). There will, however, still be an unavoidable heat loss down the current-carrying leads which go from the electrolyte to the load. This irreversibility cannot be eliminated because the thermal conductivity of these current conductors cannot be reduced below the value given by the Wiedemann-Franz Law. This type of irreversibility (or its equivalent) is inherent in all regenerative galvanic cell schemes.

Because there are no irreversibilities within the CGCC when no current is drawn, the open-circuit potential can be computed using the methods of classical equilibrium thermodynamics. These methods cannot be rigorously applied to the thermocell because even under open-circuit conditions there is an irreversible heat flux through the cell (*1*). Nevertheless, the potentials of an $I_2/AgI/I_2$ thermocell have been found to agree with the results of approximate equilibrium thermodynamic calculations (*5*). The potentials are also close to those of the $I_2/PbI_2/I_2$ CGCC.

The principal difficulty associated with the CGCC is the necessity of maintaining the integrity of a liquid electrolyte subjected to a pressure gradient. Another difficulty for some systems is the low, open-circuit potential. In Table II, the computed operating characteristics for several working fluid/electrolyte combinations are summarized. The Na/NaCl and K/KCl systems have open-circuit potentials of 0.88 and 0.71 volt, respectively, which are of the same order as conventional regenerative galvanic cells. The pressure difference for these systems is not excessive and is of the order that may be contained with surface tension effects.

Table II. Characteristics of the CGCC with Several Working Fluid/Electrolyte Systems

Working Fluid/Electrolyte	ρ Ohm-Cm.[a]	Vaporization Temp. (*T*, °C.)	Condensation Temp. (T_1, °C.)	Open-Circuit Voltage	P mm.[b]	P_1 mm.[b]
I_2/PbI_2	2.1	410	119	0.3	31,900	93.4
Hg/Hg_2Cl_2	2.0	305	100	.22	246.8	.27
Na/NaCl	.273	827	327	.88	433	.0394
K/KCl	.44	827	327	.71	1408	.635

[a] Values of resistivity are taken from Smithells (*3*) and are given for the vaporization temperature, *T*.
[b] Vapor pressures and fugacities for calculation of the open-circuit voltage were taken from Hultgren (*2*).

The pressures at the low pressure electrode are not so small that intolerable gas phase concentration polarization will occur.

Values of current density and power density referred to unit electrolyte cross sectional area have been calculated for matched load conditions. They are .394 amp./sq. cm. and .13 watt/sq. cm. for the Na/NaCl cell, and .202 amp./sq. cm. and .0537 watt/sq. cm. for the K/KCl system. For these calculations, a voltage efficiency of 0.75 was assumed. The electrolyte was taken to be 1 cm. thick and to have a resistance three times the value calculated from the resistivity of the pure electrolyte. These predicted characteristics compare favorably with other, more complex, regenerative, galvanic cell systems.

Summary

A new, thermally regenerative, galvanic cell based on the principle of continuous gas concentration cell is described. Results obtained with cells using I_2 as the working fluid and PbI_2 as electrolyte are given. The estimated operating characteristics of cells using Na/NaCl and K/KCl appear favorable in comparison with existing devices.

Acknowledgments

The author is indebted to the Valley Co. and the National Science Foundation for supporting this work and to E. E. Hucke for many stimulating discussions. C. C. Liu, M. Rothstein, R. Campbell, R. Glickman, J. Lopez, E. Horne, W. Munroe, and J. Meyer all contributed to various aspects of the experimental program.

Literature Cited

(1) Agar, J. N., "Thermogalvanic Cells," Chapter 2, Vol. 3, "Advances in Electrochemistry and Electrochemical Engineering," P. Delahay, ed., Interscience, New York, 1963.
(2) Hultgren, R., Orr, R. L., Anderson, P. D., Kelley, K. K., "Selected Values of Thermodynamic Properties of Metals and Alloys," John Wiley, New York, 1963.
(3) Smithells, C. J., "Metals Reference Book, Volume II," 3rd ed., Butterworths, Washington, 1962.
(4) Weininger, J. L., "Thermocell," U. S. Patent **2,890,259** (June 9, 1957).
(5) Weininger, J. L., *J. Electrochem. Soc.* **111**(7), 769 (1964).

RECEIVED November 10, 1965.

Solid Inorganic Electrolyte Regenerative Fuel Cell System

C. BERGER and M. P. STRIER

Astropower Laboratory, Douglas Aircraft Co., Inc., Missile and Space Systems Division, Newport Beach, Calif.

Sintered zirconium phosphate membranes containing zeolites have significant water absorptive capacities over a temperature range of from ambient to 150°C. This feature makes them sufficiently conductive for fuel cell applications over this temperature range. Such membranes have transverse strengths of 5000 to 6000 psi. They readily gain and lose water vapor in a reversible manner while maintaining good stability. This accounts for promising results obtained to date for regenerative hydrogen-oxygen fuel cells using this membrane. In addition to presenting regenerative hydrogen-oxygen fuel cell data, water absorptivity and conductivity data are given and interpreted in terms of membrane composition and structure.

The earliest reported use of zirconium phosphate membranes as a solid electrolyte for hydrogen-oxygen fuel cells dates back to 1961 (*9, 10, 13*). Astropower Laboratory has been investigating the electrochemical behavior of modified zirconium phosphate structures from both a fundamental as well as a developmental aspect. Significantly, a comprehensive investigation of composition and fabrication techniques, as they are related to membrane strength, conductivity, and hydrolytic stability, has led to deriving useful solid electrolyte structures. This is evidenced by successful hydrogen-oxygen fuel cell tests over the temperature range of 25° to 148°C. (*6*).

Most characteristic of these membranes is an incorporated zeolite component serving a water-balancing function by virtue of its high affinity for water and low rate of desorption. In this manner, the conductivity of the membrane is maintained at a suitable level over wide temperature limits. Therefore, it was our belief that such membranes were ideally suited for regenerative hydrogen-oxygen fuel cells.

Hydrogen-oxygen fuel cells employing such membranes have performed continuously for over 1000 hrs. in the 60° to 75°C. temperature range at current densities of at least 25 ma./sq. cm. at 0.5 volt. Tests have run at 50 ma./sq. cm. and 0.65 volt and at 30 ma./sq. cm. and 0.73 volt for over 300 hrs., as shown in Figure 1. Constant performance level prevails over the temperature range of 65° to 120°C. owing to the fact that the membrane tends to maintain a constant level of conductance over this temperature range. Current densities as high as 118 ma./sq. cm. at 2.5 volts have been obtained in electrolysis experiments.

This presentation is concerned with a description of the pertinent properties of the Astropower Laboratory zirconium phosphate-zeolite membrane system as they are related to independent electrolysis and fuel cell operation and subsequently regenerative fuel cell cycle.

Historical

The principal advantages to be gained from using solid electrolytes in fuel cells are compactness, simplicity of design, and few zero gravity

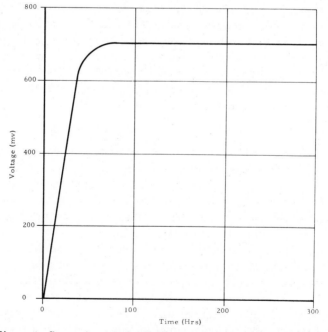

Figure 1. Synopsis of fuel cell life test at 65 ± 1°C.; Astropower zirconium phosphate-Zeolon-H membrane voltage vs. time at current density of 30 ma./sq. cm.

limitations. The first ion membrane fuel cell involving hydrogen and oxygen was described in 1959 (*22*), and its capability in a regenerative fuel cell was described initially in 1960 (*8*). The device used an organic cation-exchange membrane derived from sulfonated phenol formaldehyde polymers. This membrane system lacked strength and was unstable at slightly elevated temperatures. The temperature limitation characteristic of organic polymeric ion exchange membrane systems remains up to the present time. Efforts have been made to alleviate such shortcomings by such innovations as the Hydrogen-Bromine Fuel Cell (HBFC) and the Dual Membrane Fuel Cell (DMFC) (*7, 21*). In the former, a sulfonated polystyrene cation-exchange membrane separates the anode from the catholyte compartment (liquid phase) comprised of an aqueous solution of bromine and HBr.

In the Dual Membrane Fuel Cell, two of the same type sulfonated polystyrene cation-exchange membranes separate the anode from the cathode with an intervening $6N$ H_2SO_4 solution between the membranes. The various advantages and disadvantages of both the HBFC and DMFC systems have been discussed by Berger *et. al.*, previously (*7, 20, 21*).

Some progress has also been recorded in another kind of regenerative fuel cell in applying aqueous KOH absorbed in asbestos in a solid electrolyte (*11, 12*).

Pioneering work on zirconium phosphate used as cation-exchange material has been performed by Kraus (*14, 15, 16, 17*), Amphlett (*1, 2, 3*), and Larsen and Vissers (*19*). Hamlen has made a study of the conductivity of zirconium phosphate under various conditions of hydration and found, that at the highest level of hydration, the mechanism of conductance corresponded to that in an aqueous phase. Both Hamlen (*13*) and Dravnieks and Bregman (*9, 10*) in 1961–2 reported on hydrogen-oxygen fuel cell studies with solid zirconium phosphate membranes at ambient temperature. The performances were promising although the membranes were weak.

Astropower Zirconium Phosphate-Zeolite Membrane Studies

General Considerations. The fuel cell investigation has been in effect at Astropower for three years under NASA sponsorship (*5*). The impetus behind the selection of inorganic membranes as a route to achieving improved fuel cell performance can be outlined as follows. First, a strong skeleton network is required to provide necessary physical strength and ionizing functions for establishing an electrolytically conducting system. Second, an incorporated water-balancing agent is required to retain sufficient water in the membrane for appropriately high electrolytic conduction.

Membrane Composition and Fabrication Studies. After evaluating the strength of a number of membrane systems during the early stages of the program, it was found that the best results were achieved by the sintering of zirconium dioxide with phosphoric acid and "Zeolon H," a Norton Co. synthetic alumino-silicate zeolite. Other potential bonding materials, such as various silicate-based proprietary mixtures, yielded relatively fragile systems (5).

An explanation for the bonding characteristics of phosphate materials is as follows: Acid phosphate groups such as HPO_4^{2-} have strong ligand properties which allow them to coordinate with cations of periodic groups II and III, as well as the transition elements. Cations already incorporated in the coordination compounds may still react with acid phosphate groups if the ion concentration is sufficiently high to shift the reaction equilibrium appreciably in favor of phosphate combinations. Thus, when finally divided metal oxides are treated with concentrated phosphoric acid, oxygen atoms are partly displaced by the phosphate group. On heating, the phosphorylated oxides dehydrate and condense the acid phosphate groups into linkages between the phosphate tetrahedra. The mixture then becomes fused into a solid mass.

Such techniques for producing inorganic membranes as hot pressing, cold pressing and sintering, or by casting and sintering have been investigated. Optimum properties such as high transverse strength and low resistivity were obtained by either cold pressing and sintering or by casting and sintering. Our extensive study of the system of zirconia-phosphoric acid and "Zeolon H," based on its having shown early promise, has led to developing membranes having suitable properties for fuel cell application. Maximum transverse strengths of 5000 to 6000 psi can be obtained by using stabilized zirconia. Moreover, reactivity with phosphoric acid, and thus higher transverse strength, is enhanced by smaller crystalline size. In addition, a strong bond developed between zirconia and phosphoric acid during sintering rather than during material drying and mixing stages. Sintering temperatures in the 300° to 800°C. range have produced strong membranes, having resistivities as low as 20 ohm-cm. measured at 73% relative humidity and 105°C.

Water Vapor Adsorption Capability and Relationship to Conductivity. Water vapor adsorption characteristics were determined by means of a controlled atmosphere thermobalance. This device consisted of a McBain balance employing a quartz spring. Water pickup was measured by suspending the sample membrane in a furnace tube adjusted to the desired temperature and relative humidity. The extension of the spring was followed by a cathetometer to measure changes in weight due to moisture pickup (4).

Figure 2 shows curves depicting the water vapor adsorption characteristics at 125°C. of three different zirconium phosphate membranes pre-

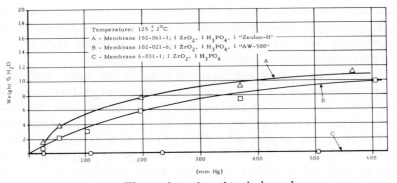

Figure 2. Water adsorption of typical membranes

pared in our laboratory at different relative humidities and partial pressures of water. The membrane made of only ZrO_2 and H_3PO_4 (Curve C) showed no water adsorption. However, for the composite membranes including the zeolites, either "Zeolon H" or "AW 500" with zirconium phosphate, appreciable water adsorption occurs. The amount of water adsorbed is much greater than can be accounted for by the presence of the one-third by-weight quantities of the respective zeolite in the membrane structure.

Water adsorption isotherms for a composite membrane system of zirconia, phosphoric acid, and "Zeolon H," prepared in equal weight ratios, are given in Figure 3. Measurements were taken at 71°C., 90°C., 125°C., and 158°C. at various partial pressures of water vapor. Lines of constant relative humidities are shown at the lower temperatures. At

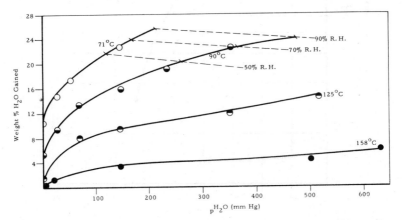

Figure 3. Water adsorption isotherms, ZrO_2-H_3PO_4-"Zeolon-H" membrane (1:1:1 composition)

constant partial pressures of water vapor the ability of the membrane to adsorb water decreases with increasing temperature. On a constant relative humidity basis, the trend is still evident. What is most significant in these measurements, however, is the fact that this membrane system has an affinity for water even at temperatures as high as 158°C.

Employing a related membrane system in the same conditioning apparatus, resistance measurements were performed at temperatures of 70°C., 90°C., and 105°C. at relative humidities ranging from 26 to 83%. Test membranes were held between platinized electrodes having approximately 1.0 sq. cm. surface area. Resistivities were calculated from the membrane resistance measured by means of an alternating current bridge circuit at 1000 cps. A plot of logarithm of the resistivity vs. % relative humidity is given in Figure 4. Resistivities decrease with increasing relative humidities, which is consistent with a gain in water content. However, this trend diminishes drastically with decreasing temperature. From Figure 3, at 71°C., the moisture content is somewhat higher than at 90°C. and apparently at 105°C. as well, for the same relative humidity. There-

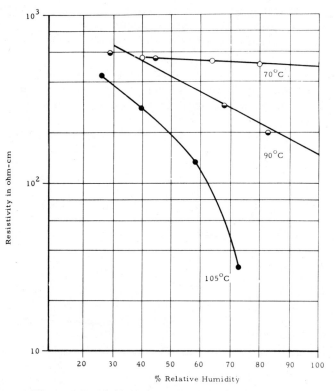

Figure 4. Log resistivity vs. % relative humidity for the membrane at 70°C., 90°C., and 105°C.

fore, the increase in conductivity with rising temperature is apparently not related to the change in water content of the membrane. According to the data in Figure 3, membrane resistivities at 90°C. and 105°C. approach the resistivity level at 70°C. as the environmental humidity decreases. This means that despite the tendencies of these membranes to dehydrate at higher temperatures their conductivities do not decrease to levels lower than those of lower temperatures. Fuel cell performance is invariant over the temperature range of 65°C. to 120°C., which could be related to the tendency of the conductance of the membrane to remain constant over this temperature range.

Arrhenius plots of the resistivity data at constant relative humidity over the 70° to 90°C. temperature range give activation energies ranging from 3 kcal./mole at 50% relative humidity to 16 kcal./mole at 90% relative humidity. This means that the rate of decrease in resistivity with rising temperature increases directly with higher relative humidity; this may be due to an increase in the amount of current-carrying ions resulting from the increased humidity.

On the basis of such studies, it must be concluded that the zirconium dioxide-phosphoric acid-"Zeolon H," membrane system offers promise in regenerative fuel cell operations as high as 100°C.

In the sections which follow the results of electrolytic fuel cell and regenerative fuel studies with this membrane are described.

Electrolysis Studies. Electrolysis studies were conducted on a zirconia-phosphoric acid-"Zeolon H" membrane. This material had a resistivity at 110°C. of 10.3 ohm-cm. and 4.0 ohm-cm. at 50% and 100% relative humidity, respectively.

The two-inch membrane was sandwiched between a Teflon-bonded platinum black-tantalum electrode screen. A small amount of platinum black was added to the screen electrodes. Then, the assembly was clamped between one sq. cm. platinized electrodes and placed in a test chamber maintained at 60% relative humidity at 25°C. The configuration is shown in Figure 5. Current-voltage characteristics as a function of time are given in Figure 6. Figure 7 shows the variation in current density for this membrane maintained continuously at 2.5 volts for 400 min. at 25°C. and 60% relative humidity. There is a relatively slow decline in current density with time at each voltage level in Figure 6. That the cell could operate for almost 7 hrs. at 2.5 volts (Figure 7) indicates that a continuous process of water vapor adsorption is possible for these membrane systems. Water vapor is continuously being adsorbed by the membrane and moves through the membrane to the electrodes, where it is electrolyzed, forming oxygen and hydrogen.

Under the proper design conditions, adsorption and electrolysis rates could be properly balanced at the desired voltage and current operating levels so that the unit would operate as a continuous water vapor electrol-

Figure 5. Experimental electrolysis cell

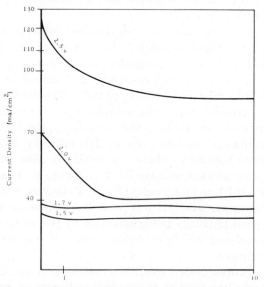

Figure 6. Current density at various voltages (membrane
191–047) at 25 ± 1°C. and 60% relative humidity

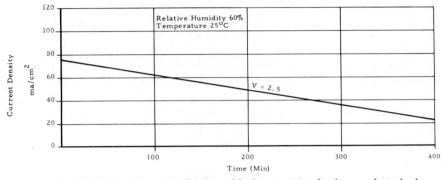

Figure 7. *Variation of current density with time at 2.5 volts for an electrolysis cell using inorganic membrane electrolyte No. 191–047 (continuous operation)*

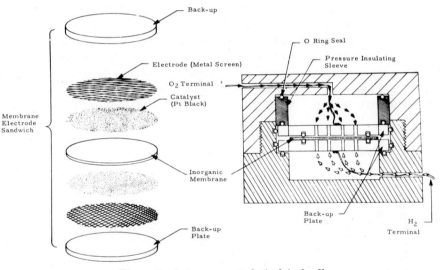

Figure 8. *Astropower analytical fuel cell*

ysis unit. These data show that such solid membrane electrolytes can be effectively and efficiently used in regenerative fuel cells.

Fuel Cell Studies. The zirconium phosphate-"Zeolon H" membrane systems have been evaluated in laboratory type fuel cells at temperatures ranging from ambient up to 148°C. A schematic diagram of one type of Astropower Laboratory fuel cell designed to accommodate a 2-in. diameter membrane is given in Figure 8.

The electrodes were of a Teflon-platinum black, tantalum screen configuration obtained from American Cyanamid. About 0.3 gram powdered, platinum black was sprinkled on each side of the membrane prior to assembling the membrane-electrode-backup plate wafer.

The membrane used in the results to be described was prepared in the following manner. An initial mixture of ZrO_2 and 85% H_3PO_4 was prepared in 1:1 weight ratio and sintered at 200°C. Then, the sintered material was crushed and ground to minus 80 mesh and mixed with equal parts of 85% phosphoric acid and "Zeolon H." After drying and pressing into 2-in. diameter membranes having a thickness of approximately 0.7 mm., it was sintered at 500°C. for 2 hrs. This membrane had a transverse strength of 5200 psi.

Figure 9 summarizes the fuel cell operational characteristics—i.e., current densities plotted against time, for this membrane in separate life tests performed at 25°C., 64°C., and 75°C., respectively, all at 0.5 volt. (Electrolysis experiments were performed at the conclusion of each test and will be described below. Actually, the fuel cells were all still functioning at the moment of termination of the discharge cycle. At 25°C., current densities of 20 to 28 ma./sq. cm. for 624 hrs. operation were recorded. They ranged from 20 to 52 ma./sq. cm. for 1174 hrs. at 64°C. and at 75°C.; the range was 22 to 32 ma./sq. cm. for 912 hrs. This is not considered the optimum performance capability for such membranes because we do not consider that membrane properties or catalyst configurations have been optimized. For example, by improving the mode of platinum catalyst application such as impregnating it into the membrane

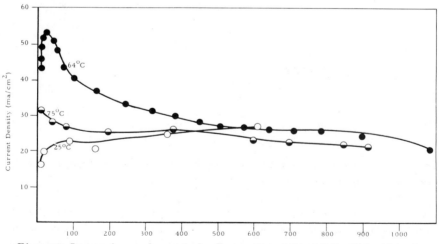

Figure 9. Inorganic membrane fuel cell operating data at 0.5 volt for zirconium dioxide-phosphoric-"Zeolon H" membranes at 25°C., 64°C., and 75°C.

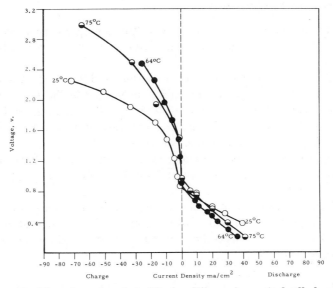

Figure 10. Zirconium phosphate-"Zeolon H" membrane fuel cell charge and discharge operational characteristics

system by a sintering procedure, it has been possible to improve performance by as much as 20% (*6*).

Regenerative Fuel Cell Study. The fuel cells performing for the indicated number of hours in Figure 9 were utilized as regenerative fuel cells at these three temperature levels. Electrode polarity was reversed and voltages ranging from 3.0 to 0.8 were applied across the cell. The corresponding currents were recorded as generated hydrogen and oxygen. The results obtained are plotted in Figure 10 as charge-discharge curves. According to these curves, the highest current densities for electrolysis are obtained at 25°C., with the results at 64°C. and 75°C. being essentially the same. This is consistent with the results of the prior electrolysis studies described above which indicated that the absorptive capacity of these membranes for water was inversely related to temperature. At 25°C. the decomposition potential for water appears to be approximately 1.9 volts at a current density of 30 ma./sq. cm.

These data show that such zirconium phosphate-"Zeolon H" membrane systems are applicable to regenerative hydrogen-oxygen fuel cells. They are physically strong, thermally stable, have low resistivity, and absorb water efficiently. Therefore, by appropriate design consideration, a unit capable of electrolyzing water to hydrogen and oxygen on the charging cycle can be constructed, and the stored gases on discharge can be utilized. The membrane will have absorbed sufficient H_2O during this discharge process to regain its initial equilibrium moisture content.

Summary and Conclusions

(1) Zirconium phosphate membranes containing incorporated zeolites serving as water-balancing agents do have significant water absorptive capacities.

(2) By virtue of extensive composition and fabrication studies, it has been possible to prepare zirconium phosphate-"Zeolon H" membranes having transverse strengths in the 5000 to 6000 psi range and higher, while simultaneously possessing low enough resistivities to be suitable for hydrogen-oxygen regenerative fuel cell application.

(3) Electrolysis studies on these membranes at 25°C. have indicated that current densities as high as 125 ma./sq. cm. at 2.5 volts can be achieved.

(4) Because such membrane systems gain and lose water vapor readily in a reversible manner while maintaining good stability, their potential as the solid electrolyte in regenerative hydrogen-oxygen fuel cells appears favorable.

Acknowledgment

The authors wish to thank F. Arrance, M. Plizga, and G. Belfort of Astropower Laboratory for their experimental contributions. Some of this work has been supported by NASA-Lewis Research Center Contracts NAS 7-150 and 3-6000.

Literature Cited

(1) Amphlett, C. B., McDonald, L. A., Burgess, J. S., Maynard, J. C., *J. Inorg. Nucl. Chem.* **10,** 69 (1959).
(2) Amphlett, C. B., McDonald, L. A., Redman, M. J., *Chem. Ind.* **1956,** 1314.
(3) Amphlett, C. B., McDonald, L. A., Redman, M. J., *J. Inorg. Nucl. Chem.* **6,** 220 (1958).
(4) Astropower, Inc., "Investigation of Zeolite Electrolytes for Fuel Cells," NASA Contract NAS 7-150, Quarterly Progress Report 108-03, period ending 18 March 1963.
(5) Astropower, Inc., "Investigation of Zeolite Electrolytes for Fuel Cells," NASA Contract NAS 7-150, Final Report 108-F, March 1964.
(6) Astropower Laboratory, "Inorganic Ion Exchange Membrane Fuel Cell," NASA-Lewis Research Center, Contract NAS 3-6000, Quarterly Report SM-46221-Q3, period ending April 1965.
(7) Berger, C., "The Current State of Development of Fuel Cells Utilizing Semipermeable Membranes, "Presented before the Division of Fuel Cell Chemistry, American Chemical Society, New York (Sept. 8-13, 1963).
(8) Bone, J. S., "Regenerative Ion-Exchange Fuel Cell System," Proceedings of the 14th Annual Power Sources Conference, Atlantic City, New Jersey, May 1960.
(9) Dravnieks, A., Boies, D. B., Bregman, J. I., Proceedings of the 16th Annual Power Sources Conference (May 22-4, 1962), Session on Fuel Cell Materials and Mechanisms, p. 4-6.
(10) Dravnieks, A., Bregman, J. I., Fuel Cell Symposium of the Electrochemical Society, Detroit, October 1961.

(11) Electro-Optical Systems, Inc., "Fuel Cell Assemblies," JPL Contract 950258, NAS 7-100, EOS Report 3070, Final, March 25, 1963.

(12) Electro-Optical Systems, Inc., "Hydrogen-Oxygen Electrolytic Regenerative Fuel Cells," NASA-Lewis Research Center, Contract NAS 3-2781, EOS Report 4110-2Q-1, period ending June 26, 1964.

(13) Hamlen, R. P., *J. Electrochem. Soc.* **109,** 746 (1962).

(14) Kraus, K. A., Abstracts of Papers, 135th Meeting, ACS, April 1959, p. 17M-48.

(15) Kraus, K. A., *Chem. Eng. News* **34,** 4760 (1956).

(16) Kraus, K. A., *J. Am. Chem. Soc.* **78,** 694 (1956).

(17) Kraus, K. A., Proc. Intern. Conf. on Peaceful Uses of Atomic Energy, Vol. 7, 113, 131 United Nations (1956).

(18) Kraus, K. A., *Nature* **177,** 1128 (1956).

(19) Larsen, E. M., Vessers, D. R., *J. Phys. Chem.* **64,** 1732 (1960).

(20) Lurie, R. M., Berger, C., Shuman, R. J., "Ion Exchange Membranes in Hydrogen-Oxygen Fuel Cell," Presented at the American Chemical Society Fuel Cell Symposium, Chicago, Ill., September 6 and.7, 1961.

(21) Lurie, R. M., Berger, C., Viklund, H., *J. Electrochem. Soc.* **110,** 1173 (1963).

(22) Nedrach, L. W., "The Ion-Exchange Membrane Fuel Cell," Proceedings of the 13th Annual Power Sources Conference, Atlantic City, New Jersey (April 29, 1959).

RECEIVED January 21, 1966.

4

Development of a Thermally Regenerative Sodium-Mercury Galvanic System

Part I. Electrochemical and Chemical Behavior of Sodium-Mercury Galvanic Cells[1]

L. A. HERÉDY, M. L. IVERSON, G. D. ULRICH,[2] and H. L. RECHT

Research and Technology Division, Atomics International, A Division of North American Aviation, Inc., P. O. Box 309, Canoga Park, Calif.

The chemical and electrochemical characteristics of sodium amalgam galvanic cells were studied. A static electrode cell, contained in a stainless steel pressure vessel, was operated at temperatures from 477 to 510°C. under 140 to 180 psig argon cover gas pressure. A molten eutectic mixture of sodium salts was used as the electrolyte. Current densities as high as 200 ma./sq. cm. were achieved without appreciable electrode polarization. A flowing electrode cell with a tubular electrode matrix was designed, built, and tested. In this cell the anode and the cathode compartments were supplied with continuous streams of concentrated and dilute amalgam, respectively. A complete thermally regenerative system (a flowing electrode cell coupled with a regeneration loop) was successfully operated for a period of 1200 hrs. at a cell temperature of about 490°C.

The application of thermally regenerative fuel cells for the conversion of heat into electrical energy has been discussed recently (9). Thermally regenerative systems using liquid metal electrodes and fused salt electrolytes appear to be particularly promising because energy losses through electrode polarization and electrolyte resistance can be much

---

[1] Work performed under company-sponsored, independent research and development program.

[2] Present address: Billerica Research Center, Cabot Corp., Billerica, Mass.

lower than in any other system. Experimental studies on several systems with liquid metal electrodes have been reported (*1, 7*). The aim of the present work was to investigate the feasibility of this concept for application in a space-power plant to convert heat from a compact nuclear reactor into electricity. The system consists of two major parts. One is a regeneration section in which the constituents of an alloy (in the present system, mercury and sodium) are separated from each other by distillation. The other part is the galvanic cell-battery in which the alloy is reconstituted electrochemically at a lower temperature with the production of useful electrical energy. The operation of the complete Atomics International system (called TRAC for Thermally Regenerative Alloy Cell system) is discussed elsewhere (*4*). Work on the development of the alloy cell for the TRAC system is discussed in this paper.

Cell Component Studies

High specific output for space systems often requires a heat reject (i.e., radiator) temperature of about $\frac{3}{4}$ths the (absolute) temperature of the heat source. With a reactor source ($t \cong 700°C.$), a radiator temperature of about 460°C. is desired. A battery operating temperature somewhat above 460°C. is therefore desirable for this application. Alkali metal-mercury systems appear to be the most promising for use at this temperature. The sodium-mercury system was selected for these studies because sodium has several advantages over the other alkali metals. Lithium had to be excluded because of the high melting temperatures of its amalgams (up to 600°C.). Among the other alkali metals sodium has the lowest vapor pressure and, therefore, it can be separated from mercury by distilling more efficiently at the expected boiler temperature ($\sim 700°C.$). Another advantage of using sodium is that the mutual solubilities of several sodium-sodium salt systems are lower than those of the corresponding higher atomic weight alkali metal systems (*2*).

EMF of Sodium/Sodium Amalgam Galvanic Cells. High temperature emf measurements with sodium-sodium amalgam systems have been carried out previously only with amalgams of high sodium content (*5*). Since emf values for dilute sodium amalgams could be calculated only crudely from mercury vapor pressure data using the Gibbs-Duhem equation, experimental verification was desired. Therefore, it was decided to carry out experimental emf measurements on dilute sodium amalgams at elevated temperatures.

The measurements were carried out with galvanic cells of the type Na(l)/Na$^+$(glass)/Na-Hg(l) in the temperature range of 350–400°C. The emf *vs.* composition curve determined at 375°C. is shown in Figure 1.

The curve in the low sodium mole fraction region (0–20 mole% Na) represents new data (6); additional measurements in the high sodium mole fraction region agree well with the results obtained by Hauffe (5). Details of this investigation will be published elsewhere (6). Complete emf measurements with this system have not been extended to temperatures above 400°C. However, open-circuit voltages were determined between 480 and 500°C. in static cell experiments (described below) using a molten salt electrolyte with amalgams of known composition. The values obtained agreed within 10–15 mv. with corresponding cell voltage values calculated from the emf *vs.* composition measurements made between 350 and 400°C. This indicates that only minor changes may be expected in the emf *vs.* composition curve at temperatures near 500°C.

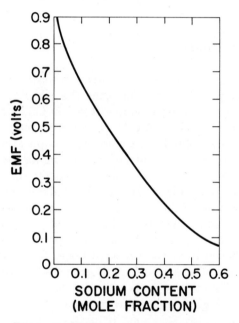

Figure 1. EMF vs. composition for sodium-sodium amalgam galvanic cells

Selection and Testing of the Electrolyte.   In order to function properly in the TRAC cell, the electrolyte is required to satisfy the following conditions:

a) It must melt below 500°C.

b) It must be thermally stable at 500°C.

c) The resistivity of the electrolyte should be low, preferably less than 1.0 ohm-cm.

d) It should contain Na^+ as the only cation, and oxidation and reduction at the electrodes should involve only this ionic species.

e) The mutual solubility of the electrolyte-sodium amalgam system must be low.

f) It must not react chemically with other cell components (e.g., ceramic seals or matrices, sodium amalgam, etc.).

Ternary or quaternary mixtures composed of sodium halides and a few other sodium salts were found to satisfy these requirements. The composition of the sodium salt mixture, which was selected as electrolyte, is proprietary. The electrolyte melts in the temperature range of 475–479°C. It was heated for extended periods at 550°C. and found to be thermally stable at that temperature.

The conductivity of the electrolyte was measured over the temperature range of 515–630°C. in a sealed quartz conductivity cell. The cell wall appeared to be etched slightly during the measurement, but the conductivity of the electrolyte did not change within experimental error ($\pm 2\%$) over a period of 6 hrs. The logarithm of conductivity, κ, varied linearly with the reciprocal of the absolute temperature (I) and fit the equation as follows:

$$\log \kappa = 1.074 - \frac{595}{I}.$$

The resistivity of the electrolyte at 500°C. was calculated from this equation to be 0.50 ohm-cm.

A preliminary experimental study of the mutual solubility of the electrolyte and sodium amalgams of various compositions was carried out. The electrolyte and amalgam were equilibrated and then isolated by decantation or by using ball check-valves (*3*). The tests were made in sealed stainless steel (Type 304) tubes in the temperature range of 500–600°C., using sodium amalgams of 40–80 atom% sodium content. It was found that the solubility of the liquid metals in the electrolyte was very low. The solubility of sodium was less than 0.2 weight% in every sample; no mercury at all could be detected. The results on determining the solubility of electrolyte in amalgams were widely scattered. This was probably a result of salt dispersions forming. However, values as low as 0.1 and 0.3 weight% salt were obtained at 550 and 650°C., respectively. Chemical interaction between the electrolyte and sodium amalgam was not indicated either in the compatibility tests or in the cell experiments.

Ceramic matrices of 40–55% apparent porosity were used to contain the electrolyte. The ceramic was found to be compatible with the electrolyte. The ceramic material also resisted attack by sodium amalgam. No significant damage to the ceramic matrix was observed after a cell operation at 480–530°C. for a period of 1200 hrs.

Experiments with a Static Electrode Cell

The aim of these experiments was to study the general electrochemical behavior of the system and to obtain information necessary for the design of a continuously fed (flowing electrode) cell. A schematic drawing of a flowing electrode cell, with the cell processes, is shown in Figure 2. The cell is supplied with a sodium-rich amalgam (anode) and essentially pure mercury (cathode). The cell process involves oxidation of Na to Na$^+$ at the anode, transport of Na$^+$ through the electrolyte, and reduction of Na$^+$ to Na at the cathode. At both electrodes, a series of sodium-mercury compounds is formed. Products of the cell reaction are sodium-poor amalgams.

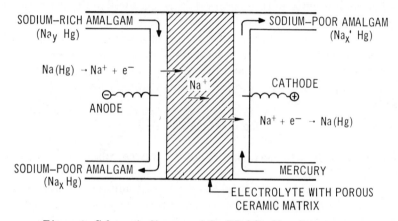

Figure 2. Schematic diagram of the TRAC cell and processes

The main emphasis in the static cell experiments was placed on determining cell resistance and electrode polarization as a function of current density, at various temperatures, electrode compositions, and electrolyte-matrix configurations. Because at the temperature of operation the vapor pressure of mercury is 100–140 psia, the cell was contained in a stainless steel pressure vessel and operated under an argon atmosphere at 140–175 psig total pressure. Figure 3 is a drawing of the cell. The mercury cathode is contained in a type 410 stainless steel crucible located at the bottom of the pressure vessel. The electrolyte matrix is fastened by a spring loaded stainless steel supporting frame to the bottom of a dense ceramic cylinder which is immersed in the mercury pool. The sodium amalgam is contained in the inner part of the cylinder-matrix assembly. Two stainless steel rods passing through the top of the cell dip into each of the liquid metal electrodes and serve as electrode terminals. The lower part of the cell was heated in an electric pot furnace; the upper half was cooled to permit the use of silicone rubber and Teflon gaskets.

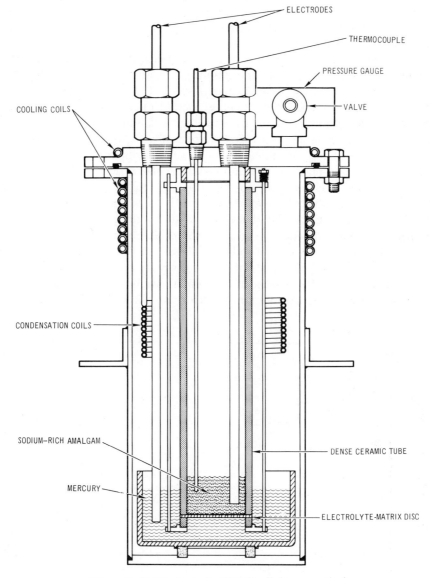

Figure 3. Static electrode TRAC cell (cross-section)

The amalgam electrodes were prepared, and the cell was assembled in a controlled atmosphere box under argon. The results of some typical experiments are discussed below. These serve to illustrate the operation of the static electrode cell. In one of these experiments, the cell was operated for a period of 176 hrs. and was shut down voluntarily. A ceramic

disc (effective surface area: 11.4 sq. cm., thickness: 0.254 cm.) of 41%
apparent porosity was used as electrolyte matrix. It was impregnated
with the molten salt at 500°C., first in vacuum then under 15 psig argon
pressure, for a total period of 2 hrs.

The starting composition of the two liquid metal electrodes was 37.6
atom% sodium in the anode and 2.9 atom% sodium in the cathode. The
cell was operated in the temperature range of 470–510°C. under 150–175
psig argon pressure. After a discharge period of 5–15 hrs., the cell was
recharged electrically to about the starting electrode composition. Several
such discharge-recharge cycles were carried out. Figure 4 shows a typical
example of the change of cell voltage with time during discharge at various
current densities. There was no appreciable polarization of the electrodes
up to current densities close to 200 ma./sq. cm., as indicated by the
nearly constant value of the apparent resistivity of the electrolyte-matrix
combination during most of this experimental period. The last two resistivity values may indicate the onset of appreciable concentration polarization caused by the low rate of sodium diffusion in the amalgam electrodes
at a current density of about 200 ma./sq. cm. It appears, however, that
the magnitude of the concentration polarization also depends on the
composition of the electrodes and therefore on the cell voltage. This was

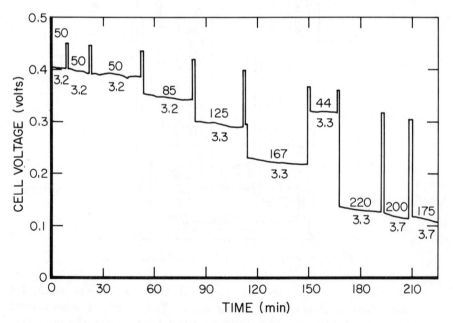

Figure 4. Discharge characteristics of a static TRAC cell

Figures *above curve are current densities (ma./sq. cm.); those below are calculated
resistivities (ohm-cm.)*

shown during another experimental period, when the open-circuit voltage of the cell was 0.48 volts, corresponding to a higher sodium content in the anode. At that time, a current density of 200 ma./sq. cm. could be maintained without any appreciable polarization of the electrodes. At higher current densities, in the range of 300 to 360 ma./sq. cm., considerable polarization was observed.

During recharge, strong concentration polarization was observed above a current density of about 100 ma./sq. cm. in a cell with an open-circuit voltage of 0.32 volts. When the current density was decreased to 70 ma./sq. cm., continuous recharging could be maintained without appreciable concentration polarization.

It should be pointed out that the above results indicate that, at the same bulk electrode compositions, concentration polarization begins at a lower current density during recharging than during discharge. These results agree generally with the conclusions reached by Wright (8) in his studies on concentration polarization of potassium amalgam electrodes. In that work, the diffusion coefficient of potassium was reported to be lower in dilute amalgams than in concentrated ones. Assuming that this holds true for sodium amalgams, at a given bulk concentration and current density, the differential sodium concentration (surface to bulk) in the amalgam will be lower on discharge than on charge. This will then correspond to a lower concentration polarization on discharge. The above results suggest that convection streams (due to density differences) do not play a significant role in adjusting the amalgam concentration at the amalgam-electrolyte interface. If the surface concentrations in the amalgam were determined by convection, the onset of appreciable concentration polarization would occur at higher current densities during charging because convection streams would tend to replenish the sodium content of the amalgam in the surface layer.

The value of the current density at which concentration polarization begins also seems to depend on the quality of the matrix. In another static cell experiment when a ceramic disc was used which had the same apparent porosity (41%), but had been prepared under different conditions, appreciable concentration polarization on discharge was observed at a current density as low as 120 ma./sq. cm. under otherwise similar experimental conditions.

The measured resistivity of the electrolyte-matrix combination was as low as 3.0 ohm-cm. in most of the static electrode cell experiments. This resistivity value is six times greater than the resistivity of the molten electrolyte itself. If one assumes that the effective area of contact between the liquid metal electrodes and the fused salt electrolyte is directly proportional to the porosity of the matrix (41%), and that all the pores are open straight channels perpendicular to the surface, one obtains a calculated optimum value of 1.23 ohm-cm. for the resistivity of the molten electrolyte. The experimental electrolyte resistivity value is 0.5 ohm-cm., $\frac{4}{10}$ as great as this, indicating an effective tortuosity factor of this magnitude. A systematic investigation of porous ceramic matrices should bring about improvements in their structural characteristics related to the tortuosity factor.

Experiments with a Flowing Electrode Cell

The basic features of the flowing electrode cell design were developed on the basis of the experience gained with the static electrode cell. Additional laboratory experiments (corrosion tests, study of various seal designs) were carried out as required by the progress of the work.

A cross-sectional sketch of the continuous cell is shown in Figure 5. A photograph of the assembled cell is shown in Figure 6. The main cell components are a cylindrical ceramic assembly and a tubular stainless steel structure which holds the ceramic parts. The electrolyte is contained in a porous ceramic tube which is supported by two dense ceramic end pieces. The dense-to-porous ceramic seal is pressurized by spring-loaded bellows which also serve to compensate for the difference in thermal expansion of the porous ceramic tube and the stainless steel cylinder. On the basis of corrosion tests, 410 stainless steel was selected for this design. High purity iron or tantalum gaskets were found to provide a satisfactory seal between the dense ceramic end pieces and the stainless steel flanges. The two liquid metal streams are pumped through the cell countercurrently, the mercury flowing upwards in the annulus and the amalgam flowing downward inside the porous tube. The presently used model has only one porous tube. An advanced design would have several porous tube matrices connected in parallel.

The use of tubular matrices has the following advantages over discs or rectangular plates:

1) The inherent structural strength of a tube is greater than that of a disc of the same surface area and wall thickness.

2) The size of the porous ceramic-to-dense ceramic and dense ceramic-to-stainless steel seal surface per effective electrolyte matrix surface area is smaller in the case of the tubular design than for a cell of the same capacity equipped with disc matrices.

3) The tubular construction lends itself better to countercurrent operation than a design utilizing disc matrices.

4) The use of tubular matrices makes the construction of very compact cell units possible. Preliminary designs of cell units with a capacity of several hundred watts indicate a "specific weight" of about 3 grams/sq. cm. of active electrolyte surface for a cell unit filled with liquid metal electrodes.

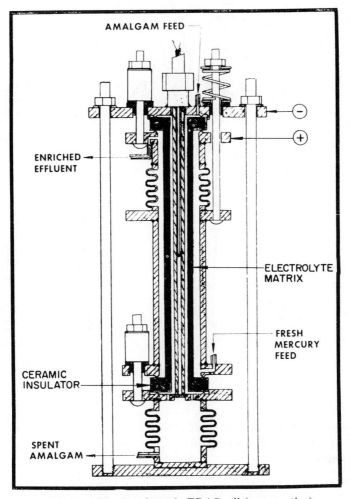

Figure 5. Flowing electrode TRAC cell (cross-section)

In the first experiments the regeneration of the amalgam was carried out electrically. In this case, two feed tanks and two receiver tanks were connected to the cell. After filling up the feed tanks with amalgams and electrolyte the whole assembly was placed in an electrically heated oven. The exit lines of the four tanks were connected to a control panel which served to regulate the flow of the liquid metals by argon pressure. In these experiments current densities of 50–100 ma./sq. cm. were maintained, and a power of 35 mw./sq. cm. was achieved at electrode flow velocities of 0.5–2.5 cm./min. The resistivity of the electrolyte-matrix varied from 6.0–12.0 ohm-cm. These resistivity values are 2–4× greater than the resistivity of the porous disc electrolyte-matrices used in the

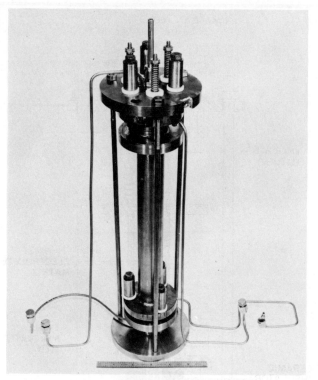

Figure 6. Flowing electrode TRAC cell

static cell experiments and indicate a requirement for modified fabrication methods for achieving a favorable pore structure in producing tubular porous ceramic matrices.

Two experiments were carried out with a complete cell incorporated in a regeneration loop system. In these experiments the amalgam exit streams were connected to the feed line of a continuous distillation unit (4), and the cell was supplied with mercury and concentrated amalgam from the distillate and distillation residue streams, respectively.

In the first experiment the complete system was operated for a period of 118 hrs., after which the run was terminated voluntarily. In the second experiment, operation was maintained at a temperature of about 490°C. for a total period of nearly 1200 hrs. During this test, after the complete system had run for 625 hrs., the loop portion was shut down for about 440 hrs. to replace two leaking valves (the cell remained in operation in an electrically rechargeable mode). The regeneration loop was then re-started and was operated together with the cell for an additional 130 hrs. The test was terminated when a bottom iron gasket of the cell began to leak. Later examination indicated that this leak was caused by air oxidation of the iron gasket, following failure of the external nitrogen purge system—not by corrosion caused by the TRAC materials.

Because of difficulties in the experimental production of porous ceramic tubes of proper porosity and pore size distribution, a low-porosity ceramic tube was used as matrix in these experiments. The apparent porosity of these tubes was only 15%, and this resulted in high electrolyte-matrix resistivity (50 to 55 ohm-cm.). These tubes held up very well during both experiments. The electrical resistivity of the electrolyte-matrix did not change during the experiment, indicating that both the fused salt electrolyte and the ceramic matrix were very stable under the operating conditions.

Conclusions

A mercury-sodium amalgam cell has been developed for a thermally regenerative, fuel cell system. The molten salt electrolyte has a low resistivity (0.5 ohm-cm. at 500°C.) and is chemically compatible with both the amalgam and the ceramic. The electrolyte-matrix showed resistivities as low as 3 ohm-cm.

A static electrode cell was constructed for electrochemical measurements with the system. Current densities as high as 200 ma./sq. cm. were achieved without appreciable electrode polarization at an operating temperature of 480–510°C. A flowing electrode cell with a tubular electrolyte-matrix was constructed. This cell, coupled with a regeneration loop, was successfully operated for a period of 1200 hrs. at a temperature of about 490°C. No deterioration of the electrolyte matrix occurred during the experiment.

The results of the chemical compatibility studies and the electrochemical measurements with the static and flowing electrode cells indicate that the described system is applicable for developing a reliable high-power density, thermally regenerative power unit.

Literature Cited

(1) Agruss, B., *J. Electrochem. Soc.* **110,** 1097 (1963).
(2) Bredig, M. A., "Molten Salt Chemistry," M. Blander, ed., Interscience Publishers, New York, 1964.
(3) Bredig, M. A., Johnson, J. W., Smith, W. T., Jr., *J. Am. Chem. Soc.* **77,** 307 (1955).
(4) Groce, I. J., Oldenkamp, R. D., ADVAN. CHEM. SER. **64,** 43 (1967).
(5) Hauffe, K., *Z. Electrochem.* **46,** 348 (1940).
(6) Iverson, M. L., Recht, H. L., "The Activity of Sodium in Sodium Amalgams from EMF Measurements," in preparation.

(7) Mangus, J. D., "Research and Development of an Advanced Laboratory Liquid Metal Regenerative Fuel Cell," Technical Documentary Report No. APL-TDR-64-41, Allison Division, General Motors Corp., Indianapolis, 1964.

(8) Wright, R. B., "Diffusion of Potassium in a Liquid Metal Cell," Engineering Department Report No. 3814, Allison Division, General Motors Corp., Indianapolis, 1964.

(9) Yeager, E., Proceedings of the 12th Annual Battery Research and Development Conference, Asbury Park, N. J., 1959, pp. 2–4.

RECEIVED May 9, 1966.

Development of a Thermally Regenerative Sodium-Mercury Galvanic System

Part II. Design, Construction, and Testing of a Thermally Regenerative Sodium-Mercury Galvanic System[1]

I. J. GROCE and R. D. OLDENKAMP

Research and Technology Division, Atomics International, A Division of North American Aviation, Inc., Canoga Park, Calif.

In operating Atomics International's Thermally Regenerative Alloy Cell (TRAC) system, the sodium amalgam stream from the cell battery must be converted to a sodium-rich amalgam and mercury. This is done in the regenerator which distills and separates a mercury fraction, condenses the mercury vapor, cools both streams, and then recirculates them to the cells. A test loop was built and operated to study these regeneration processes. Two tests were made with the regeneration loop connected to single-matrix TRAC cells—one for 116 hours, and another for 1197 hours. The cell internal resistance did not change during either test, indicating that the cell materials are compatible with the working fluids under flow conditions. The tests also demonstrated the long-term operability of the TRAC system.

The thermally-regenerative energy conversion system under development at Atomics International has been named the "TRAC System," from the initials of the words "thermally-regenerative alloy cell." The TRAC system uses galvanic cells, in which liquid metal streams of sodium and mercury are allowed to combine electrochemically to produce an alloy plus electrical energy. The alloy produced by the cells is regenerated

---

[1] Work performed under company-sponsored, independent research and development program.

with heat, yielding the two liquid metal streams which are recirculated to the cells to continue the process.

The TRAC system can be considered in two parts—the galvanic cell battery and the regeneration system. The TRAC cell and the cell development program are described elsewhere (4). This paper summarizes the regeneration system development and describes the test program carried out to study first the regeneration system alone, and then a complete TRAC system.

The TRAC system flow diagram is shown in Figure 1. The regeneration system includes all components except the cell battery. Each cell in the battery consists of an anode chamber and a cathode chamber, separated by the electrolyte matrix. Continuous streams of sodium-rich amalgam and nearly pure mercury flow through these chambers, and sodium is transferred from anode to cathode in each cell, causing an electrical current to flow through an external circuit connecting the electrodes. This mass transfer reduces the anode sodium concentration and increases the cathode sodium concentration, so that both of these streams leave the cells as dilute amalgams. They then go to the regeneration system.

In the regeneration system, the two dilute amalgam streams are combined and pumped to a boiler, where heat from an external heat source is used to boil the mixture. This produces a vapor phase of nearly pure mercury and a liquid phase of sodium-rich amalgam. The liquid and vapor phases are then separated, both are cooled to the cell temperature, and the vapor phase is condensed. The two liquid streams are then returned to the cells to repeat the process.

The regenerator consists of a pump, boiler, heat source, vapor-liquid separator, cooler, condenser, and associated tubing, valves, and controls.

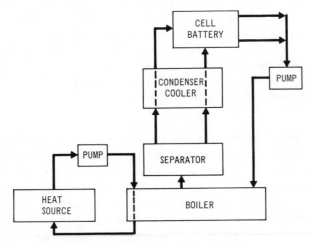

Figure 1. Basic TRAC flow diagram

For a space power system, the vapor-liquid separator will have to perform well under zero-gravity conditions, where there is no weight difference between the two phases. Also, the heat rejected in the cooler and condenser will have to be transferred to space through a radiator. The thermal efficiency of the system can be improved by heat exchange between the relatively cool material leaving the cells and the hot material leaving the separator. Further, if the pump is electromagnetic and powered by the TRAC cells, the system will have no moving parts. This will eliminate bearing wear and rotating seal problems and add to the inherent dependability of the power plant. A space TRAC system would then have the flow diagram shown as Figure 2.

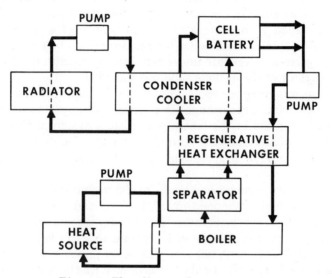

Figure 2. Flow diagram for a space system

None of these components is unique in concept; all are required, for example, in a mercury Rankine-cycle power plant. However, the conditions of high sodium concentration and low flow rate under which they must operate are unique to TRAC. Because of this, existing liquid metal loop technology for mercury Rankine-cycle plants cannot be used directly in designing TRAC components. For this, additional data for boiling, cooling, condensing, separating, and pumping sodium-mercury amalgams under TRAC conditions were needed. Further, TRAC has other unique features to be studied. It was necessary to know the extent of any chemical and/or physical reactions between the molten salt electrolyte, the ceramic matrix, and the flowing amalgam streams and the effect of any such reactions on the regeneration system performance. To study these problems experimentally requires an actual regeneration test loop, built to be operated under different conditions with various component designs. Such a loop has been designed, built, and operated at Atomics International. It is described below, along with the results of the first tests.

Design and Construction of the Test Loop

In designing the test loop, it was decided that emphasis should be placed on testing and evaluating components which should work well under zero gravity conditions, evaluating materials of construction, and studying cell-loop interactions. For simplicity of operation, the heat exchanger and radiator were omitted, cooling water was used to remove waste heat, and electrical heaters were used. An electromagnetic pump operated by a separate laboratory power supply was provided. The entire loop was designed to operate at the temperature of a nuclear reactor powered system—i.e., with a boiler temperature of up to 1300°F., and the boiler was designed to operate under zero gravity conditions. Also, a centrifugal separator of the cyclone type was included.

The loop was designed to use 5 kw. of electrical heat. This size loop was chosen as being large enough for practical tests, yet small enough to be built and operated in the laboratory. Also, a system with this power input would ultimately be able to produce enough electricity to power its own pump and provide a good demonstration of an integrated cell-loop system.

In preliminary calculations made to determine flow rates and heat requirements, a boiler temperature of 1280°F. and cell temperature of 900°F. were chosen. Then, because the mercury stream entering the cell contains almost no sodium, the cell pressure was the vapor pressure of mercury at 900°F., or about 100 psia. The boiler pressure was only slightly higher than the cell pressure, or about 105 psia. With the boiler temperature and pressure known, the equilibrium compositions of the vapor and liquid leaving the boiler could be determined from equilibrium data for the sodium-mercury system. The vapor pressures of sodium-mercury amalgams were measured and used to calculate the equilibrium compositions of the liquid and vapor phases. At 1280°F. the vapor composition was 0.2 atom percent (a/o) sodium and the liquid was 38.5 a/o sodium. It was assumed that the streams entering the cell would have these compositions. It then remained to estimate the flow rates, cell power, and efficiency.

The method used to estimate cell output as a function of the anode and cathode flow rates and inlet compositions is described elsewhere (7). For the case where the anode and cathode exit compositions are the same and the voltage is the same at both ends of the cell, mass balances indicated the sodium concentration in the effluent streams would be 13 a/o sodium, and that the molar flow rate of mercury through the cathode compartment would be 3.2 times that through the anode compartment. Under these conditions the 5 kw. boiler could distill the cathode material (mercury) at the rate of about 0.8 gram mole/sec. Cells using this material would produce about 300 watts at 0.3 volt for a system efficiency of 6%. The individual components used in the test loop were then designed based on these calculations.

The flow diagram for the test loop is shown in Figure 3. Because no cells were available at the beginning of the test program, two reservoirs were used in their place. The temperature range of the TRAC loop, 900 to 1300°F., was not so high that refractory metals or other exotic materials were needed. However, a consideration affecting choice of materials of construction was the corrosion or dissolution caused by sodium and mercury metal and mercury vapor. Recent data (*6, 7*) indicated that the 400-series stainless steels would probably be suitable materials for components exposed to high temperature mercury, so these materials were used in the boiler, separator, and condenser, and in the amalgam line between the separator and reservoir. Other lower temperature components were made of type 316 stainless steel.

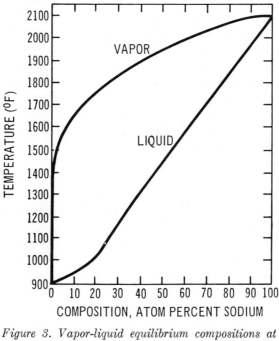

Figure 3. Vapor-liquid equilibrium compositions at 100 psia

The boiler was based on the design concept of a SNAP-2 mercury boiler (*5*). A $\frac{1}{2}$-in. I.D. tube of type 410 stainless steel was chosen for the boiler tube, and a twisted-ribbon turbulator was included to insure improved contact between the heat transfer surface and the working fluid, as would be required under zero gravity. Using the flow rates and heat requirements previously calculated, a heat transfer area was calculated which required a tube 12.6 ft. long, coiled into a helix. The pressure drop in the boiler was estimated at 5 psi.

Electrical heaters were used to heat the boiler tube. This was done by inserting the tube inside a shell of stainless steel, with the shell filled with sodium metal. A 3-kw. electrical immersion heater was inserted into the sodium in the middle of the coil, and five 400-watt strip heaters were mounted around the outside of the shell. An argon blanket was provided above the sodium to allow room for thermal expansion.

The separator was designed as a centrifugal cyclone. Mercury vapor and liquid amalgam enter the separator tangentially, where their velocities cause them to spin around the inside wall, forcing the vapor to the center and out the top.

It should be noted that equilibrium between liquid and vapor is approached in the separator. Thus, if the boiling material reaches the separator well-mixed, as it should, then a one-theoretical-plate separation should occur. This is the most that can be achieved with one stage separation under zero gravity conditions.

The condenser was a single straight tube made of 410 stainless steel. This tube had four fins on the outside parallel to the tube axis and spaced 90° apart, which were cooled by water in copper cooling coils. The finned tube design was used to simulate space radiator heat transfer conditions.

The estimated pressure drop around the complete loop, including pressure losses in the cells, was 8 psi. With a 2-psi safety margin a pump capable of developing 10 psi was needed. The pump throughput was known from the flow rates and compositions of the cell exit streams, and the pump operating temperature was taken to be 900°F. A Faraday electromagnetic pump was designed to these specifications (2). The pump used a permanent magnet of 4700 gauss field strength, and a power source of up to 600 amp., at 0.8 volt. This power was supplied by a high-current rectifier system, operated from the laboratory service A-C supply.

The reservoirs were type 316 stainless steel cylinders, designed to provide a storage capacity for the liquid metals plus an argon blanket space above the liquid metal surfaces. This gas blanket was used to control the system pressure. The gas spaces at the tops of the two reservoirs were connected to equalize the pressure on the anode and cathode legs of the loop. The connecting tubing was type 316 stainless steel everywhere except between the separator and amalgam reservoir, where type 410 stainless steel was used. Stainless steel bellows valves were used to avoid contamination from packing and to assure leak tightness. Two of the valves were on sample lines which were used to sample the amalgam and mercury stream compositions.

Chromel-alumel thermocouples were used to measure the temperature at 22 different points on the outside of the loop, including the boiler tube, condenser tube, and separator. The system pressure was measured at the argon blanket above the liquid metal level in the reservoirs, using a stainless steel Bourdon tube gage.

Flow measurements were provided by two electromagnetic flowmeters, one in the amalgam line and one in the mercury line. These operated much like the pump and used identical magnets. Their output signal was an emf of the order of 0.1 mv. These flowmeters were positioned so as to avoid interference by signals from the pump.

All tubing connections were welded except for those in the argon lines, which used "Swagelok" fittings. The loop was assembled in a vented, fireproof enclosure. The final assembly is shown, with the front panels of the enclosure removed, in Figure 4.

Operation of the Test Loop

The loop was filled with a 14 atom percent sodium amalgam, and then operated at boiler temperatures of 1000°F. and 1200°F., with the reservoirs maintained at 900°F. Samples of amalgam and mercury were taken to determine the separation obtained in the boiler (Figures 5 and 6) and to calibrate the flowmeters. The enriched amalgam compositions from the separator were found to be 35 atom percent sodium at 1200°F. and 90 psia, and 17 atom percent sodium at 1000°F. and 90 psia. These values are almost identical to the values for a one-theoretical-plate distillation under the same conditions. Flow rates equal to design values were obtained.

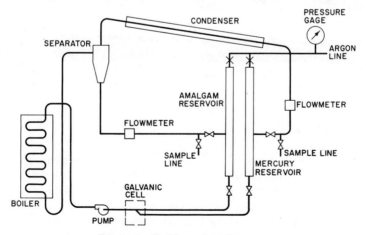

Figure 4. Test loop flow diagram

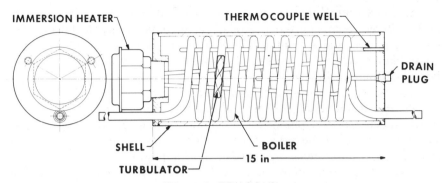

Figure 5. TRAC boiler

Figure 6. Assembled TRAC test loop

Testing of the Complete System

When a flowing electrode TRAC cell became available, tests of the combined system—cell plus regeneration loop—were carried out. Two such tests were performed. In both tests, the cell used was a single tube matrix cell of the type described by Heredy *et al.* (*4*).

Type 304 stainless steel feed and return lines were used to connect the cell into the loop between the reservoirs and the pump inlet. A bypass line and bypass throttle valve were provided and used to regulate the flow rate of material through the cell. The cell was installed in a constant temperature electric oven, and electric heaters were provided for the cell feed and return lines.

In the first test, the boiler temperature was kept at about 1250°F. and the cell at 950°F. The system was operated for 116 hrs. and then shut down. The regeneration loop performed satisfactorily during the test, but the pressure drop in the loop increased slowly as the test proceeded. This was evidently due to the build-up of corrosion product deposits, since loose corrosion products, mainly iron with traces of other stainless steel constituents, were found on cleaning out the loop. Excess salt from the cell (introduced during the matrix impregnation) was also found in the loop. However, no significant loss of electrolyte from the cell matrix pores occurred, because the cell internal resistance did not change measurably during the test. The performance of the cell during this test and the second test is described in Reference *4*.

When the cell was disassembled after the first test, the iron gasket seals were found to be corroding externally, evidently from oxygen in the air. To avoid this in the second test, a system was installed in the cell oven to purge the gas spaces around the seals with dried, deoxygenated nitrogen. The regeneration loop was drained, cleaned, dried, and reloaded with fresh amalgam for the second test.

The second test lasted for a total of 1197 hrs. but was interrupted by a repair period after 625 hrs. of continuous operation. In this test, the boiler temperature was kept between 1240 and 1280°F. and the cell at about 910°F. The loop performance was quite satisfactory at first, but then again a gradual increase in pressure drop was observed. Then, after 625 hrs. of operation, the stainless steel bellows in two of the valves began to leak. These valves were replaced, which necessitated draining, cleaning, and reloading the loop. During this period, the cell was kept filled with amalgam and mercury and maintained at 910°F., but with no flow through it. After the loop was repaired, flow through the cell was reestablished and the test continued, with the system functioning as before. After a total of 1197 hrs. of testing, a lower cell gasket failed due to a broken lower nitrogen purge line, and the test had to be terminated.

During the test, the cell and loop had been operated together for a total of 750 hrs., and the cell had been in contact with the liquid metals for the entire 1197 hrs. The cell internal resistance had not changed during this time, indicating that the electrolyte was not leached out or removed from the matrix pores. Mercury corrosion products were again evident in the loop; the failure of the two valve bellows was probably due to mercury corrosion. Another factor which may have caused or contributed to the bellows failure is carbon transfer between the various steels—caused by the sodium. Sodium is an effective transport medium for carbon (*1, 3*), tending to carry it from regions of high activity to regions of low activity. The valve bellows were made of type 347 stainless steel, and there were also types 304, 316, and 410 present in the loop. The flowing sodium may have decarburized the high carbon type 410 stainless steel and carburized the other steels. A single alloy such as "Haynes 25" should work better than the mixture of steels used. For TRAC systems operating with boiler temperature of 1600°F. or higher, it will probably be necessary to use refractory metals such as tantalum to avoid the mercury and sodium corrosion problems.

The system tests successfully demonstrated the operability of the TRAC system and showed that the TRAC cell materials will perform satisfactorily for long periods.

Literature Cited

(1) Anderson, W. J., Sneesby, G. V., "Carburization of Austenitic Stainless Steel in Liquid Sodium," NAA-SR-2582.
(2) Guon, J., AI-64-TDR-68, April 8, 1964.
(3) Hayes, W. C., Shipard, O. C., "Corrosion and Decarburization of the Ferritic Chromium-Molybdenum Steels in Sodium Coolant Systems," NAA-SR-2973.
(4) Herédy, L. A., Iverson, M. L., Ulrich, G. D., Recht, H. L., ADVAN. CHEM. SER. 64, 30 (1967).
(5) NAA-SR-7945.
(6) Nejedlik, J. F., Vargo, E. J., Electrochem. Technol. 3, 250 (1965).
(7) Oldenkamp, R. D., Recht, H. L., ADVAN. CHEM. SER. 64, 53 (1967).
(8) Scheuermann, C. M., Barrett, C. A., Londermilk, W. H., Rosenblum, L., Astronautics and Aerospace Engineering 1, 40 (1963).

RECEIVED May 9, 1966.

Development of a Thermally Regenerative Sodium-Mercury Galvanic System

Part III. Performance Analysis for a Nuclear Reactor-Powered, Thermally Regenerative Sodium-Mercury Galvanic System[1]

R. D. OLDENKAMP and H. L. RECHT

Research and Technology Division, Atomics International, A Division of North American Aviation, Inc., Canoga Park, Calif.

The Thermal Regenerative Alloy Cell (TRAC) system is a closed-cycle apparatus which converts thermal energy into electricity, with an overall efficiency limited to the Carnot-cycle value. Necessary irreversibilities reduce this by about one-half. For space application, efficiency must be considered primarily in its effect on the specific power of the system. In designing a TRAC system, component weights can be reduced at the cost of efficiency, but this requires a heavier heat source and radiator and increases pumping power requirements. A performance analysis, considering component weights and pumping power requirements, determines the best system design for space application. Component weights estimated for many different sets of anode and cathode stream cell exit compositions indicate that the optimum system will have a specific power of about 10 watts/lb., unshielded, and an overall efficiency of about 7%.

T he Thermally Regenerative Alloy Cell (TRAC) system is a device which uses heat to regenerate the cell products which, in turn, produce electricity. It is composed of two main parts: the liquid alloy galvanic cell battery which produces the electricity, and the regeneration system

[1] Work performed under company-sponsored independent research and development program.

which uses primary heat and supplies the reactants to the cells. The experimental programs undertaken at Atomics International to develop these two separate parts have been described elsewhere in this volume.

For specific application as an auxiliary power plant for spacecraft, the cell battery and regeneration system must not only be combined into a complete system but generally combined so as to produce the most power/lb. of total system weight—i.e., to give maximum specific power output. To build such an optimized system, the proper combination of component capacities and system operating conditions must be found. This was done using certain limiting assumptions, by a mathematical analysis, which predicted the maximum specific power obtainable and the conditions required for its achievement. This paper describes the analysis and discusses the results which were obtained.

The TRAC systems can use heat from any source producing this heat at temperatures over 1100°F. ($\sim$ 600°C.). These sources include nuclear reactors, radioisotopes, solar collectors, and even fossil fuels. A reactor heat source was selected for this analysis.

The system studied was one powered by a SNAP-8 nuclear reactor which could supply 600 kw. of thermal power at a maximum temperature of 1300°F. (704°C.).

When the TRAC cell battery and regeneration system are combined, the complete power plant, whose flow diagram is shown in Figure 1, results. The cell battery receives a continuous supply of nearly pure mercury cathode material (0.2 atom% sodium amalgam under conditions herein considered) and molten sodium-rich amalgam anode material (38.5 atom% sodium) from the regeneration system. This material is allowed to react electrochemically in the cell battery, producing electrical power, and the spent streams are returned for regeneration.

In the regeneration system, the spent streams are combined and pumped electromagnetically through a heat exchanger to a boiler-separator. Here heat from the SNAP-8 NaK coolant stream is used to vaporize

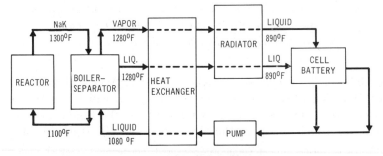

Figure 1. TRAC flow diagram

mercury, producing the cathode material in vapor form. The liquid remaining becomes the enriched anode material.

The cathode vapor phase is then separated from the liquid, and the two streams are passed back through the heat exchanger where they give up heat to the incoming boiler feed. Both cathode and anode feed streams then pass into a radiator, where they are cooled to the 890°F. (477°C.) cell temperature and where the cathode material is condensed. The streams are then returned to the cells to repeat the process and generate more electricity.

The analysis was done to study the interactions of the individual components in a complete system, to determine the capacities of the components required to produce the maximum power per unit system weight, and to assess the maximum specific power obtainable.

In performing the analysis, certain technical requirements which imposed limits on the range of system operating conditions had to be considered. These limits were fixed by the temperature requirements of the TRAC cells and by the reactor heat source temperature limit. The TRAC cells use a molten sodium salt electrolyte which has a melting point of 890°F. (477°C.). This fixes the lowest temperature at which the cells can operate. It also fixes the cell pressure, because the cathode stream entering each cell is nearly pure mercury at its own vapor pressure. This pressure is 100 psia at the cell temperature. With the cell pressure fixed, the pressures at all other points in the system are also fixed and can be estimated by adding calculated pressure drops to the cell pressure. In this way, the pressure at the boiler-separator exit was calculated to be 105 psia.

The boiler temperature is limited by the reactor operating temperature. The SNAP-8 reactor will operate with coolant inlet and exit temperatures of 1100°F. (593°C.) and 1300°F. (704°C.), respectively. This puts upper limits on the boiler inlet and exit temperatures. Because the boiling temperature of the amalgam increases with increased sodium concentration, a relatively constant temperature drop between the reactor coolant and the boiling amalgam throughout the boiler-separator can be maintained with countercurrent operation. Thus, heat transfer occurs at a high rate over the entire temperature range between boiler inlet and exit. This should make it possible to achieve a small temperature difference between the reactor coolant and the boiler-separator stream. In this analysis, a 20°F. temperature drop between the reactor coolant and the boiler stream was assumed so that the temperature of the material leaving the boiler-separator was taken to be 1280°F. (693°C.).

With the temperature and pressure at the boiler-separator exit both fixed, the equilibrium compositions of the liquid and vapor leaving this component were also fixed. At 1280°F. (693°C.) and 105 psia, these compositions were 38.5 atom% (a/o) sodium in the liquid (anode) and 0.2 a/o sodium in the vapor (cathode). These were then the inlet concentrations of the streams fed to the cells. Only an equilibrium separation, equivalent to a one-theoretical-plate distillation, was assumed here because a multistage distillation cannot be carried out under zero-gravity conditions without actual mechanical separation of the phases between each stage.

A cell in the TRAC battery may be designed to consist of many parallel ceramic tubes contained within a hexagonal cylindrical shell. The cross-section of such a cell is shown in Figure 2. The ceramic tubes are porous, and the pores are filled with the molten salt electrolyte. The anode stream flows through the inside of each tube, and the cathode stream flows countercurrently outside the tubes and inside the shell. This arrangement was chosen so that the cathode-electrolyte interface was the larger, because it was felt that any concentration polarization which occurred would occur principally at the cathode.

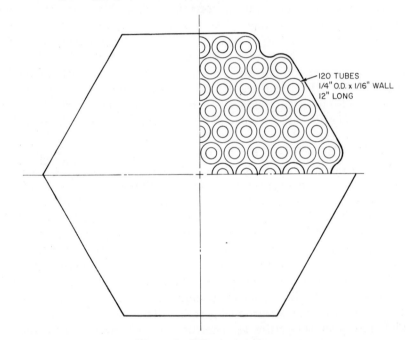

120 TUBES
1/4" O.D. x 1/16" WALL
12" LONG

Figure 2. Cell cross section

Figure 3 illustrates the electrochemical reactions which occur in the cells. Sodium from the anode stream is oxidized to sodium ions at the anode-electrolyte interface, and these ions pass through the molten salt electrolyte in the pores of the ceramic tubes. They are then reduced at the cathode-electrolyte interface and form sodium-mercury compounds. As the cell reaction takes place, with a current flowing through a load connected to the electrodes, a net transfer of sodium occurs. This causes the anode and cathode concentrations to change in the directions of the

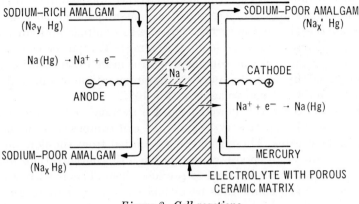

Figure 3. Cell reactions

flowing streams. Because the concentrations, and hence the interface potentials, vary along the tube length, the cell voltage and power produced is a rather complex function of the stream flow rates and the inlet compositions.

In general, larger flow rates cause larger concentration gradients across the electrolyte throughout each cell and thus produce more power per cell. However, larger flow rates are also less efficient because the anode and cathode streams leave the battery with more unreacted material. Thus, more heat input per unit of cell power output is required. There is, then, a relationship between efficiency and weight. The optimum TRAC plant must be the best compromise between one with high power per cell, using a lighter cell battery but producing less power from a given heat source, and a more efficient system, which produces more power but which requires a heavier cell battery.

In the cells, for a given flow rate, the concentration of sodium in the anode and cathode streams varies from inlet to exit. The cell potential at any point along a cell tube is determined by the concentration difference between the anode and cathode streams at that point. This dependence is shown in Figure 4, which gives the potential of a sodium amalgam with reference to a pure sodium electrode. Part of this curve was obtained at Atomics International. The remainder had been measured by Hauffe (5). Note that this curve is nonlinear. It would be desirable to determine the concentrations, potential, and sodium transfer rate along each tube from the solutions to a set of partial differential equations describing the mass transfer processes in each cell. These equations, however, are made nonlinear by the above relationship so that it is difficult to obtain explicit solutions for them. As an approximation, for this analysis, the average of the potentials across the cell at the anode inlet and exit was calculated and used to estimate the average cell current from the known cell resistance and load resistance. In this, the load resistance was assumed to be equal to the internal cell resistance, and it was assumed that no polarization other than the IR drop occurred. The average voltage and current then gave the cell power and sodium transfer rate. The power calculated by this averaging method was compared with a more exact solution for one case, obtained by a finite difference approximation of the differential equations, and was found to agree within 10%.

To estimate the cell power using the average of the inlet and exit voltages, it was first necessary to know the exit compositions of the anode and cathode streams. These could be calculated from the flow rates, but it was more direct to choose values for the exit concentrations and then calculate the flow rates required to produce them. This is what was done. The power per cell could thus be estimated for any pair of anode and cathode exit compositions, and the rate of sodium transfer per cell could then be calculated from the cell current. After this, mass balances were used to calculate the flow rates of the anode and cathode streams into, and out of, each cell. Thus, for a given pair of anode and cathode exit compositions, the power produced per cell and the anode and cathode feed rate requirements per cell were determined. These were then used to calculate the heat requirements per cell and, with a fixed total heat input, determine the number of cells which could be supplied. The total system electrical power output was then calculated. The capacities and weights

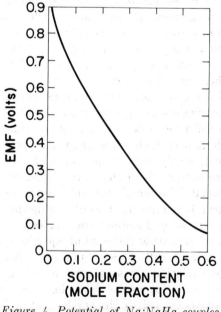

Figure 4. Potential of Na:NaHg couples at 375°C.

of the other components were then estimated. The total system weight was thus obtained and used to calculate the specific power output.

The entire set of calculations was then repeated for each paired set of exit compositions until the pair yielding the maximum specific power under the assumed conditions was found.

In calculating the weights of components having given capacities, individual design optimization studies could not be performed. Instead, weights were estimated using the results of existing calculations for other systems and available design calculation guidelines. The methods used and parameter values assumed in treating each component will now be discussed briefly.

The cells were assumed to contain 120 tubes, each $\frac{1}{4}$-in. OD with $\frac{1}{16}$-in. thick walls, 12 in. long. The shell of each cell was $3\frac{1}{2}$-in. ID. The log-mean mass transfer area per cell was 820 sq. in. (5300 sq. cm.), and the weight varied from 30 to 33 lb., depending on the average densities of the amalgams it contained. The resistivity-thickness product of the tubes was taken to be 0.35 ohm-sq. cm. The power produced per cell depended on the anode and cathode flow rates, as previously discussed.

The pump was a direct-current Faraday pump requiring low-voltage and high-current, which is operated with power from the cells. It was required to develop 10 psi and was assumed to be 5% efficient. The weight was taken as 1 lb./watt of output. These values were based on design calculations for existing pumps (*4*). The NaK pump in the reactor coolant loop was of similar type.

The heat exchanger was assumed to have an overall heat transfer coefficient of 1000 Btu/hr., sq. ft., °F. (*2*) and to weigh 10 lb./sq. ft. of heat transfer area, including amalgam inventory. Its weight varied with the anode and cathode flow rates, which determined the temperature of the incoming material. The material leaving this component was assumed to be at 1080°F. (582°C.) in all cases.

The boiler-separator was planned to be a heated-wall cyclone separator, with heat supplied by the reactor NaK coolant stream. The momentum of the liquid-vapor mixture would hold the liquid against the walls, enhancing heat transfer, and separate out the vapor which would be forced to the center. The overall heat transfer coefficient here was taken to be 2000 Btu./hr., sq. ft., °F., and the weight to be 10 lb./sq. ft. of heat transfer area (*2*), including inventory. With a temperature gradient of 20°F. and a heat input of 600 thermal kw., the boiler-separator heat transfer area was fixed at 51.2 sq. ft. for all cases, giving a boiler weight of 512 lb.

The reactor heat source was a 600-kw. (thermal) SNAP-8 reactor, which was taken to weigh 835 lb., including the core, case, pump, piping, NaK inventory, and controls (*1*).

The condenser-radiator was assumed to reject all waste heat at its exit temperature of 890°F. (477°C.). The heat rejection rate was taken to be 1.2 kw./sq. ft. and the weight to be 2 lb./sq. ft., including amalgam inventory and meteoroid shield. These values were based on use of a stainless steel tube radiator with aluminum fins (3).

The above values were used to estimate the weights of the components required for each set of anode and cathode exit compositions investigated. The specific power for each set was then calculated and plotted as a function of cathode exit composition for different anode exit compositions. The results are shown in Figure 5. The optimum plant, on the basis of the assumptions previously described, corresponds to cathode and anode exit compositions of about 27.5 and 35 a/o sodium, respectively. The specific power of this plant was calculated to be 10 watts/lb., unshielded, and the efficiency was 7.0%. The plant would thus weigh 4200 lb. and produce 42 kw. (electrical) of net power.

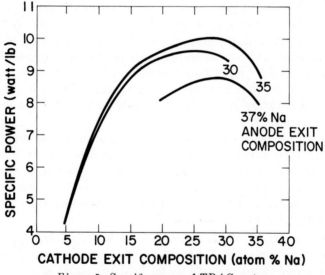

Figure 5. Specific power of TRAC systems

The characteristics of this plant are shown in Table I. Here, it can be seen that the cell battery makes up nearly half of the total weight. Reducing this battery weight is most important if plant specific power is to be increased beyond the calculated value. One way this can be done is to reduce the amalgam holdup in each cell. Alternate cell configurations are being considered to accomplish this.

The rather small radiator area required should be noted, because it will make a compact plant possible. This is a result of the high heat rejection temperature.

Table I. Calculated Characteristics of a TRAC Plant

Weight, Cells	1850
Radiator	930
Reactor	835
Boiler-Separator	512
Heat Exchanger	13
Pump	48
Tubing and Structure	50
Total	4238 lbs.

Radiator Area	465 sq. ft.
Heat Input	600 kw.
Heat Rejected	557 kw.
Pumping Power	2 kw.
Output Power, Net	42 kw.
Specific Power	$\sim$ 10 watts/lb.
Efficiency	7%

In conclusion, it should be restated that the analysis presented was only approximate. However, the results indicate the potential of TRAC systems for space power plants.

Literature Cited

(1) A.I.-7437, Aug. 6, 1962.
(2) Allison Division, General Motors Corp., E. D. Report 3113 (Dec. 5, 1962).
(3) Coombs, M. G., Stone, R. A., "Space Heat Rejection," A.I.-9068, Oct. 11, 1963.
(4) Guon, J., A.I.-64-TDR-68, Apr. 8, 1964.
(5) Hauffe, K., *Z. Electrochem.* **46,** 348 (1940).

RECEIVED May 9, 1966.

7

The Thermally Regenerative Liquid Metal Concentration Cell

B. AGRUSS and H. R. KARAS

Allison Division, The Energy Conversion Division, General Motors Co., Indianapolis, Ind.

Three basic schemes are described herein for thermal regeneration of fuel cell reaction products. A program was initiated to investigate a system wherein a liquid metal alloy product of a liquid metal concentration cell is thermally separated into solute and solvent-rich phases which are returned to the cell. It was seen that an alkali metal anode would contribute to a high cell potential, and a molten salt electrolyte would yield excellent conductivity and polarization characteristics. Na/Sn, Na/Hg, and K/Hg concentration cells have been investigated, and a three-cell, regenerative K/Hg battery was operated for a period of 60 hrs. Power densities better than 100 watts/sq. ft. have been attained at a potential of 0.55 volt. System efficiencies for thermally regenerative, liquid metal concentration cells compare favorably with projected system efficiencies for other types of thermally regenerative cells and systems.

Developing fuel cells to produce electrical power has come to the fore within the past 10 to 15 years. It is historically noteworthy that from 1956 to the present, the number of fuel cell papers has increased sharply. The five-year period extending from 1956 through 1960 shows no papers published and just one introductory round-table discussion, held by the Battery Division of the Electrochemical Society. In marked contrast, the second five-year period, from 1961 through 1964, saw 131 papers published by industry, government, and academic institutions. At the Power Sources Conference of 1958, five papers were contributed at the solitary session of fuel cells. At the 1964 conference, the number of papers advanced to 12, and the number of sessions doubled. During the year 1964, there were 10 different symposia on fuel cells.

There is, then, a consensus in a significant segment of the scientific community that fuel cells have a potentially important role in our future, due to the direct, clean, and efficient conversion of chemical to electrical energy expected from such devices. The approaching Apollo mission can well be considered as the end of a gestation period leading to the birth of a practical, primary, hydrogen-oxygen device. A comparison might be drawn with the automobile industry at the turn of the century, when the feasibility of many different mechanisms had been shown in workshops all over the world. Apollo corresponds to the first "wheel-out" of a practical device.

The next step beyond the practical fuel cell is the coupling of an electrochemical system in a closed cycle with a thermal source freely accessible or of long duration—e.g., solar, nuclear, or isotopic heat. This would, of course, be essential in special applications (space missions), limiting the carrying of the large bulk of fuel needed for long operating periods. With the internal combustion engine, regenerative operation with a single charge of fuel is difficult owing to the complexity of reactions involved. Closed cycle regenerative systems using metal and organic vapor turbines are being investigated mainly to reduce weight and bulkiness. But if the fuel cell is considered with the multiplicity of reactions available, could not some regenerative scheme be worked out to compete with the vapor cycle? The approaching ready availability of thermal energy generated by solar, nuclear, or isotopic devices almost demands a strong case for a fuel cell system in which reaction products are thermally regenerated.

Thermal Regeneration

There are three general schemes for thermal regeneration, as follows:

a) Identical cells are operated in opposition with a thermal gradient placed between them.

b) Reaction products are thermally decomposed to their original reactant form.

c) A liquid metal alloy, product of a liquid metal concentration cell, is thermally separated into solute and solvent-rich phases which are returned to the cell (A special case of B).

In cells of Scheme A, reactants are chosen such that there is a large thermal coefficient of voltage. The load circuit is placed in series with the two cells (Figure 1); hence, products formed in the first cell are transferred to the second cell, where electrolysis occurs. The restored reactants are now returned to the first cell for further reaction. These systems have been reviewed (*1, 13*) but little encouragement was given for practical systems.

In Scheme B the reaction products are broken down thermally, such as is done in the lithium-hydride system (Figure 2). Alternatively, the

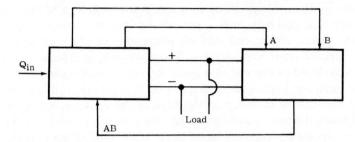

Figure 1. Schematic of thermally regenerative fuel cell (electrothermal regeneration)

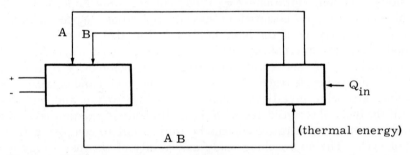

Figure 2. Schematic of thermally regenerative fuel cell (thermomechanical regeneration)

reaction products can be broken down to the reactants electrochemically
by reversing the current through the cell.

Scheme C is really a special case of Scheme B but does not necessarily
involve compound formation. Cell products are restored by normal distillation procedures. Reactants A and B are now metals, not compounds.

All the above schemes are essentially heat engines subject to the
second law of thermodynamics. They require both a heat source and a heat
sink. The thermodynamics and theoretical efficiencies of regenerative systems (3, 4, 7, 9) have been more than adequately covered by many authors
and need not be repeated here. The special case of regenerative liquid
metal systems was covered by Henderson (5) and also by Oldenkamp and
Recht, and Hesson in this monograph. Expressions for thermal efficiency
are derived and compared to Carnot cycle efficiencies. These papers can
be consulted to obtain approximate theoretical efficiencies.

Liquid Metal Concentration Cells

A survey was made of the literature (6) in a search for thermally
decomposable inorganic compounds, based on the following criteria:
   a) Easy separation of reaction products
   b) Simple reactions

c) Proper temperature range

d) Reasonable kinetics

e) Thermodynamic considerations

The findings of the survey gave a list of 20 compounds which would offer reasonable regenerative schemes. Further detailed analysis reduced this list until just a few suitable combinations were left.

A re-evaluation affirmed that a system having the desired high power-to-weight ratio must be based on a molten salt electrolyte, because the conductivity of molten salt electrolytes is an order of magnitude higher than those of comparable aqueous systems (Figure 3). In addition, the temperature of operation and general characteristics of fused salts would lead to excellent electrode kinetics and consequently low polarization. Interest then became centered on a concentration cell utilizing a molten salt electrolyte and liquid metals as cell reactants. Such a cell can be represented schematically as:

$$A_{a_1} \;\; (B) \quad | \;\; A^+ \;\; | \quad A_{a_2} \;\; (B) \tag{1}$$

$$A_{a_0} \qquad | \;\; A^+ \;\; | \quad A_{a_2} \;\; (B) \tag{1a}$$

in which A and B represent a wide variety of metals, and a_1 and a_2 are the activities of A in each electrode. The free energy associated with Cell 1 can be expressed as:

$$-\Delta \overline{G} = n\,FE = -RT \ln \frac{a_2}{a_1}. \tag{2}$$

In the case of Cell 1a, the cell potential can be expressed as

$$E = -\frac{RT}{nF} \ln a_2, \tag{3}$$

because the activity of a pure metal is unity by definition. Alloying reactions with high equivalent free energies yield high voltages, and the cell potential declines logarithmically with an increase in the concentration of A in the alloy AB. Because liquid metal electrodes are used, electron transfer and the diffusion of alloy AB away from the electrode surface should be very rapid. Exchange currents at metal electrodes in molten salts can be very high, which would allow relatively small activation polarization at high current densities. There can be some concentration polarization at the alloy-electrolyte interface at high current densities: when A can be discharged at a faster rate than surface tension effects and diffusion can remove it, resulting in a thin, high alloy concentration layer. The significant voltage loss in a cell of this type should be due primarily to IR losses. Because molten salts have conductivities of the order of 1–5 mhos while the best aqueous electrolytes have conductivities in the range of 0.5–0.9 mhos, these cells should be capable of high power densities.

Actual operation of a single cell is shown schematically in Figure 4. A and A_xB_y are chambers containing A and A_xB_y, respectively, separated by a porous ceramic matrix. The electrolyte is a molten salt or mixture of molten salts of cations of metal A and convenient anions, held in the pores of the ceramic matrix. The electrolyte is selected for its melting point range, lack of reaction with the liquid metals, and absence of thermal decomposition. As the cell operates:

a) A gives up an electron and becomes the ion A^+.

b) The ion A^+ migrates into the electrolyte.

c) The electron passes through the load in the external circuit furnishing electrical power and unites at the electrolyte-cathode interface, with A^+ forming the neutral atom A.

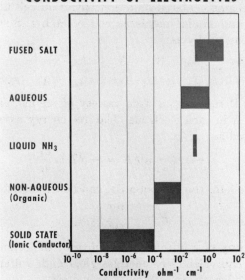

Figure 3. Conductivity of electrolytes

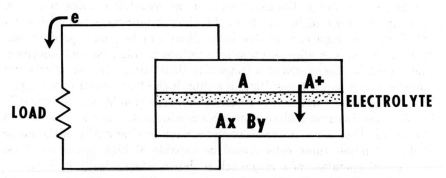

Figure 4. Schematic representation of liquid metal cell

d) A reacts with the alloy A_xB_y, forming the alloy A'_xB_y, which is now richer in component A.

e) The enriched alloy now flows out of the cell into the regenerator, where thermal energy is used to distill the alloy into the original reactant concentrations.

The thermal energy would be derived from the most convenient source for the particular application. Thus by operating in a closed loop, and by flowing reconstituted alloy back into the cell, a steady power output can be maintained as long as thermal energy is directed to the regenerator.

In choosing a system for initial laboratory evaluation, the following factors were considered:

a) An alkali metal anode would contribute to a high cell potential. Free energy values are high (*10*) for alkali metal alloys with base metals.

b) The molten salt electrolyte should be mono-cationic.

c) The cathode metal should have vapor pressure characteristics far removed from that of the anode material, in order to provide for the simplest thermal separation.

d) The system should present the least formidable problems with materials of construction with the temperatures required.

Specific Systems

The first system chosen for laboratory work was the combination of sodium and tin. Initially, thermodynamic data were determined from the cell Na/glass/Sn at temperatures between 500° and 700°C. and have been previously reported as shown in Figure 5 as activity of Na *vs.* $1/T$ with concentration of sodium as a parameter. Laboratory cells of the type Na/NaCl-NaI/Na$_x$Sn were operated singly and then in a regenerative fashion. It was shown (*2*) that the sodium-tin cell could operate between cathode alloy composition limits of 15–30 mole% Na, with open-circuit voltages between 0.33 and 0.43 volt at 700°C.

In these cells no polarization was observed up to current densities of 700 ma./sq. cm., the limit of the power supply. One cell was cycled like a secondary cell on a 20 min. charge-discharge cycle for 31 days. During this period it was observed that the cell was reversible and that it had operated at about a 95% coulombic efficiency.

Separate regeneration experiments were carried out to study the efficacy with which varying mixtures of Na/Sn could be separated. The results are shown in Figure 6, indicating the amount of Na condensate in the regenerator collection tube as a function of time. Because the kinetics of separation were slower than desired at temperatures less than 1100°C., it was realized that a new liquid metal system would need to be chosen in

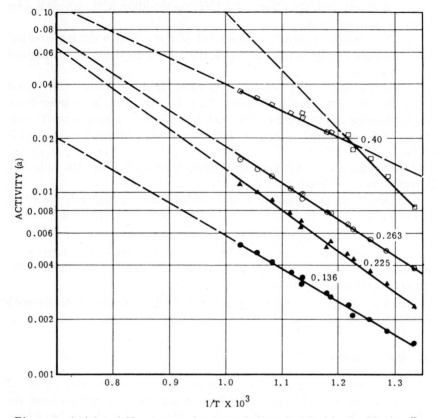

Figure 5. Activity of Na vs. temperature at indicated mole fraction Na in alloy

order to keep regeneration temperatures below this previously imposed, arbitrary temperature limit.

One additional test was run, however, in which a complete regenerative loop was operated for a short time until the insulating seals were attacked by hot Na vapor. The cell is shown in Figure 7. At the start of the run a 31 mole% Na-Sn alloy was placed in the regenerator, but no Na was placed in the anode cup on the right. The anode cup, which separated the Na anode from the Na-Sn cathode, and which served as the electrolyte, was a porous alumina thimble impregnated with a eutectic mixture of NaI and NaCl. The cell was maintained at 625–650°C. in a furnace, and the regenerator was heated in another furnace to a temperature of 1000°C. Thus, no power could be obtained until sufficient Na metal had distilled over into the anode compartment to constitute the cell. This cell was operated for 15 min. at 0.3 volt and 0.1 amp. until the seals failed.

Program effort was then directed to the potassium-mercury system because the kinetics of separating K-Hg were felt to be far superior to the

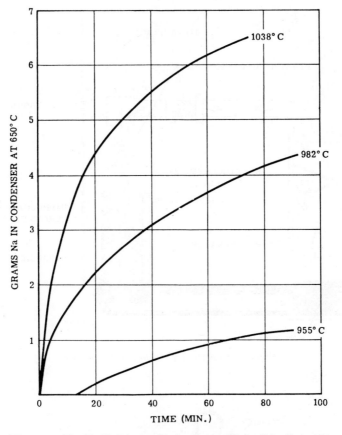

Figure 6. Na distilled from 8% (wt.) or 31% (mole) alloy; 150 grams alloy in still at start

earlier Na-Sn system. Also, its regeneration temperature would be close to that achieved by present day nuclear reactors. A schematic representation of a thermally regenerative K-Hg system is shown in Figure 8. K and Hg react to produce electricity in the fuel cell and at the same time form a K amalgam. The amalgam is pumped through a boiler where it is heated above the boiling point of the Hg contained therein. In a separator the Hg vapor is separated from a rich K liquid. The Hg vapor and K liquid pass to a condenser-cooler where the Hg vapor is condensed and cooled to cell temperature, while the K liquid is cooled, also to cell temperature. The two reactant streams enter the fuel cell to repeat the cycle.

The vapor-liquid equilibrium diagram shown in Figure 9 was developed in our laboratories. It shows the acceptable low separation temperature and the theoretical composition of the fluid streams to and from the cell. This shows that regenerative operation is feasible and practical.

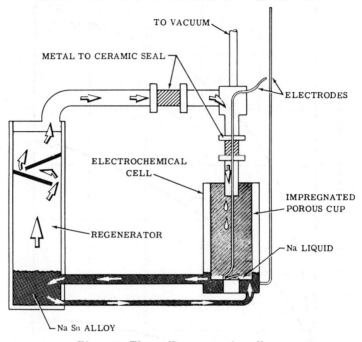

Figure 7. Thermally regenerative cell system

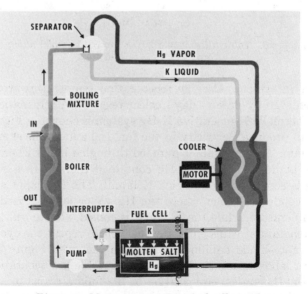

Figure 8. Mercury-potassium fuel cell system

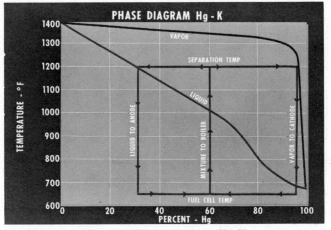

Figure 9. Phase diagram, Hg-K

As in the Na/Sn system, it was necessary to know the variation in cell voltage with alloy composition. Fortunately there was enough literature data (8) available to plot the curve shown in Figure 10. Operating laboratory cells and a special K/K glass/K amalgam cell confirmed the data at a few points in the operating range. This curve, then, has been used throughout the work.

Three electrolyte systems (two binary and one ternary) were considered for use with this fuel cell. The binary systems were (1) KOH-KBr with a eutectic at 300°C., and (2) a mixture of KOH-KI with a eutectic at 250°C. The ternary system is a 70 mole% KOH, 15% KBr, 15% KI eutectic, and melts at 225°C. when properly dried. The melting points for all three eutectics were compatible with the cell requirements, and so the final selection of the electrolyte was based on the following considerations:

a) The greater the difference between the cell-operating temperature and the melting point of the electrolyte, the greater is the expected conductivity.

b) The greater the difference between the melting point of the electrolyte and the boiling point of Hg, the less is the danger of Hg boiling in the cathode due to internally generated cell heat.

c) The lower the percentage of KOH in the system, the less corrosion there should be on the ceramic and metal portions of the cell.

The ternary electrolyte, Figure 11, fits these qualifications best and was therefore used in the cell work. This electrolyte has a resistivity of 1 ohm-cm. at cell temperature and contains less KOH than either of the binary systems. Some of the physical properties of this eutectic are shown in Figure 12. Mutual solubility was determined to see whether any adverse effects would be experienced by the system because of carryover or self-

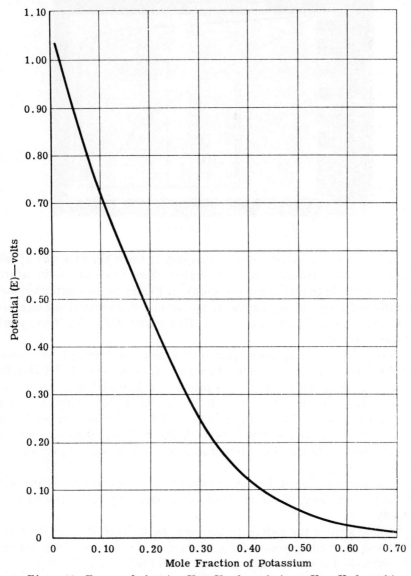

Figure 10. E_0 vs. mole fraction K at Hg electrode (pure K at K electrode)

discharge. For instance, high K solubility could lead to a high rate of self-discharge. The low mutual solubility data shown in Figure 12 indicate that no adverse effects should be experienced. Subsequent cell data confirmed the expected low, self-discharge rate.

Laboratory work with the K/Hg system involved the testing of many cell configurations and developing stackable prototype cell units. It cul-

Figure 11. Ternary phase diagram KOH-KBr-KI

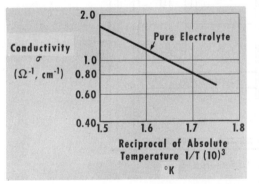

70% KOH, 15% KI, 15% KBr
ρ = 2.1 grams/cc. at 300°C.
m.p. = 225°C.
Mutual solubility with Hg—none
Mutual solubility with K—2 mole%
K saturates eutectic at 300°C.; 1
mole% eutectic saturates K at 300°C.

Figure 12. Allison eutectic

minated in the operation of single cells at power densities of up to 100 watts/sq. ft.

Early tests, Figure 13, were carried out to determine characteristics of the K/Hg couple. Figure 14 is a voltage-time plot for the cell of Figure 13 undergoing charge-discharge cycling. Charge and discharge time was 12 min. for the half-cycle, and a 3-min. open-circuit period was interposed. Current density for this test was 87 amp./sq. ft. The shape of the curve

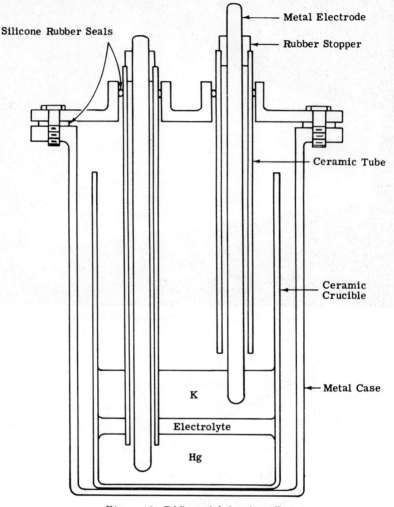

Figure 13. Differential density cell

indicates that a concentration polarization was occurring, as indicated by the curvature, as the cell was charged or discharged.

    This polarization was due to the build-up of a diffusion-controlled layer at the cathode. This situation is partially correctable by using a thinner cathode stream. Because the quantity of electricity on charge and discharge was equal, 100% coulombic efficiency would be required in order for the open-circuit voltage to remain constant over a number of cycles. The open-circuit voltage dropped from 0.84 to 0.83 volt over the five cycles, indicating that the current efficiency was slightly less than 100%, whereas the efficiency was actually about 90–95%. Thirty K/Hg cells were operated, both with and without Hg flow, in order to accumulate experience and cell data. Figure 15 is a view of the internal parts of a single, liquid-metal concentration cell and of a multi-cell, series-connected, compact battery.

The seal was effected by pressure. The ribs in the insulator coined into the Kovar metal cell halves and the electrolyte feed ring, effectively sealing the three liquid streams from each other and the outside of the cell.

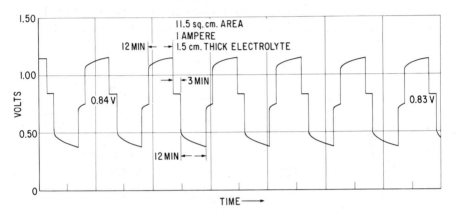

Figure 14. Voltage-time plot of cycling differential density cell

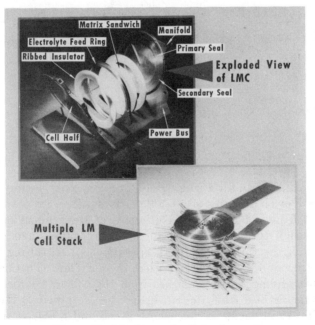

Figure 15. Liquid metal cell development

A novel sandwich matrix was used to contain the electrolyte, Figure 16. Two thin, porous MgO discs 9.531 cm. in diameter were machined so that, when they were pressed together, electrolyte had access to the free volume between the two discs. Each disc was 0.064 cm. thick and had eight 0.065 cm.-thick reinforcing ribs. The sealing edges of the discs were 0.190 cm. thick and 0.955 cm. wide. Two slots were cut in these edges to allow electrolyte access between the two discs when pressed together. Also, these slots lined up with electrolyte ports in the electrolyte feed ring. By this means, the matrix could be impregnated *in situ* after the cell had been assembled and leak-tested. Also, fresh electrolyte could be fed into the cell if and when needed.

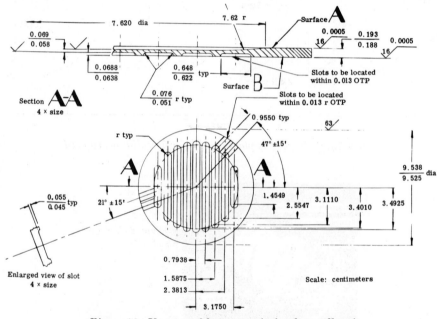

Figure 16. Upper and lower matrix for three-cell unit

Performance data for a single cell and a three cell battery are shown in Table I. Power densities of 50–100 watts/sq. ft. were obtained over a period of 430 hrs. of operation. During 75 of these hours mercury was flowing through the cell in order to maintain voltage and power. The significance of the three cell-battery operation is that during 60% of its operating time at 45 watts/sq. ft., it had mercury flow. This mercury was supplied by sending the K amalgam from the cell to a boiler where the mercury was distilled from the amalgam, then returned to the cell. This was the first experiment in which both a cell and a regenerative system operated together for such a length of time.

Table I. Battery Performance

Single Cell

Total life, hrs.	~ 430
Power output, watts/sq. ft.	50–100
Duration of Hg flow, hrs.	~ 75

Three Cell Battery

Total life, hrs.	100
Power output, watts/sq. ft.	45
Duration of Hg flow, hrs.	60

The K/Hg cell showed itself to be a feasible cell, capable of being further developed into a full scale, thermally regenerative system. More work in two prime areas should produce cells much improved over those already operated. The two areas call for further improvement in the life of materials of construction and better electrode design to yield thinner diffusion layers at the electrode surface.

System efficiencies for thermally regenerative, liquid-metal systems compare favorably with projected system efficiencies for other types of thermally regenerative cells. Figures 17 and 18 present the major parameters of a 5 kw. K/Hg system. Three curves are given, based on various degrees of development: present (laboratory cell); near future (few months with current knowledge); and 1967 objective (considerably more development). The influential operating parameter, γt_e, used for these curves, and which needs further development, is the product of electrolyte resistivity including matrix and thickness.

It has been pointed out that the cell cathode diffusion layer can markedly influence both voltage and power density. In the system analysis, therefore, the best diffusion data available were used. The complete analysis of this system design is found in References *11* and *12*. The following data were used for the "present":

γt_e = 3.68 ohm-sq. cm. (electrolyte resistivity) (electrolyte thickness)
γt_e = RA—Experimental 46 sq. cm. cell had average resistance of 0.08 ohm.
- Electrode thickness 0.6 cm.
- Bonilla's diffusion data (*9*)
- Sherwood number = 50
- Voltage = 0.5 volt
- Anode inlet = 0.60 mole fraction potassium
- Anode outlet = 0.55 mole fraction potassium
- Cathode inlet = 0.01 mole fraction potassium
- Cathode outlet = 0.07 to 0.22 mole fraction potassium
- Accessories weights (*5*)
- Cell density = grams/sq. cm.

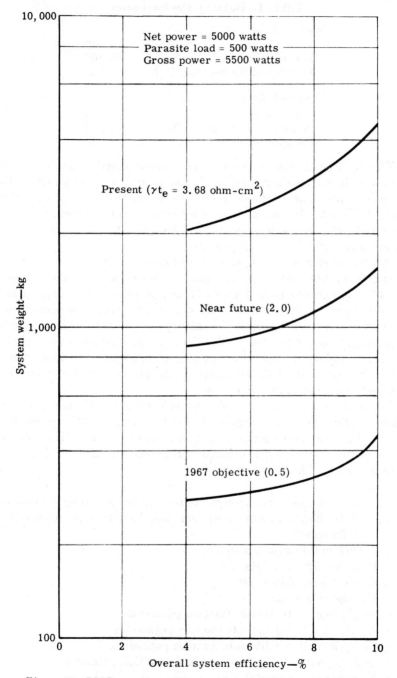

Figure 17. LMC specific weight based on efficiency and resistivity
(does not include heat source or shielding)

At a fixed thickness governed by γt_e and cell design, density then becomes an areal function.

For the "near future" the same data were used except:

- $\gamma t_e = 2.0$ ohm-sq. cm.
- Electrode thickness = 0.3 cm.
- Cell density = 10 grams/sq. cm.

For the "1967 objective" the same data were used except:

- $\gamma t_e = 0.5$ ohm-sq. cm.
- Electrode thickness = 0.1 cm.
- Cell density = 6 grams/sq. cm.

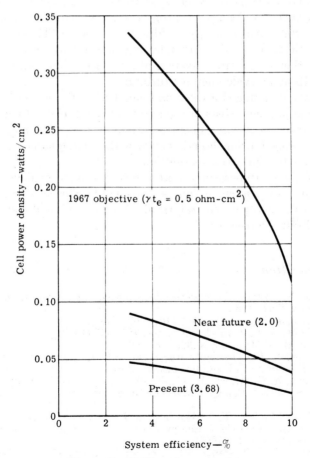

Figure 18. LMC performance data

The complete analysis is beyond the scope of this paper. It was set up on a computer program. The cell was the same as shown in Figure 4 but with counter-current, liquid-metal electrode flow. A model was used in which the cell was divided into a number of segments. The changes in voltage, concentration, diffusion layer, current density, and flow were developed mathematically for each segment. By an iterative process, the performance of the complete cell was obtained by summing up the variables of the segments.

Concentrations of amalgams entering and leaving the cell were fixed by the boiler and cell temperatures as given in the vapor-liquid phase diagram (Figure 9). These compositions also fix the changes in heat capacity, the heats of vaporization, and the thermal energy required for a given electrical output. A thermal energy balance was thus placed into the computer program along with the cell model data. Combining both computer programs and inserting the data listed above, the curves in Figures 17 and 18 were derived. The computer programs have been used to obtain many other important relationships besides those shown. These studies have confirmed that the K/Hg thermally regenerative system is competitive with any other regenerative system in the 1 to 50 kw. range, even those involving Rankine cycle mercury turbines.

Another advantage for the liquid metal cell is the ease of heat management. A real problem exists in the ability of any fuel cell to cast off internally generated heat when operating at desirable power and power densities, but using flowing liquid metals with their inherent heat transfer capabilities offers an excellent solution.

All of these studies show that the best way to achieve high power densities and low system weight at reasonable efficiency in regenerative cells, either thermally or electrolytically, is by using liquid metal electrodes with fused salt electrolytes.

Literature Cited

(1) Agar, J. N., *Advan. Electrochem. Electrochem. Eng.* V. 3, Interscience Publishers, New York, 1963.
(2) Agruss, B., *J. Electrochem. Soc.* **110,** 1097 (1963).
(3) de Bethune, A. J., *J. Electrochem. Soc.* **107,** 937 (1960).
(4) Friauf, J. B., *J. Appl. Phys.* **32,** 616 (1961).
(5) Henderson, R. E., Thermally Regenerative Fuel Cells, Sixth Agard Combustion and Propulsion Colloquium, March, 1964.
(6) Henderson, R. E., Agruss, B., Caple, W., "Resume of Thermally Regenerative Fuel Cell Systems." Energy Conversion for Space Power, V. 3, Academic Press, 1961.
(7) King, J., Jr., Ludwig, F. A., Rowlette, J. J., "General Evaluation of Chemicals for Regenerative Fuel Cells, Energy Conversion for Space Power," p. 387, Academic Press, New York, 1961.
(8) Lantratov, M. F., Tsarenko, E. V., *Zh. Prikl. Khim.*, **33,** No. 7 (1960) (Translated).

(9) Liebhafsky, H. A., *J. Electrochem. Soc.* **106,** 1068 (1959).

(10) "Selected Values for the Thermodynamic Properties of Metals and Alloys," Minerals Research Lab., Institute of Engineering Research, University of California, Berkeley, 1959.

(11) "Systems Analysis of Nuclear (SNAP II) Liquid Metal Space Power System" EDR 3113, Allison Division, General Motors Corp., Indianapolis, 1962.

(12) Wright, R. B., "Diffusion of Potassium in a Liquid Metal Cell," EDR 3814, Allison Division, General Motors Corp., Indianapolis, 1964.

(13) Zito, R., Jr., *AIAA Journal* **1,** 2133 (1963).

RECEIVED November 10, 1965.

8

Thermodynamics and Thermal Efficiencies of Thermally Regenerative Bimetallic and Hydride EMF Cell Systems

JAMES C. HESSON and HIROSHI SHIMOTAKE

Argonne National Laboratory, Argonne, Ill.

The engineering thermodynamic cycles and thermal efficiencies of bimetallic and metallic hydride emf cell systems, which are thermally regenerated by separating the reactants by distillation, are discussed. Thermodynamic equations are presented for the ideal regeneration cycles and from the ideal cycles, thermal efficiencies are estimated and compared to the Carnot cycle efficiencies. For the ideal cycle it is assumed, among other things, that the anode metal is distilled from the cathode metal which is nonvolatile. The effects of volatility of the cathode metal on the actual cycle thermal efficiencies are considered. Calculations for sodium-lead, sodium-bismuth, sodium-tin, lithium-tin, and lithium-hydride systems are tabulated. Equations for engineering thermodynamic cycles and thermal efficiencies for electrothermal regeneration are also discussed.

In this discussion we are concerned with the thermodynamics and thermal efficiencies of bimetallic cell systems in which the anode metal, cathode metal, and electrolyte are molten, and in which the anode metal is much more volatile than the cathode metal and is regenerated from it by distillation or volatilization. We are also concerned with the thermodynamics and the thermal efficiencies of hydride cell systems in which the anode metal and electrolyte are molten and in which the hydride formed in the cell is dissolved in the electrolyte (and anode metal) and is regenerated from the electrolyte (or anode metal) by thermally decomposing it to anode metal and hydrogen.

Although we are here primarily concerned with direct thermal regeneration of the cell products by evaporation or distillation, electrothermal

82

regeneration will be briefly discussed. In direct thermal regeneration as well as in electrothermal regeneration the overall efficiency is limited by the Carnot cycle (*3, 5, 9, 11, 12*).

Direct Thermal Regeneration

Figure 1 shows a flow schematic of a bimetallic cell system. In this bimetallic cell system the cathode metal with some anode metal dissolved in it is circulated to and from the regenerator in heat exchange relationship. In the regenerator anode metal is evaporated to separate it from the cathode metal. The anode metal vapor is condensed and returned to the anode of the cell.

Figure 2 shows a flow schematic of a hydride cell system. In this hydride cell system the electrolyte (or possibly anode metal) with dissolved hydride is circulated to and from the regenerator in heat exchange relationship. In the regenerator hydride is decomposed to hydrogen and anode metal. The hydrogen is returned to the cell cathode and the anode metal is returned to the cell anode.

Thermally regenerative emf cell systems are one method of converting heat energy into electrical energy and, for this reason, have been the subject of considerable interest and study (*3, 10, 11, 12*). Among the regenerative emf cell systems, which have been studied, are bimetallic (*1, 4, 6*) and metal hydride (*2, 5*) types which use fused salts as electrolytes. In the bimetallic cell systems, the anode and cathode metals are usually in the molten state. In the hydride cell systems, the anode metal is likewise usually in the molten state, and the hydrogen is in the gaseous state. In

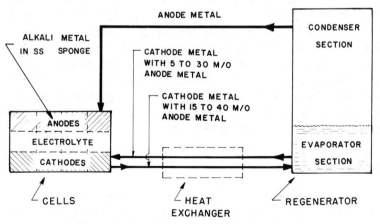

Figure 1. Bimetallic cell system flow diagram

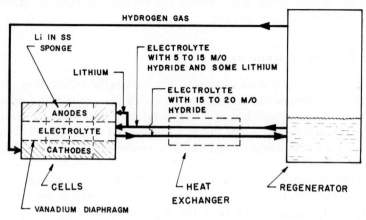

Figure 2. Lithium hydride cell system flow diagram

both the bimetallic and hydride cell systems, the molten salt electrolyte will consist, at least partially, of salts of the anode metal in order to provide anode metal ions in the electrolyte.

At the anode in the bimetallic cell systems, the metal is oxidized to positive ions, releasing electrons. The positive ions diffuse in the liquid electrolyte toward the cathode. At the cathode they are reduced to metal atoms, taking up electrons. The anode metal dissolves in or reacts with the cathode metal. The flow of electrons from the anode to the cathode through an external circuit constitutes the cell output current. In order to complete the cycle, the anode metal must be separated from the cathode metal and both returned to their separate cell compartments for reaction.

At the anode, in the hydride cell systems, the metal is oxidized to positive ions, releasing electrons. The positive ions diffuse in the liquid electrolyte toward the cathode. At the cathode, hydride ions are formed, and they diffuse in the electrolyte toward the anode to form anode metal hydride in the fused salt. The hydride ions result from reducing hydrogen gas at the cathode, removing electrons from the cathode. The anode metal hydride dissolves in the electrolyte and, to a lesser extent, in the anode metal. In order to complete the cycle, the hydride must be decomposed to hydrogen and anode metal, which are returned to the separate cathode and anode compartments in the cell.

Bimetallic Systems

Figure 3 shows a temperature entropy diagram of the idealized regeneration cycle for the bimetallic systems. In this idealized cycle it is assumed that the regeneration takes place by evaporating anode metal from the cathode metal, followed by cooling and condensing the vapor and returning it to the anode of the cell. It is assumed that no evaporation of cathode metal takes place; that there are no heat losses through insulation; that in the heat exchangers ideal heat exchange takes place; that regeneration takes place at a constant pressure which is the condensing pressure of the anode metal vapor; and that regeneration takes place at a constant mole fraction, x, of anode metal in the cathode metal. This infers that there is a very large circulation rate of the cathode metal to and from the regenerator and that there is ideal heat exchange between the cathode metal going to and from the regenerator. The cell pressure is the condensing pressure, or the vapor pressure of the anode metal at cell temperature if it is greater than the condensing pressure. In this case the cell pressure could be maintained by a hydrostatic head of liquid anode metal between the regenerator and cell.

$$\text{In Figure 3,} \qquad \Delta H_{23} = \int_{T_2}^{T_3} \overline{C}_{pl} dT \qquad (1)$$

is the net enthalpy change of, or the net heat added to, the cathode metal on cycling between the cell at temperature, T_2, and the regenerator at temperature, T_3, with ideal heat exchange, per mole of anode metal circulated. $\overline{C}_{pl}$ is the partial molar specific heat of the anode metal in the cathode metal.

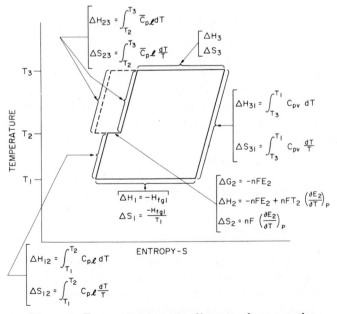

Figure 3. Temperature-entropy diagram of regeneration cycle for bimetallic cell systems

$$\Delta S_{23} = \int_{T_2}^{T_3} \overline{C}_{pl} \frac{dT}{T} \tag{2}$$

is the entropy change per mole of anode metal.

ΔH_3 and ΔS_3 are the enthalpy and entropy changes on evaporating the anode metal from the cathode metal at temperature, T_3, and x mole fraction of anode metal in the cathode metal, per mole of anode metal evaporated.

$$\Delta H_{31} = \int_{T_3}^{T_1} C_{pv} \, dT \qquad \text{and} \tag{3}$$

$$\Delta S_{31} = \int_{T_3}^{T_1} C_{pv} \frac{dT}{T} \tag{4}$$

are the enthalpy and entropy changes on cooling the anode metal vapor from temperature T_3 to T_1, per mole of anode metal circulated. C_{pv} is the specific heat of the anode metal vapor.

$$\Delta H_1 = -H_{fgl} \qquad \text{and} \tag{5}$$

$$\Delta S_1 = -\frac{H_{fgl}}{T_1} \tag{6}$$

are the enthalpy and entropy changes on condensing the anode metal vapor at temperature, T_1, per mole of anode metal vapor condensed. H_{fgl} is the latent heat of evaporation of the anode metal.

$$\Delta H_{12} = \int_{T_1}^{T_2} C_{pl} \, dT \qquad \text{and} \tag{7}$$

$$\Delta S_{12} = \int_{T_1}^{T_2} C_{pl} \frac{dT}{T} \tag{8}$$

are the enthalpy and entropy changes on heating (or cooling) the anode metal liquid from the condensing temperature, T_1, to the cell temperature, T_2, per mole of anode metal circulated. C_{pl} is the specific heat of the anode metal liquid.

$$\Delta G_2 = -nFE_2, \tag{9}$$

$$\Delta H_2 = -nFE_2 + nFT_2 \left(\frac{\partial E_2}{\partial T} \right)_P, \qquad \text{and} \tag{10}$$

$$\Delta S_2 = nF \left(\frac{\partial E_2}{\partial T} \right)_P \tag{11}$$

are the changes in free energy, enthalpy, and entropy in the cell at the cell temperature, T_2, per mole of anode metal transferred from the anode to cathode. F is Faraday's constant, E_2 is the cell potential or emf, and n is the equivalents per mole of anode metal.

This completes the regeneration cycle.

The following equations apply for the bimetallic cell system regeneration cycle:

$$\sum \Delta H = 0 \tag{12}$$

$$\sum \Delta S = 0 \tag{13}$$

Thus

$$\Delta H_3 = -\Delta H_1 - \Delta H_{12} - \Delta H_2 - \Delta H_{23} - \Delta H_{31} \tag{14}$$

$$\Delta S_3 = -\Delta S_1 - \Delta S_{12} - \Delta S_2 - \Delta S_{23} - \Delta S_{31} \tag{15}$$

Also

$$\Delta H_3 = H_{fgl} + nFE_2 - nFT_2 \left(\frac{\partial E_2}{\partial T}\right)_P - \int_{T_1}^{T_2} (C_{pl} - C_{pv})dT$$
$$- \int_{T_2}^{T_3} (\overline{C}_{pl} - C_{pv})dT \tag{16}$$

$$\Delta S_3 = \frac{H_{fgl}}{T_1} - nF\left(\frac{\partial E_2}{\partial T}\right)_P - \int_{T_1}^{T_2} (C_{pl} - C_{pv})\frac{dT}{T}$$
$$- \int_{T_2}^{T_3} (\overline{C}_{pl} - C_{pv})\frac{dT}{T} \tag{17}$$

$$T_3 = \frac{\Delta H_3}{\Delta S_3} \tag{18}$$

$$e_c = \text{Carnot cycle efficiency} = \frac{T_3 - T_1}{T_3} \tag{19}$$

$$e_i = \text{ideal cycle efficiency}$$
$$= \frac{\text{ideal electrical work}}{\text{ideal heat input}} \tag{20}$$
$$= \frac{nFE_2}{nFE_2 + H_{fgl} - A}$$

where $-A$ is the net heat rejected between T_3 and T_1, or the net accumulated negative value, if any, of

$$-\int_{T_3}^{T_2} (\overline{C}_{pl} - C_{pv})dT + nFT_2\left(\frac{\partial E_2}{\partial T}\right)_P - \int_{T_2}^{T_1} (C_{pl} - C_{pv})dT \tag{21}$$

because rejected heat can be utilized only at a temperature lower than its rejection temperature. In the case where $\overline{C}_{pl} - C_{pv} = 0$ and $T_1 = T_2$ or where $\overline{C}_{pl} - C_{pv} = 0$, $C_{pl} - C_{pv} = 0$, and $\left(\frac{\partial E_2}{\partial T}\right)_P = 0$, the ideal cycle becomes a Carnot cycle. The following equation gives the regeneration pressure.

$$P_3 = P_1 = P_{3s}\, exp\left\{ -\frac{1}{RT_3}\left[nFE_2 + nF(T_3 - T_2)\left(\frac{\partial E_2}{\partial T}\right)_P \right.\right.$$

$$\left.\left. + \int_{T_2}^{T_3} (\overline{C}_{pl} - C_{pl})\left(\frac{T_3}{T} - 1\right) dT \right]\right\} \qquad (22)^a$$

where

P_3 = regeneration pressure
P_1 = condensing pressure = vapor pressure of anode metal at T_1
P_{3s} = vapor pressure of anode metal at T_3.

A relationship between $\overline{C}_{pl}$, the partial molar specific heat of the anode metal in the cathode metal, and C_{pl}, the specific heat of the anode metal, is

$$\overline{C}_{pl} - C_{pl} = nFT \left(\frac{\partial^2 E}{\partial T^2}\right)_P \qquad (23)^a$$

In the case of the bimetallic cell,

$$E = \frac{-RT}{nF} \ln (a_x/a_o) = -\frac{RT}{nF} \ln \gamma x \qquad (24)$$

where

a_o is the activity of pure anode metal liquid = 1
a_x is the activity of the anode metal in the cathode = $\gamma x a_o$
γ is the activity coefficient of the anode metal in the cathode
x is the mole fraction of anode metal in the cathode.
Since a_x is a function of x and T, E is a function of x and T.

The relationships of the variables in regeneration of a bimetallic cell system are:

T_1 = condensing temperature
T_2 = cell temperature
T_3 = regeneration temperature
P_1 = condensing pressure determined by T_1
P_3 = regeneration pressure = P_1
x = mole fraction anode metal in cathode metal
E_2 = cell emf
E_2 is determined by x and T_2 (E_2, x, and T_2 are directly interrelated)
T_3 is determined by x and P_1 or x and T_1 (T_3, x, and P_1 or T_3, x, and T_1 are directly interrelated).

These relationships show that in the case of the bimetallic systems, the condensing temperature, T_1, of the anode metal vapor from the regenerator is determined by the regeneration pressure. The regeneration pres-

---

[a] For the derivations of Equations 22 and 23, *see* Appendix.

sure in turn is a function of both the mole fraction, x, of anode metal content of the hot cathodic alloy in the regenerator boiler and the regeneration boiler temperature, T_3. Thus, the condensing temperature, T_1 (temperature at which the bulk of the heat is rejected), increases as the regeneration temperature, T_3, increases, and the ideal regeneration cycle efficiency is nearly independent of the regeneration temperature, T_3, for a given mole fraction, x, of anode metal in the cathode. The ideal regeneration cycle efficiency increases as the mole fraction, x, of anode metal in the cathode metal is decreased; however, a reasonable cathode metal circulation rate sets a minimum mole fraction of anode metal in the cathode metal. For a given mole fraction of anode metal in the cathode metal, the minimum regeneration temperature, in the case where reflux is not required, is determined by the magnitude of the anode metal partial pressure which is required to obtain reasonable distillation rates. In the case of liquid metals, a partial pressure of at least 1 mm. Hg is usually required for reasonable distillation rates. If reflux is required in the regenerator, the minimum regeneration temperature may be determined by the need to avoid solid phase regions.

Lithium Hydride System

Figure 4 shows a temperature entropy diagram of the idealized regeneration cycle for the lithium or other types of hydride cell. In this idealized cycle it is assumed that the regeneration takes place by decomposing to lithium and hydrogen the lithium hydride from the electrolyte (or anode

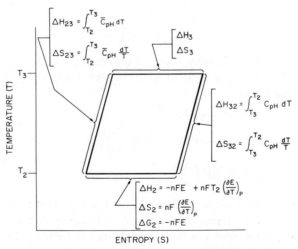

Figure 4. Temperature-entropy diagram of regeneration cycle for hydride cell systems

metal) and then returning the gaseous hydrogen to the cell cathode and the lithium to the cell anode. It is assumed that no evaporation of electrolyte or lithium metal takes place; that there are no heat losses through insulation; that ideal heat exchange takes place in the heat exchangers; and that regeneration takes place at constant pressure, temperature, and mole fraction of lithium hydride in the electrolyte. This implies that there is a very large circulation rate of the electrolyte to and from the cell and regenerator, and that there is ideal heat exchange between the electrolyte going from the cell to the regenerator and returning.

In Figure 4

$$\Delta H_{23} = \int_{T_2}^{T_3} \overline{C}_{p\mathrm{H}} \, dT \tag{25}$$

is the net enthalpy change of, or the net heat added to, the electrolyte on going from the cell at temperature, T_2, to the regenerator at temperature, T_3, and returning, with ideal heat exchange, per mole of hydride regenerated, where

$$\overline{C}_{p\mathrm{H}} = \overline{C}_{phye} - C_{pl} \tag{26}$$

and $\overline{C}_{phye}$ is the partial molar specific heat of lithium hydride in the electrolyte, and C_{pl} is the specific heat of lithium metal.

$$\Delta S_{23} = \int_{T_2}^{T_3} \overline{C}_{p\mathrm{H}} \left(\frac{dT}{T}\right) \text{ is the entropy change.} \tag{27}$$

ΔH_3 and ΔS_3 are the enthalpy and entropy changes, respectively, per mole of hydride regenerated at pressure, P_3, and temperature, T_3.

$$\Delta H_{32} = \frac{n}{2} \int_{T_3}^{T_2} C_{p\mathrm{H}} \, dT \qquad \text{and} \tag{28}$$

$$\Delta S_{32} = \frac{n}{2} \int_{T_3}^{T_2} C_{p\mathrm{H}} \left(\frac{dT}{T}\right) \tag{29}$$

are the enthalpy and entropy changes on cooling the hydrogen gas from temperature T_3 to T_2 per mole of hydride regenerated. $C_{p\mathrm{H}}$ is the specific heat of hydrogen gas.

$$\Delta G_2 = -nFE_2, \tag{30}$$

$$\Delta H_2 = -nFE_2 + nFT_2 \left(\frac{\partial E_2}{\partial T}\right)_P, \qquad \text{and} \tag{31}$$

$$\Delta S_2 = nF \left(\frac{\partial E_2}{\partial T}\right)_P \tag{32}$$

are the changes per mole of hydride formed in free energy, enthalpy, and entropy in the cell at temperature, T_2. F is Faraday's constant, E_2 is the cell potential or emf, and n is the equivalents per mole of the anode metal or per mole of the hydride.

This completes the cycle.

The following equations apply for the hydride cell system regeneration cycle:

$$\sum \Delta H = 0 \tag{33}$$

$$\sum \Delta S = 0 \tag{34}$$

Thus

$$\Delta H_3 = -\Delta H_{23} - \Delta H_{32} - \Delta H_2 \tag{35}$$

$$\Delta S_3 = -\Delta S_{23} - \Delta S_{32} - \Delta S_2 \tag{36}$$

Also

$$\Delta H_3 = nFE_2 - nFT_2 \left(\frac{\partial E_2}{\partial T}\right)_P - \int_{T_2}^{T_3} \left(\overline{C}_{pH} - \frac{n}{2} C_{pH}\right) dT \tag{37}$$

$$\Delta S_3 = -nF \left(\frac{\partial E_2}{\partial T}\right)_P - \int_{T_2}^{T_3} \left(\overline{C}_{pH} - \frac{n}{2} C_{pH}\right) \frac{dT}{T} \tag{38}$$

$$T_3 = \frac{\Delta H_3}{\Delta S_3} \tag{39}$$

$$e_c = \text{Carnot cycle efficiency} = \frac{T_3 - T_2}{T_3} \tag{40}$$

$$e_i = \text{ideal cycle efficiency}$$
$$= \frac{\text{ideal electrical work}}{\text{ideal heat input}} \tag{41}$$

$$= \frac{nFE_2}{nFE_2 - nFT_2 \left(\frac{\partial E_2}{\partial T}\right)_P - A}$$

where $-A$ is the net heat rejected between T_3 and T_2 or the net accumulated negative value, if any, of

$$-\int_{T_3}^{T_2} \left(\overline{C}_{pH} - \frac{n}{2} C_{pH}\right) dT \tag{42}$$

because rejected heat can be reutilized only at a temperature lower than its rejection temperature. In the case where $\overline{C}_{pH} - \frac{n}{2} C_{pH} = 0$, the ideal cycle becomes a Carnot cycle. The following equation gives the regeneration pressure.

$$P_3 = P_{oH} \, exp \left\{ -\frac{2}{RT_3} \left[nFE_2 + nF \left(T_3 - T_2\right) \left(\frac{\partial E_2}{\partial T}\right)_P \right. \right.$$
$$\left. \left. + \int_{T_2}^{T_3} \left(\overline{C}_{pH} - \frac{n}{2} C_{pH}\right) \left(\frac{T_3}{T} - 1\right) dT \right] \right\} \tag{43a}$$

where P_3 = regeneration pressure.

P_{oH} = hydrogen pressure at which values of E_2 were measured.

[a] For the derivations of Equations 43 and 44, *see* Appendix.

A relationship between $\overline{C}_{p\mathrm{H}}$ and $C_{p\mathrm{H}}$ is

$$\overline{C}_{p\mathrm{H}} - \frac{n}{2} C_{p\mathrm{H}} = nFT \left(\frac{\partial 2_E}{\partial T^2} \right)_P. \tag{44}^a$$

In the case of the lithium hydride cell

$$E = Eo - \frac{RT}{nF} \ln \frac{a_{\mathrm{LiH}}}{a_{\mathrm{H}}^{1/2} a_{\mathrm{Li}}} \tag{45}$$

$$= - \frac{RT}{nF} \ln \frac{f_{\mathrm{H(LiH)}}^{1/2}}{f_{\mathrm{H}}^{1/2}}$$

where

a_{LiHo} is the activity of pure lithium hydride $= 1$

a_{LiH} is the activity of lithium hydride in the electrolyte

a_{Lio} is the activity of pure lithium $= 1$

a_{Li} is the activity of lithium in the anode

$a_{\mathrm{H}} = f_H$ is activity or fugacity of the hydrogen in the cathode

$f_{\mathrm{H(LiH)}}$ is the fugacity of the hydrogen in equilibrium with the lithium hydride in the electrolyte

Z is the mole fraction of the hydride in the electrolyte

$f_{\mathrm{H(LiH)}}$ is a function of Z and T, and f_{H} is a function of the cathode or regeneration hydrogen pressure, P; hence, E is a function of Z, T, and P.

The relationships of the variables in regeneration of a hydride cell, where the hydride is regenerated from the electrolyte, are as follows:

$T_2 =$ cell temperature

$T_3 =$ regeneration temperature

$P_3 =$ regeneration hydrogen pressure

$Z \ =$ mole fraction hydride in the electrolyte

$E_2 =$ cell emf

E_2 is determined by P_3, Z, and T_2 (or E_2, P_3, Z, and T_2 are directly interrelated)

T_3 is determined by Z and P_3 (or T_3, Z, and P_3 are directly interrelated).

These relationships show that in the case of the hydride systems the cell operating temperature, T_2 (temperature at which the heat is rejected), is independent of the regeneration temperature, T_3. The hydrogen regeneration pressure, P_3, however, increases with increased regeneration temperature, T_3, and with increased mole fraction, Z, of hydride in the electrolyte. The cell emf increases with increased hydrogen pressure; it decreases with increased cell temperature and with increased dissolved mole fraction, Z, of hydride in the electrolyte. The ideal regeneration

---

[a] For the derivations of Equations 43 and 44, *see* Appendix.

cycle efficiency is dependent upon the regenerator and cell operating temperatures, T_3 and T_2, but is nearly independent of the mole fraction, Z, of hydride in the electrolyte.

Electrothermal Regeneration

Where the cell voltage at a high temperature, T_3, is substantially less than the voltage at a lower temperature, T_2, electrical regeneration for a power producing system can be considered. (Electrothermal regeneration could also be accomplished if the voltage at high temperature, T_3, were substantially greater than the voltage at the lower cell temperature, T_2. This would be unusual, but thermodynamically possible.) In this case a cell in the system would be used to regenerate electrically the reactants at temperature, T_3, and another cell in the system would be used to produce electric current at temperature, T_2. Also, the regenerator cell along with the electrical load would be connected in series with the power cell. Figure 5 shows a flow schematic for such a system. Figure 6 shows a temperature-entropy diagram for the ideal cycle.

In Figure 6, C_{pp} is the specific heat of the cell product going from temperature T_2 to T_3. C_{pR} is the specific heat of the cell reactants going from temperature T_3 to T_2.

In a bimetallic cell system, cathode metal with some anode metal could be circulated to and from the regenerator cell, where anode metal would be electrically removed and returned to the anode of the power cell:

$$C_{pp} = \overline{C}_{pl} \quad \text{and} \tag{46}$$

$$C_{pR} = C_{pl} \tag{47}$$

In a cell system such as lead-bromine, lead bromide electrolyte would be sent to the galvanic regenerator, and lead and bromine would be separated and returned to the anode and cathode compartments of the power cell:

$$C_{pp} = C_{p(\text{Pb Br}_2)} \quad \text{and} \tag{48}$$

$$C_{pR} = C_{p(\text{Pb})} + \tfrac{1}{2} C_{p(\text{Br}_2)} \tag{49}$$

In a lithium hydrogen cell system, electrolyte containing lithium hydride could be circulated to and from the regenerator cell, where lithium and hydrogen would be removed and returned to the power cell:

$$C_{pp} = \overline{C}_{phye} \quad \text{and} \tag{50}$$

$$C_{pR} = C_{pl} + C_{pH} \tag{51}$$

The ideal cycle electrical output per mole of anode material is

$$-\Delta G_2 - \Delta G_3 = n F (E_2 - E_3). \tag{52}$$

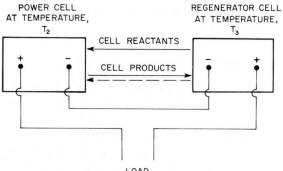

Figure 5. Flow schematic for electrical regeneration in a cell system

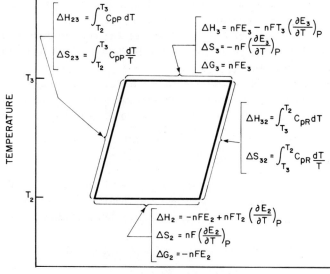

Figure 6. Temperature-entropy diagram for electrical regeneration cycle in cell systems

The ideal cycle efficiency

$$e_i = \frac{-\Delta G_2 - \Delta G_3}{\Delta H_3 - \Delta G_3 + A} \tag{53}$$

$$= \frac{nF\,(E_2 - E_3)}{-nFT_3\left(\dfrac{\partial E_3}{\partial T}\right)_P + A} \tag{54}$$

where A is the net heat added between T_2 and T_3 or the net accumulated positive value, if any, of

$$\int_{T_2}^{T_3} (C_{pp} - C_{pR}) \, dt \qquad (55)$$

because rejected heat at temperatures between T_2 and T_3 can be reutilized only at a lower temperature than its rejection temperature. Where $C_{pp} - C_{pR} = 0$, the ideal cycle becomes a Carnot cycle.

The electrical efficiency of the power cell on discharge is a product of the voltage and current or coulombic efficiencies, e_{E2} and e_{I2}, respectively. The electrical efficiency of the regenerator cell on charge is a product of the voltage and current or coulombic efficiencies, e_{E3} and e_{I3}, respectively, where

$$e_{E2} = \frac{E_2 - R_2 I_2}{E_2} \qquad (56)$$

$$e_{E3} = \frac{E_3}{E_3 + R_3 I_3} \qquad (57)$$

R_2 and R_3 are the cell resistances
$e_{E2}e_{I2}$ = power cell electrical efficiency
$e_{E3}e_{I3}$ = regenerator cell electrical efficiency

The system electrical energy output per equivalent of anode material used in the power cell is

$$nF\left[E_2 e_{E2} e_{I2} - \frac{E_3}{e_{E3} e_{I3}}\right] = nF\left[(E_2 - R_2 I_2)e_{I2} - \frac{E_3 + R_3 I_3}{e_{I3}}\right] \qquad (58)^a$$

The overall thermal efficiency of the system, which is the electrical output divided by the heat input, is

$$e_T = \frac{nF\left[(E_2 - R_2 I_2)e_{I2} - \dfrac{E_3 + R_3 I_3}{e_{I3}}\right]}{-nF\, T_3 \left(\dfrac{\partial E_3}{\partial T}\right)_P + A - nF\left[\dfrac{E_3 + R_3 I_3}{e_{I3}} - E_3\right]} \qquad (59)^a$$

where e_T is the efficiency of heat utilization to the regenerator cell.

From the above it can be noted that to obtain a net electrical output from the system, the following is necessary:

$$(E_2 - R_2 I_2)\, e_{I2} > \frac{E_3 + R_3 I_3}{e_{I3}} \qquad (60)$$

or

$$E_2 - R_2 I_2 > \frac{E_3 + R_3 I_3}{e_{I2} e_{I3}} \qquad (61)$$

or

$$e_{E2} e_{E3} e_{I2} e_{I3} > \frac{E_3}{E_2}. \qquad (62)$$

---

[a] For the derivations of Equations 58 and 59, *see* Appendix.

As an example, if

$$e_{I2} = e_{I3} = 0.90$$

$$e_{E2} = e_{E3} = 0.75 \tag{63}$$

then E_3/E_2 must be less than $(0.9)^2$ $(0.75)^2$ or less than 0.455 to obtain useful electrical output from the system.

When the coulombic efficiency of either the power or regenerator cell is less than 1.0, the current produced in one power cell is insufficient to regenerate the cell products in one regenerator cell, so that some type of compound or multiple cell system must be used. For example, if the coulombic efficiency of each cell is 0.90, four power cells in series with five regenerator cells could be used.

Computed Thermal Efficiencies for Direct Thermal Regeneration

From the experimental values of E_2 and $\left(\dfrac{\partial E_2}{\partial T}\right)$ for a given bimetallic or hydride cell and from values of C_{pl}, C_{pv}, and C_{pH} for the anode metal and hydrogen, as well as estimated values of $\overline{C}_{pl}$ and $\overline{C}_{pH}$, the efficiencies of the ideal regeneration cycles for bimetallic and hydride cell systems may be estimated using the previously discussed equations. The actual thermal efficiency of a system will be less than the ideal cycle efficiency because of losses. These losses will consist of cell electrical losses; losses due to differences in the mole fraction of anode metal in the cathode (or mole fraction of hydride in the electrolyte) in the cell and regenerator; heat losses in the regenerator due to heat exchanger inefficiencies and heat losses through the insulation; losses due to the necessity of reflux in the regenerator because of cathode metal evaporation; and miscellaneous losses.

The cell electrical efficiency is a product of the voltage and current efficiencies. The voltage efficiency is equal to the cell voltage at load divided by the cell open-circuit voltage or emf. The current efficiency is the actual coulombs of electricity obtained per mole of anode metal used divided by the electrochemical equivalent of the anode metal. Cell electrical efficiencies of 60% are reasonable values to use in estimates. Cell electrical efficiencies of this order have been obtained in our laboratory units.

The mole fraction of anode metal in the cathode metal (or of hydride in the electrolyte) will be greater in the cell than in the regenerator because of the finite circulation rate. This results in an irreversible loss. The reduction in efficiency due to this effect is equal to the ratios of the open-circuit cell voltages or emfs corresponding to the mole fractions of anode metal in the cathode metal (or hydride in the electrolyte) in the cell and in the regenerator. As an example, Figure 7 shows the open-circuit voltage or emf

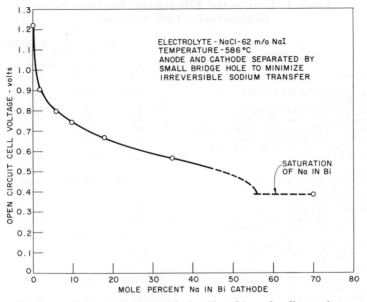

Figure 7. Open circuit potential of sodium bismuth cell as a function of m/o Na in Bi cathode

of a sodium-bismuth cell at 586°C. as a function of the mole fraction of sodium in the bismuth cathode. If the mole fractions of sodium in the bismuth cathode metal is 0.45 in the cell and 0.40 in the regenerator, the factor for reduction in efficiency due to this effect is 0.555/0.58 = 0.956. The loss due to this effect could be included in the cell electrical efficiency or in the regenerator heat utilization efficiency.

The thermal utilization efficiency in the regenerator is the ratio of the heat computed for the ideal cycle including reflux to the actual heat required. In this connection, efficiencies as high as 80% are reasonable since the problem is mainly one of heat exchange.

The reduction in efficiency due to reflux is a function of the internal reflux ratio. If there is no reflux, the factor for efficiency reduction is 1.0. If one assumes that the latent heat of evaporation per mole of anode-cathode metal is independent of composition, the factor for reduction of efficiency due to reflux is (1-R), where R is the internal reflux ratio.

Miscellaneous losses include any power for pumping liquid metals, etc.

The thermal efficiencies of sodium-bismuth, sodium-lead, sodium-tin, and lithium-tin bimetallic cell systems were computed for values of 0.1, 0.2, 0.3, and 0.4 mole fraction of anode metal in the cathode metal and are shown in Table I. In the case of the sodium-bismuth system, a regeneration internal reflux ratio requirement of 30% was assumed and, in the case of the sodium-lead, sodium-tin, and lithium-tin systems, it was assumed that no reflux would be required. A regeneration thermal efficiency

Table I. Computed Efficiencies for Bimetallic Regenerative Cell Systems

Bimetallic System	Mole Fraction of Anode Metal in Cathode Metal			
	0.1	0.2	0.3	0.4
Sodium-Bismuth				
Cell open circuit volts at 859°K. (586°C.)[a]	0.74	0.64	0.58	0.53
Efficiency (Per cent)				
Regeneration, Ideal Cycle—No Reflux	41	38	36	34
Regeneration, Ideal Cycle—30% Reflux	29	27	25	23
Regeneration, 75% of Ideal Cycle—30% Reflux	21	20	19	18
System, 60% Cell Electrical Efficiency	13	12	11	10
Estimated Regeneration Temp. to Avoid Solid				
Phase Region, °K.	1325	1310	1300	1290
Sodium-Lead				
Cell open circuit volts at 698°K. (425°C.)[b]	0.483	0.401	0.327	0.260
Efficiency (Per cent)				
Regeneration, Ideal Cycle	31	27	23	19
Regeneration, 75% of Ideal Cycle	23	20	17	14
System, 60%, Cell Electrical Efficiency	14	12	10	8
Regeneration Pressure, mm. Hg at 1100°K.				
(827°C.)	2.62	6.38	13.8	28.0
Sodium Condensing Temperature, °K. for				
1100°K. Regeneration Temperature	750	795	840	880
Sodium-Tin				
Cell open circuit volts at 773°K. (500°C.)[c]	0.47	0.41	0.36	0.31
Efficiency (Per cent)				
Regeneration, Ideal Cycle	30	27	23	20
Regeneration, 75% of Ideal Cycle	22	20	17	15
System, 60% Cell Electrical Efficiency	13	12	10	9
Regeneration Pressure, mm. Hg, at 1073°K.				
(800°C.)	1.3	5.3	10.0	16.6
Sodium Condensing Temperature, °K. for				
1073°K. Regeneration Temperature	735	785	830	855
Lithium-Tin				
Cell open circuit volts at 823°K. (550°C.)[a]	0.74	0.63	0.58	0.54
Efficiency (Per cent)				
Regeneration, Ideal Cycle	27	24	20	17
Regeneration, 75% of Ideal Cycle	20	18	15	13
System, 60% Cell Electrical Efficiency	12	11	9	8
Regeneration Pressure, mm. Hg, at 1323°K.				
(1050°C.)	0.33	0.75	1.75	3.3
Lithium Condensing Temperature, °K. for				
1323°K. Regeneration Temperature	960	1005	1055	1090

[a] From determinations made at Argonne National Laboratory.
[b] From Hultgren (8), p. 869.
[c] From Hultgren (8), p. 876.

of 75% of the ideal cycle including the loss due to concentration differences between the cell and regenerator was assumed. A cell electrical efficiency of 60% was assumed. Values of cell, open-circuit voltages for the sodium-bismuth and lithium-tin systems were taken from measurements made at Argonne National Laboratory, and values for the sodium-lead and sodium-tin system were taken from the literature (8). Values of the specific heats of the liquids and vapors, the latent heats of evaporation, and the vapor pressures of the anode metals were taken from the literature (8). Values of the partial molar specific heats of the anode metals in the cathode metals were estimated. The heat or enthalpy changes due to the specific heats are small compared to the latent heats of evaporation. Errors due to estimations of the partial molar specific heats are small.

Table II. Computed Efficiencies for Lithium Hydride Cell System

Regeneration Temperature, °K.	Cell Temperature, °K.	Cell Open Circuit Volts[e]		Efficiency (%)		
		10 m/o LiH in Electrolyte	20 m/o in Electrolyte	Ideal Regeneration Cycle	Expected[a] Regeneration	Expected[b] System
1200	773	0.25	0.24	35	24	12
	873	0.19	0.18	27	19	9
1300	773	0.29	0.28	41	29	14
	873	0.24	0.23	33	23	11
1400	773	0.33	0.31	45	31	16
	873	0.28	0.26	38	26	13
1500	773	0.36	0.34	48	33	17
	873	0.31	0.30	45	31	15

[a] Based on 70% of ideal cycle.
[b] Based on 70% of ideal cycle and 50% cell electrical efficiency.
[e] From measurements made at Argonne National Laboratory.

The thermal efficiency values of the lithium-hydride system were computed for cell temperatures of 773 and 873°K. and regeneration temperatures of 1200, 1300, 1400, and 1500°K. and are shown in Table II. A regeneration thermal efficiency of 70% of the ideal cycle, including the losses due to concentration differences between the cell and regenerator, was assumed. A cell electrical efficiency of 50% was assumed. Values of cell, open-circuit voltages or emf's for the lithium hydride system were taken from measurements made at Argonne National Laboratory, and values of the specific heats of lithium liquid, hydrogen gas, and lithium hydride were taken from the literature (*2, 8*). Values of the partial molar specific heats of lithium hydride in electrolyte were estimated.

The expected overall thermal efficiencies of from 8% to 12% for these thermally regenerative cell systems compare favorably with the expected overall thermal efficiencies of other systems for similar applications—for example, mercury vapor cycle, 10%; thermoelectric cycle, 5%; and thermoionic system at 1610°K., 8% maximum, and at 2050°K., 15% maximum.

Nomenclature

A = a constant as defined in the text
a = activity, dimensionless
C_{pl} = specific heat of anode metal liquid, cal./mole °K.
C_{pv} = specific heat of anode metal vapor, cal./mole °K.
C_{pH} = specific heat of hydrogen gas, cal./mole °K.
C_{plx} = specific heat of cathode metal liquid with x mole fraction anode metal, cal./mole °K.
C_{ply} = specific heat of anode metal liquid with y mole fraction hydride, cal./mole °K.
C_{plZ} = specific heat of electrolyte liquid with Z mole fraction hydride (saturated with anode metal), cal./mole °K.

$\overline{C}_{pl}$ = partial molar specific heat of x anode metal in liquid cathode metal, cal./mole °K.

$\overline{C}_{phy}$ = partial molar specific heat of y hydride in liquid anode metal, cal./mole °K.

$\overline{C}_{phye}$ = partial molar specific heat of Z hydride in electrolyte liquid (saturated with anode metal), cal./mole °K.

$\overline{C}_{pH}$ = $\partial C_{ply}/\partial y$ in the case of regeneration of hydride from anode metal, cal./mole °K.

$\overline{C}_{pH}$ = $\overline{C}_{phye} - C_{pl}$ in the case of regeneration of hydride from the electrolyte, cal./mole °K.

$\overline{C}_{pl} = C_{plx} + (1 - x)(\partial C_{plx}/\partial x)$, cal./mole °K.

$\overline{C}_{phy} = C_{ply} + (1 - y)(\partial C_{ply}/\partial y)$, cal./mole °K.

$\overline{C}_{phye} = C_{plZ} + (1 - Z)(\partial C_{plZ}/\partial Z)$, cal./mole °K.

$\overline{C}_{pl} - C_{pl} = nFT \ (\partial^2 E/\partial T^2)_P$, cal./mole °K.

$\overline{C}_{pH} - (n/2)C_{pH} = nFT \ (\partial^2 E/\partial T^2)_P$, cal./mole °K.

C_{pp} = specific heat of cell products, cal./mole °K.

C_{pR} = specific heat of cell reactants, cal./mole °K.

e_c = Carnot cycle efficiency, dimensionless

e_i = ideal cycle efficiency, dimensionless

e_E = cell voltage efficiency, dimensionless

e_I = cell current or coulombic efficiency, dimensionless

E = cell reversible open circuit emf, volts

F = Faraday's constant, 23061 cal./volt eq.

f = fugacity, atm.

ΔG = change in free energy per mole of anode metal, cal./mole

H_{fg} = latent heat of condensation of anode metal vapor, cal./mole

ΔH = change in enthalpy per mole of anode metal or per mole of hydride circulated, cal./mole

I = cell current, amperes

n = equivalents per mole of anode metal, eq./mole

P = pressure, atm.

P_H = hydrogen pressure, atm.

P_v = anode metal saturation vapor pressure, atm.

P_3 = regeneration pressure, atm.

$P_1 = P_{1s}$ = condensation pressure, atm.

R = gas constant, 1.9865 cal./mole °K.

R = internal reflux ratio (distillation), dimensionless

R = cell electrical resistance, ohms

ΔS = change in entropy per mole of anode metal or per mole of hydride circulated, cal./mole °K.

T = temperature

x = mole fraction of anode metal in cathode metal, dimensionless

y = mole fraction of hydride in anode metal, dimensionless

Z = mole fraction of hydride in electrolyte, dimensionless

Subscripts

o refers to a standard condition or to a standard hydrogen pressure

1 refers to conditions at condensing temperature of anode metal vapor from regenerator

2 refers to conditions at cell operating temperature

3 refers to conditions at regeneration temperature

12, 23, 32, 31, and 21 refer to conditions in going from 1 to 2, 2 to 3, 3 to 2, 3 to 1, and 2 to 1

s refers to anode metal vapor pressure

H refers to hydrogen gas

LiH refers to lithium hydride

Li refers to lithium

x, y, z refer to x, y, z mole fractions

Literature Cited

(1) Agruss, B., *J. Electrochem. Soc.* **110**, 1097 (1963).

(2) Ciarlariello, T. A., McDonough, J. B., Shearer, R. E., Study of Energy Conversion Devices, Final Report No. 7, July 1959 to May 1961, MSAR61-99, Contract DA-36-039-SC-78955 Task No. 3A99-09-022-03 to U. S. Army Signal Research and Development Laboratory, Ft. Monmouth, N. J., September 14, 1961 AD 270212.

(3) de Bethune, A. J., *J. Electrochem. Soc.* **107**, 937 (1960).

(4) Foster, M. S., Wood, S. E., Crouthamel, C. E., *Inorg. Chem.* **3**, 1428 (1964).

(5) Fuscoe, J. M., Carlton, S. S., Laverty, D. P., Regenerative Fuel Cell System Investigation, Thompson Ramo Woolridge, Inc., Report No. ER-4069, May 1960 WADD Technical Report 60-442 AD249256 Contract AF33(600)-39573 Project No. 3145 Task No. 60813.

(6) Henderson, R. E., Liquid Metal Cells, Fuel Cells-A CEP Technical Manual p. 17, AICHE, 1963.

(7) Henderson, R. E., Agruss, B., Caple, W., Résumé of Thermally Regenerative Fuel Cell Systems "Energy Conversion for Space Power," Vol. 3, p. 411, Academic Press, New York, 1961.

(8) Hultgren, R. D. *et al.*, "Thermodynamic Properties of Metals and Alloys," p. 869, 876, J. Wiley and Sons, New York, 1963.

(9) King, J., Jr., Ludwig, R. A., Rowlette, R., General Evaluation of Chemicals for Regenerative Fuel Cells, "Energy Conversion for Space Power," Vol. 3, p. 387, Academic Press, New York, 1961.

(10) Liebhafsky, H. A., *J. Electrochem. Soc.* **106**, 1068 (1959).

(11) Roberts, R., *J. Electrochem. Soc.* **105**, 428 (1958).

(12) Yeager, E., Proceedings 12th Annual Battery Research and Development Conference, Asbury Park, N. J., 1958, 2.

RECEIVED November 10, 1965.

Appendix

Derivation of Equation 22. The regeneration pressure, P_3, is equal to the condensing pressure, P_1, which is the vapor pressure of the anode metal at temperature, T_1. P_3 is the partial pressure of the anode metal in the cathode metal, and P_{3s} is the vapor pressure of pure anode metal at temperature, T_3.

The free energy of change of the anode metal in going from the pure state to the condition of X_3 mole fraction in the cathode metal is:

$$\Delta G_3 = RT_3 \, \ell n \, (P_3/P_{3s})$$

or

$$P_3 = P_{3s} \exp (\Delta G_3/RT_3).$$

But

$$\Delta G_3 = \Delta G_2 - \int_{T_2}^{T_3} \Delta S \, dT$$

or

$$\Delta G_3 = -nFE_2 - \int_{T_2}^{T_3} \Delta S_2 \, dT - \int_{T_2}^{T_3} \left[\int_{T_2}^{T} (\overline{C}_{p\ell} - C_{p\ell}) \frac{dT}{T} \right] dT$$

since

$$\Delta S = \Delta S_2 + \int_{T_2}^{T_3} (\overline{C}_{p\ell} - C_{p\ell}) \frac{dT}{T}$$

By substituting $nF \left(\frac{\partial E_2}{\partial T} \right)_p$ for ΔS_2 and integrating the double integral by parts, one obtains

$$\Delta G_3 = -nFE_2 - nF(T_3 - T_2) \left(\frac{\partial E_2}{\partial T} \right)_p - \int_{T_2}^{T_3} (\overline{C}_{p\ell} - C_{p\ell}) \left(\frac{T_3}{T} - 1 \right) dT$$

Substituting this value of ΔG_3 in the equation above yields:

$$P_3 = P_{3s} \exp \left\{ - \frac{1}{RT_3} \left[nFE_2 + nF(T_3 - T_2) \left(\frac{\partial E_2}{\partial T} \right)_p \right. \right.$$
$$\left. \left. + \int_{T_2}^{T_3} (\overline{C}_{p\ell} - C_{p\ell}) \left(\frac{T_3}{T} - 1 \right) dT \right] \right\} \quad (22)$$

Derivation of Equation 23. By differentiating the expression for ΔS,

$$\Delta S = \Delta S_2 + \int_{T_2}^{T} (\overline{C}_{p\ell} - C_{p\ell}) \frac{dT}{T} = nF \left(\frac{\partial E}{\partial T} \right)_p$$

with respect to T, one obtains:

$$\frac{\overline{C}_{p\ell} - C_{p\ell}}{T} = nF \left(\frac{\partial^2 E}{\partial T^2} \right)_p$$

or

$$\overline{C}_{p\ell} - C_{p\ell} = nFT \left(\frac{\partial^2 E}{\partial T^2} \right)_p \quad (23)$$

Derivation of Equation 43.   The regeneration hydrogen pressure is P_3, and the hydrogen pressure at which values of E_2 are measured is P_{oH}. The hydrogen free energy change per mole H in going from P_{oH} to P_3 at temperature, T_3, is:

$$\Delta G_3 = \frac{1}{2} RT_3 \, \ell n \, \frac{P_3}{P_{oH}}$$

or

$$P_3 = P_{oH} \exp \frac{2\Delta G_3}{RT_3}$$

In a manner similar to that for Equation 22, ΔG_3 is found to be

$$\Delta G_3 = -nFE_2 - nF(T_3 - T_2)\left(\frac{\partial E_2}{\partial T}\right)_p - \int_{T_2}^{T_3} \left(\overline{C}_{pH} - \frac{n}{2} C_p{}^H\right)\left(\frac{T_3}{T} - 1\right) dT$$

from which

$$P_3 = P_{oH} \exp \left\{ -\frac{2}{RT_3}\left[nFE_2 + nF(T_3 - T_2)\left(\frac{\partial E_2}{\partial T}\right)_p \right.\right.$$

$$\left.\left. + \int_{T_2}^{T_3} \left(\overline{C}_{pH} - \frac{n}{2} C_p{}^H\right)\left(\frac{T_3}{T} - 1\right) dT \right]\right\} \qquad (43)$$

Derivation of Equation 44.   Equation 44 is derived in a manner similar to that for Equation 23. The expression

$$\Delta S = \Delta S_2 + \int_{T_2}^{T} \left(\overline{C}_{pH} - \frac{n}{2} C_{pH}\right)\frac{dT}{T} = nF\left(\frac{\partial E}{\partial T}\right)_p$$

is differentiated with respect to T yielding

$$\overline{C}_{pH} - \frac{n}{2} C_{pH} = nFT\left(\frac{\partial^2 E}{\partial T^2}\right)_p$$

Derivation of Equations 58 and 59.   The electrical energy output from the power cell per mole of anode material used is:

$$nFE_2 e_{E_2} \quad e_{I_2}$$

(output = input times efficiency).

The electrical energy input to the regenerator cell per mole of anode material regenerated is:

$$\frac{nFE_3}{e_{E3}e_{I3}}$$

(input = output divided by efficiency).

The net electrical output is:

$$nFE_2 e_{E2} e_{I2} - \frac{nFE_3}{e_{E3}e_{I3}} = nF\left[E_2 e_{E2} E_{I2} - \frac{E_3}{e_{E3}e_{I3}} \right]$$

or

$$nF\left[(E_2 - R_2I_2)e_{I2} - \frac{E_3 + R_3I_3}{e_{I3}}\right] \tag{58}$$

since

$$(E_2 - R_2I_2)/E_2 = e_{E2}$$

and

$$\frac{E_3}{E_3 + R_3I_3} = e_{E3}.$$

The overall efficiency of the system is the electrical output divided by the heat input.

The electrical output from Equation 58 is:

$$nF\left[(E_2 - R_2I_2)e_{I_2} - \frac{E_3 + R_3I_3}{e_{I3}}\right].$$

The heat input ΔH_3 for the regenerator cell is:

$$nFE_3 - NFT_3\left(\frac{\partial E_3}{\partial T}\right)_p,$$

minus the electrical input,

$$nF\frac{E_3 + R_3I_3}{e_{I3}},$$

plus any net heat added to the reactant and product streams between the regenerator cell, 3, and the power cell, 2, A, which is given by Equation 21 or 42.

The net heat input is then

$$-nFT_3\left(\frac{\partial E_3}{\partial T}\right)_p + A - nF\left[\frac{E_3 + R_3I_3}{e_{I3}} - E_3\right].$$

Equation 59 follows.

$$e_T = \frac{nF\left[(E_2 - R_2I_2)e_{I2} - \dfrac{E_3 + R_3I_3}{e_{I3}}\right]}{-nFT_3\left(\dfrac{\partial E_3}{\partial T}\right)_p + A - nF\left[\dfrac{E_3 + R_3I_3}{e_{I3}} - E_3\right]}. \tag{59}$$

Thermodynamics of the Lithium Hydride Regenerative Cell

CARL E. JOHNSON and ROBERT R. HEINRICH

Argonne National Laboratory, Argonne, Ill.

Fundamental investigations have been conducted on all phases of the lithium hydride, regenerative emf cell. These studies have demonstrated the feasibility of using a hydrogen permeable membrane as the cathode in a cell. Emf techniques have been used to determine the fundamental thermodynamic quantities (ΔG_f^0, ΔH_f^0, ΔS_f^0) for the lithium hydride cell product. Temperature-composition data are given defining electrolytes suitable for use in the lithium hydride cell. Included in the considerations here presented for potential application of this cell are an examination of the complete cycle, cell operation and regeneration and the inherent problems and advantages associated with this system.

The purpose of this chapter is to describe in detail the work that has been carried out at Argonne National Laboratory in order to understand better the regenerative, lithium hydride, cell system. Primary emphasis of this research has been to provide the fundamental data necessary to solve those problems encountered in attaining a successfully operative, regenerative, lithium hydride system. Further, such investigations were restricted mainly to laboratory studies.

Recent interest in thermally regenerative emf cells has been due to their potential application as an energy conversion device capable of relatively low temperature operation and as an energy storage device. In a thermally regenerative cycle, two components react together electrochemically in a cell to produce electrical power, heat, and the cell product. The product formed in the cell is then heated and dissociated to the reactants. The reactants are separated, cooled, and recycled to their respective anode and cathode compartments in the cell. Because the cell reactants are being regenerated in a closed cyclic operation, there is no need for the further introduction of reactants (fuel) to the system. The cyclic system then absorbs heat at a high temperature, rejects heat at a low temperature, and produces electric power. Thus, this direct conversion of thermal energy into electrical power is accomplished with virtually no mechanical equipment. The practical application of a lithium hydride cell to such conversion is feasible because the cell product shows a fairly large change in free energy with temperature, and regeneration can be achieved at reasonable temperatures.

The lithium hydride cell was selected for initial investigation after a careful study of the total available literature (2, 22, 23, 24, 25, 26, 28), which is not extensive. The lithium hydride cell appears promising if the difficulties associated in using porous metal frits for the hydrogen gas cathode could be eliminated. The primary difficulties of using a porous metal electrode were the occurrence of variable catalytic activity at the surface of the frits and the flooding of the frits, alternately, by hydrogen gas and fused salt electrolyte. Despite these difficulties, Mine Safety Appliance Research Corp. developed a hydride cell operating at 570°C., which produced an emf of 0.3 volt with a current density of 200 amp./sq. ft. (22, 23, 24, 25, 26). The cell consisted of a liquid lithium anode, a lithium fluoride-lithium chloride fused salt eutectic mixture as an electrolyte, and a stainless steel cathode. The cathode was in the form of a screen or a porous, micrometallic gas electrode. The duration of cell operation and the other conditions under which it was achieved are not known.

Other studies on lithium hydride cells have also been carried out by Thompson Ramo Wooldridge, Inc. (1, 4, 21). The results of this work indicated that iron and niobium are the only materials which possess the requisite characteristics for use as hydrogen diffusion diaphragms—i.e., the rate of diffusion of hydrogen through both materials was appreciable at 400–500°C., and both materials were compatible with the electrolyte environment of the cell. Most of the galvanic experiments at Thompson Ramo Wooldridge were carried out with iron diaphragms; however, the results of a single, 45-min. run in which a niobium diaphragm was utilized have been reported (1). This run indicated that at 549°C. and 1 atm. pressure current densities of over 1000 ma./sq. cm. of electrode area could be achieved by a lithium hydride cell using a niobium diaphragm. Much effort had to be expended, however, to keep the niobium diaphragm free of oxide surface contamination at the operating temperature of the cell.

Inert Atmosphere Box

The experimental program for the lithium hydride cell involved working with metals and salts which are extremely sensitive to the chemically active gases. Lithium, for example, may be expected to combine with oxygen, nitrogen, and water vapor. The commonly used lithium halides form hydrates at room temperature; at high temperatures, volatile halogen acids may be lost.

The problem, then, concerns not only achieving the absolute purity of the original charge of blanket gas, but also maintaining the purity of the box atmosphere in the face of continuing contamination. Water vapor, for example, is continually diffusing into the box through rubber gloves. There is continual contamination of the inert atmosphere by chemically active gases released when new equipment is moved into the box and during heating operations. A unit was developed (*3*), therefore, in which helium gas was cycled through the purification system and then returned to the box.

A schematic diagram of the helium-purification unit is shown in Figure 1. The contaminated gas from the boxes is passed first through a palladium catalytic unit (Deoxo-unit) where any hydrogen contaminant in the gas stream is combined with oxygen present in gas stream and converted to water. The helium then passes through a dryer unit of Linde Molecular Sieves, next through a countercurrent heat exchanger, and finally through an activated carbon bed immersed in liquid nitrogen. The gas returning from the carbon bed is heated first in the countercurrent heat exchanger, then to about 20°C. by an electric heater, and finally recycled back to the boxes. A Rotron blower sealed in the gas stream is used to move the helium gas through the completely closed system. Impurity levels in the box atmosphere during normal experimental operation were below 5 p.p.m. for both oxygen and nitrogen and below 1 p.p.m. water.

HELIUM-PURIFICATION SYSTEM

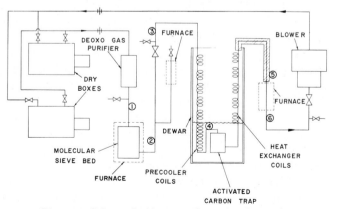

Figure 1. Schematic diagram of regeneration unit

Electrodes

Certainly a most significant problem in the development of a workable lithium hydride cell has concerned the gas electrode, or cathode. The immediate region of contact between the reactant, electrolyte, and electrode is important because it is here that electron transfer takes place. The hydrogen gas must transfer electrons from the electrode at the same time as it enters into the electrolyte as an ion. In conventional operation, the gas electrode requires a three-phase site which must be as large as possible in order to achieve a practical rate for the electrode process. Gases, being nonconductors and having no strength, must be supplied through a medium which conducts electricity and yet provides the greatest possible area wherein the gas, conductor, and electrolyte are in mutual contact. In the past, electrically conducting porous media, such as sintered metals, have been employed as gas electrodes. Through careful control of pore size the electrode area can be made quite large and, with appropriate catalysts, the efficiency of the electrode is adequate.

A problem exists with such electrodes, however, in that porous media inherently tend to absorb liquids by capillary action, causing the gas-electrode-electrolyte interface to retreat within the electrode. When this condition, known as flooding, occurs, the electrode is prone to severe polarization and, as a result, the cell output is decreased considerably.

Because certain metals are readily permeable to hydrogen at the cell temperature, it was recognized that an unusual opportunity existed for circumventing the problems of flooding and the need for catalysts for the gas electrode. It was postulated that the gas electrode could be formed of a solid thin sheet of metal through which the hydrogen could be transmitted by means of interatomic diffusion. Hydrogen would thus be supplied in the atomic state at the metal fused-salt interface.

Hydrogen permeation studies were therefore initiated on selected metals compatible with the lithium hydride, lithium metal, and fused salt environment. Materials such as palladium and silver-palladium alloys which have high hydrogen permeability were not considered because of their incompatibility with lithium metal; hence, the permeation studies were restricted to iron, iron-molybdenum alloys, vanadium, and niobium.

Figure 2 shows some of the data obtained from these permeation studies. Even though the permeation rate of hydrogen through iron is low (*6*), and for this reason would be capable of supporting about $\frac{1}{10}$ the current densities of interest, iron is still somewhat attractive because it is self-cleaning at cell operating temperatures in a hydrogen atmosphere. The possibility of special cathode design to effect a significant increase in current density may still be practical in a cell using an iron diaphragm. Alloys of molybdenum and iron gave results (*6*) which were essentially the same as pure iron. Vanadium, on the other hand, appears to be an excellent diaphragm material (7). It has a high hydrogen permeability at moderate temperatures and is compatible with the cell environment. If a higher cell operating temperature is desired, this material can sustain a theoretical current density in excess of 1000 ma./sq. cm. at 600°C. Because vanadium, however, is not self-cleaning at normal cell temperatures, some preparation of the metal is needed before its maximum permeation rate is achieved. This preparation consists of baking the metal in vacuum at a

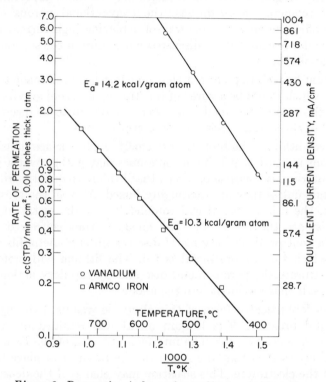

Figure 2. Permeation isobars of vanadium and Armco iron

temperature of 850°C. to remove as much of the surface oxide contamination as possible. Further, vanadium is one of a group of metals (V, Nb, Ta) which have a negative absorption coefficient with temperature; therefore, the metal absorbs greater quantities of hydrogen at lower temperatures than at higher temperatures. If vanadium metal is cooled in hydrogen, the metal lattice will be expanded, which will further increase the permeation rate at the low temperatures.

No permeation data are presented for niobium because of the difficulty in obtaining reproducible results. Such data as were collected, however, corresponded reasonably well with the available literature information (20). Studies reported (1) on the lithium hydride cell utilizing a niobium diaphragm are inconsistent with the literature data. The authors are not familiar with any permeation studies that will support the current densities mentioned in this report (1); rather, it appears that at 500°C. for a 0.010 in.-thick metal diaphragm, the maximum theoretical current density is about 300 ma./sq. cm.

Although it does seem that hydrogen permeable membranes offer distinct advantages, other parameters such as operation at lower cell temperatures to give higher cell voltages may be more important. Under these low temperature conditions, the conventional porous electrodes appear to offer the only possible way of achieving high current densities. This particular feature will be discussed more fully in the section on practical cell applications.

It might be well to point out that no effort has been made to develop electrodes which would be assured of functioning in a zero gravity environment. In the case of the anode, however, the design to be discussed may serve well in this and a variety of other applications.

Molten lithium exhibits an extremely high surface tension. Our observations indicate that lithium sometimes may gather over a $\frac{1}{2}$-in. hole without entering. It was also observed that lithium frequently will not wet other metals unless they are thoroughly fluxed. Also, in the presence of a fused salt, the lithium metal will completely wet the metal surface and readily displace the fused salt. The anode is thus conceived as being basically a controlled porosity-metal disc (or sintered-metal fiber sponge) through which the lithium metal is fed. The lithium will preferentially wet and saturate the porous metal disc and by capillary action displace any fused salt that has crept into the anode.

A less sophisticated form of this electrode was used throughout our experimental program. The lithium metal was retained on a sintered metal fiber sponge (SS-430). The interfacial tension of the liquid lithium on the sponge is such that the metal can be retained in place below the surface of the electrolyte. This situation may change if the density of the electrolyte is very high (e.g., the fused salt iodides), producing a greater buoyancy on the light metal.

Electrolyte

An electrolyte, to be suitable for use in a lithium hydride cell, should have the following properties: (1) reasonable solubility for lithium hydride, (2) thermodynamic stability with respect to the very electropositive lithium metal, (3) stability at regeneration temperatures, preferably with a low vapor pressure at this temperature, and (4) a low anode metal solubility. Halides of lithium metal are the only substances which meet these requirements. Data describing the solid-liquid equilibrium for the lithium hydride-lithium halide systems (*8, 9*) were obtained by thermal analyses, and the pertinent data are given in the following table.

Components	Eutectic Melting Point (°C.)	Eutectic Composition LiH, m/o
LiH-LiCl	495.6	34.0
LiH-LiBr	453.3	29.7
LiH-LiI	390.8	23.5
LiH-LiF	684 min.	solid solution

The first three systems are simple eutectics with the stated melting points and compositions. Data for the LiH-LiF system were obtained from the work of Messer (*16*) and are included here for the sake of completeness.

Analysis of the solid-liquid equilibrium data (*8, 9*) for the first three systems given above has indicated that these systems all show positive deviations from ideality. Such positive deviations are usually caused by dispersion forces or association of one of the components in the mixture. The thermodynamic behavior of the lithium halide systems is similar in regions rich in lithium hydride. The interpretation which seems most consistent with all of the experimental results is that LiH is ionic, and the lithium halides behave ionically probably as an ionic aggregate such as LiY_2^-. This situation corresponds to the same equations suggested previously (*9*) but with the present interpretation in terms of the ionic nature of the melt. The apparent success of this treatment in fitting the data does not prove that these species exist. Only independent measurements which bear directly on the properties of the species in question can confirm their existence.

In order to increase the Carnot cycle efficiency and cell voltage, the lithium hydride cell should be operated at low temperatures; thus, low melting electrolytes are desirable. Precautions should also be taken to prevent possible metal dispersions during cell operation. The fluoride ion is reported (*12*) to be an agent which effectively breaks dispersions of this kind. Two systems are available for use as electrolytes in cell operation as follows: the LiH-LiCl-LiF system (*10*), which is predominantly a solid solution with a minimum of 456°C. and the LiH-LiCl-LiI system, presently under study, which is a ternary eutectic with a melting point of 330°C.

Electrochemical Cell

The only available thermodynamic data for lithium hydride are enthalpy data derived from calorimetric measurements (*5, 16*). With this paucity of systematic thermodynamic data on lithium hydride, it was decided to establish the standard thermodynamic functions (ΔG_f^0, ΔH_f^0, ΔS_f^0) for the formation of solid lithium hydride by an emf method over as wide a temperature range as possible.

The lithium hydride formation cell may be represented as $Li(l)/LiX(l)$ saturated with $LiH(s)/H_2(g)$ 1 atm., Fe. The half-cell reactions, at the anode, $Li(l) \rightarrow Li^+ + e$; and at the cathode, $\frac{1}{2}H_2 + e \rightarrow H^-$, sum to give the cell reaction $Li(l) + \frac{1}{2}H_2(g) \rightarrow LiH(s)$. With the standard states of pure liquid lithium metal, pure solid lithium hydride, pure hydrogen gas at one atmosphere pressure, and the Nernst equation, $\mathrm{E} = \mathrm{E}^0 - RT/nF \ln \left(\dfrac{a_{LiH}}{a_{Li}\, a_{H_2}^{1/2}} \right)$, it is readily seen that the equation reduces to $\mathrm{E} = \mathrm{E}^0$ for the actual cell with all three substances in their standard states.

The essential parts of the standard lithium hydride cell assembly are illustrated in Figure 3. The cell is isolated from the inert atmosphere box by a cover through which the stainless steel support tubes extend. Both the lithium anode and the hydrogen cathode were insulated by beryllia tubing. The lithium metal was contained on the sintered-metal, fiber sponge as described previously. The cathode consists of a stainless steel bubbler tube to which an Armco iron bubbler cap was welded. Pure hydrogen gas, purified by diffusion through a silver palladium alloy, was passed over the iron surface for the catalytic reduction of hydrogen to hydride ions. Emfs were taken at a pressure of one atmosphere.

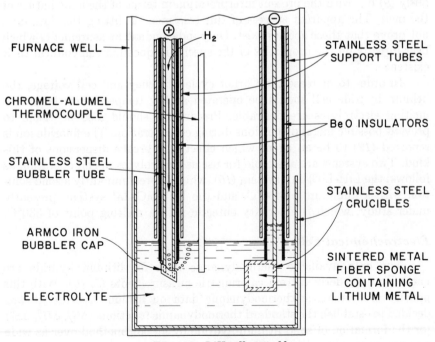

Figure 3. LiH cell assembly

Table I. EMF-Temperature Data for Lithium Hydride Cell

59.8 m/o LiI 40.2 m/o LiH		59.8 m/o LiBr 40.2 m/o LiH		55.1 m/o LiCl 44.9 m/o LiH		40.0 m/o LiCl 60.0 m/o LiH	
EMF (Volt)	Temp. °K.	EMF (Volt)	Temp. °K.	EMF (Volt)	Temp. °K.	EMF (Volt)	Temp. °K.
0.3934	673.2	0.3440	733.7	0.3076	777.2	0.2845	803.2
0.3915	674.2	0.3412	738.7	0.3033	782.2	0.2822	810.2
0.3864	683.2	0.3368	744.2	0.2993	788.2	0.2764	813.2
0.3822	687.2	0.3324	749.7	0.2951	792.2	0.2747	819.7
0.3797	693.2	0.3275	754.2	0.2908	798.2	0.2690	823.2
0.3739	698.2	0.3253	758 2	0.2870	803.2	0.2690	828.2
0.3698	704.2	0.3247	762.2	0.2828	808.7	0.2605	838.2
0.3628	708.2	0.3197	764.2	0.2828	813.2	0.2629	843.2
0.3598	716.2	0.3183	767.7			0.2520	844.2
0.3522	722.2	0.3183	769.7			0.2517	847.7
0.3520	723.7	0.3178	773.2			0.2510	852.2
0.3440	734.2	0.3120	778.2				
0.3387	742.7						
0.3325	747.2						
0.3318	756.2						
0.3228	766.2						

Reagent grade lithium chloride, lithium bromide, and lithium iodide were purified before use by standard techniques (*13, 14*). Lithium hydride was made by a technique described by Messer (*15*).

Data for cells of differing lithium halide-lithium hydride compositions are summarized in Table I. A comparison of the individual cell data with the composite set showed no apparent inconsistencies, and the data are treated as a whole. The uncertainty in the data obtained with the chloride cells is somewhat greater than that obtained with the bromide and iodide cells, because of higher cell-operating temperatures resulting in significant corrections in the chloride emf data. In order to derive an equation giving the emf as a function of temperature, the emf data obtained for the bromide and iodide cells were combined and fitted to an equation linear with respect to temperature, and the data for the chloride cells were fitted to a second linear equation. For the temperature range considered, a linear function seemed to fit all the data best. The intercept and slope of the final linear equation were obtained by using an average of the values in the above two equations, weighted according to the number of experimental points in each set of data. The resultant equation, $E^0 = 0.9081 - 7.699 \times 10^{-4}T$, is for the temperature range 673–853°K. with a standard deviation of ±2 mv. Calculations were made of ΔG_f^0, ΔH_f^0, and ΔS_f^0 at 800°K.; these data are given in Table II, and the data were transposed to 298°K. by integration of the best available heat capacity data over the temperature range 800–298°K.

Table II. Calculated Values[a] and Literature Values for the Enthalpy, Free Energy, and Entropy of Lithium Hydride

	This Work 800°K.	This Work 298°K.	Literature 298°K.
ΔH_f^0 cal. mole^{-1}	$-20{,}940$	$-21{,}790 \pm 290$	$-21{,}340$ (16) $-21{,}670$ (5)
ΔG_f^0 cal. mole^{-1}	$-6{,}740$	$-16{,}160 \pm 50$	$-16{,}450$ (11, 16) $-16{,}800$ (5, 11)
ΔS_f^0 cal. deg.$^{-1}$ mole^{-1}	-17.7	-18.9 ± 0.4	-16.3 (11)

^{a} $\Delta H_f^0 = nF\left[T\left(\frac{\partial E^0}{\partial T}\right)_p - E^0\right]$, $\Delta G_f^0 = -nFE^0$, $\Delta S_f^0 = nF\left(\frac{\partial E^0}{\partial T}\right)_p$, where $E^0 800°K. =$ 0.2922 volt, $\left(\frac{\partial E^0}{\partial T}\right)_p = -7.699 \times 10^{-4}T$ volt deg.$^{-1}$.

Studies have also been made of the reactions taking place at the cathode. The equilibrium potential obtained during the entire experimental program was always the same for any metal used: pure iron, vanadium, or niobium. The rate of achieving this equilibrium potential for vanadium and niobium, however, was very slow.

The hydrogen electrode in a lithium hydride cell is required to assume the potential defined by the overall equilibrium between molecular hydrogen gas and hydride ions in the cell electrolyte. But, since this equilibrium is not freely established in the absence of an active surface, the electrode must serve in this capacity as well. The establishment of an equilibrium population of atomic hydrogen on the metal surface is achieved only after the bulk metal is saturated with hydrogen. Hydrogen solubility in niobium and vanadium is about four to seven thousand times greater than in iron.

The following mechanism agrees with the experimental results and delineates the important features in establishing the equilibrium potential at the hydrogen-hydride electrode.

$$H_2 \text{ (g)} \rightleftharpoons 2H \text{ (surface)}; \quad R_1 \text{ (moderate)}$$
$$H \text{ (surface)} \rightleftharpoons H \text{ (bulk)}; \quad R_2 \text{ (slow)}$$
$$H \text{ (surface)} \rightleftharpoons H^- \text{ (solution)}; \quad R_3 \text{ (very fast)}$$

Rate 1 is the activated adsorption of hydrogen on the metal surface. Rate 2 combines the formation of the gas-metal solid solution and the diffusion of atoms into the metal as a composite rate. The diffusion of hydrogen through the metal lattice is the rate-controlling step. The slow rate at which hydrogen saturates the metal also controls the rate at which the cell equilibrium potential is established.

The reaction rate, R_3, was assumed to be very fast with respect to rates R_1 and R_2. Atomic hydrogen on the electrode surface is rapidly stripped off as the hydride ion by an electron exchange.

The diffusion of atomic hydrogen from the metal surface into the bulk metal lattice was considered the slowest rate. This was consistent with the fact that, in the operation of a metal diaphragm under a hydrogen gas pressure differential of one atmosphere, the permeation rate is inversely proportional to the diaphragm thickness. Vanadium and niobium, compared with iron, are unique in their extremely high, hydrogen solubility. It is thus not surprising that an equilibrium population of atomic hydrogen could not be maintained on the fresh vanadium or niobium electrode surfaces until the bulk metal was saturated. Evidence of this condition was the low, initial, cell potentials for these metal electrodes compared with the virtually immediate attainment of equilibrium potentials for iron electrodes. For vanadium, equilibrium was attained in hours to days, depending on the cell temperature. Once equilibrium had been attained, on the other hand, the potential of a lithium hydride cell, using a vanadium cathode, dropped only slowly even when the hydrogen gas atmosphere was removed from the cell, contrasting with the very rapid potential drop when iron cathodes were used.

Voltammetric and chronopotentiometric (*19*) studies using an iron microelectrode in a lithium chloride-potassium chloride electrolyte have confirmed the rapid rate of R_3, the stripping of atomic hydrogen from the electrode surface as hydride ion, in the above sequence. These studies also indicate that not all metals will be suitable for use as electrodes in a lithium hydride, galvanic cell system. For example, it was demonstrated that the overall process using an iron electrode is much faster than that for a tungsten electrode.

Regeneration Characteristics

Certainly one of the more attractive features of the lithium hydride cell system is the apparent ease of regeneration. Literature data (*15*) indicate that at 900°C., lithium hydride readily dissociates to give an equilibrium hydrogen gas pressure of one atmosphere. The relatively low temperature and ease of separation of the gas-liquid metal cell reactants make for convenient cyclic operation in a thermally regenerative cell system. At 900°C. hydrogen diffuses rapidly through iron to give virtually perfect gas phase separation of hydrogen.

The purpose of the regenerator is to dissociate the cell product, lithium hydride, into the reactants, lithium and hydrogen, which may then be returned to their respective electrode compartments for completion of the cycle. Studies on regeneration conditions should determine the characteristics of the reactions and processes concerned with this phase of the lithium hydride cell. Because of the scope of the present work, the conditions for regeneration were approached by a circuitous route. It was convenient to extend the work on the emf studies of the hydrogen-hydride systems in solutions saturated with lithium hydride to unsaturated solutions. Once the standard emf of the reaction $Li(l) + \frac{1}{2}H_2(g) \rightarrow LiH(s)$

had been determined as a function of temperature, the activity of lithium hydride could be obtained in unsaturated electrolytes of similar cells.

Computed thermodynamic data for lithium hydride obtained from emf-temperature-composition studies of the lithium hydride cell are given in Table III. Using the relation $\Delta G = -nF\text{E}$, the free energy of formation of lithium hydride was calculated from the cell emf, E. The partial molal free energy, $\overline{G}$, of lithium hydride in solution is then $\overline{G} = \Delta G - \Delta G^0$, where ΔG^0 refers to pure solid lithium hydride. The entropy of formation,

Table III. Energy Relationships in LiH-LiCl System

N (LiH)	Saturated	0.3019	0.2019	0.1020	0.0503	0.0252	0.0104
$(\partial\text{E}/\partial T)_p \times 10^4$	−7.699	−5.817	−5.891	−5.416	−5.523	−3.902	−3.230
ΔS cal./deg.	−17.7	−13.4	−13.6	−12.5	−12.7	−9.0	−7.4
$\overline{S}$	0	4.3	4.1	5.2	5.0	8.7	10.3
ΔH cal./mole	−16,060	−14,110	−14,860	−15,420	−16,550	−15,500	−16,370
$\overline{H}$	0	1,950	1,200	640	−490	560	−210
600°C. E(volts)	0.2358	0.2632	0.2904	0.3437	0.3873	0.4379	0.5176
600°C. ΔG (cal.)	−5,437	−6,069	−6,696	−7,925	−8,931	−10,097	−11,935
600°C. $\overline{G}$	0	−632	−1,259	−2,488	−3,494	−4,660	−6,498
600°C. a	1.0	0.6947	0.4840	0.2384	0.1335	0.0682	0.0242
700°C. E(volts)	0.1588	0.2050	0.2314	0.2895	0.3321	0.3989	0.4853
700°C. ΔG (cal.)	−3,662	−4,727	−5,336	−6,676	−7,658	−9,198	−11,190
700°C. $\overline{G}$	0	−1,065	−1,674	−3,014	−3,996	−5,536	−7,528
700°C. a	1.0	0.5765	0.4207	0.2104	0.1266	0.0571	0.0204
800°C. E(volts)	0.0819	0.1469	0.1725	0.2353	0.2768	0.3599	0.4530
800°C. ΔG (cal.)	−1,888	−3,387	−3,978	−5,426	−6,383	−8,299	−10,446
800°C. $\overline{G}$	0	−1,499	−2,090	−3,538	−4,495	−6,411	−8,558
800°C. a	1.0	0.4951	0.3753	0.1903	0.1215	0.0495	0.0181
900°C. E(volts)	0.0048	0.0887	0.1136	0.1812	0.2216	0.3209	0.4207
900°C. ΔG (cal.)	−111	−2,045	−2,619	−4,178	−5,110	−7,400	−9,700
900°C. $\overline{G}$	0	−1,934	−2,508	−4,067	−4,999	−7,289	−9,589
900°C. a	1.0	0.4362	0.3410	0.1747	0.1172	0.0439	0.0164

ΔS, is obtained from $\Delta S = nF(\partial\text{E}/\partial T)_P$ and the partial molal entropy, $\overline{S} = \Delta S - \Delta S^0$. The activity of lithium hydride in solution, a, is calculated from $\overline{G} = RT \ln a$. Other tabulated quantities are the corresponding enthalpies, ΔH and $\overline{H}$.

With the activity of lithium hydride, determined from the cell emf, one can use these data with the Nernst equation

$$\text{E} = \text{E}^0 - \frac{RT}{nF} \ln \left(\frac{a_{\text{LiH}}}{a_{\text{Li}} \, P_{\text{H}_2}^{1/2}} \right)$$

to calculate the hydrogen equilibrium pressure at each temperature and composition. With the restrictions that $a_{\text{Li}} = 1$ because we are using pure lithium metal anodes and E = 0 because we are calculating the hydrogen equilibrium pressures, the equation reduces to the form

$$2 \left(\frac{-\text{E}^0}{1.984 \times 10^{-4}T} + \log a_{\text{LiH}} \right) = \log P_{\text{H}_2}$$

Assuming the cell emf to be a linear function of temperature, the equation relating cell emf with temperature $E^0 = 0.9081 - 7.699 \times 10^{-4}T$ was extrapolated to 900°C. in order to make an estimate of the hydrogen equilibrium pressure at temperatures near regeneration conditions. The data are shown graphically in Figure 4 where the logarithm of the hydrogen pressure and the reciprocal of the absolute temperature is plotted. For a solution containing 0.302 atom fraction lithium hydride, a dissociation pressure of 129 mm. was calculated for a temperature of 900°C.

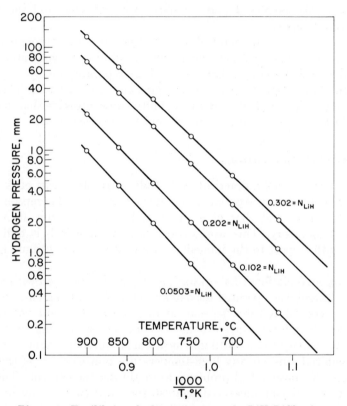

Figure 4. Equilibrium hydrogen pressure in LiH-LiCl mixtures

The validity of this experimental approach seems confirmed by the fact that these data check well with the direct measurements made on several lithium hydride-lithium chloride compositions by the group at Thompson Ramo Wooldridge, Inc. (4). One cannot overlook, however, the apparently low pressure obtained under nominal, regeneration conditions. The full import of this particular phase of the cell work will be evaluated in greater detail in the section on Practical Cell Applications.

Although no design work has been carried out to define a particular regeneration system, some possibilities in equipment design are noteworthy. For regeneration of the lithium hydride system, separating the hydrogen gas from the liquid metal-electrolyte mixture and separating the lithium metal from the electrolyte are required. Both separations have been examined in some detail by the group at Thompson Ramo Wooldridge (27) using a compact gas-liquid-liquid separator, a cylinder in which the liquid-gas mixture is introduced tangentially at a high velocity. Beneath the cylindrical section is a conical chamber. The gas is removed from the base of the cone, the heavier liquid removed from its side, and the lighter liquid, from its apex.

Exploiting the high permeability of hydrogen gas through certain metals at regeneration temperatures helps simplify the regenerator. In its design, a metal diaphragm can be used to separate the hydrogen gas component from the other gaseous components in the system. There will thus be no problem in dealing with the finite vapor pressure that is caused by the electrolyte and is sure to be present in the regenerator.

Practical Cell Applications

To date, the only practical cell studies are the early ones of the groups at Mine Safety Appliance Research Corp. and Thompson Ramo Wooldridge, Inc., and that of a single cell which was run at Argonne National Laboratory. This work, being largely empirical, is difficult to evaluate with respect to the immediate application of the lithium hydride cell.

At Argonne National Laboratory, a lithium hydride cell with a vanadium diaphragm was operated for 540 hrs. at 525°C., giving current densities that exceeded 200 ma./sq. cm. at one-half open-circuit voltage (0.3 volt). Even though this current density is only about one-half the theoretical current density (for a 0.010 in.-thick, vanadium diaphragm at 500°C.), it was achieved without any high-temperature pretreatment of the metal diaphragm. No mechanical problems arose during the cell run. The slope of a plot of cell emf measured against the logarithm of the hydrogen pressure corresponded to the expected Nernst slope of one, indicating the reversibility of the H_2, H^- couple at the vanadium electrode.

The electrolyte or the cathode construction, for the most part, determines design parameters. Because lithium metal has unique characteristics, the anode design incorporating either a sintered-metal or controlled-porosity disc will be most suitable. If one uses the LiH-LiCl-LiF electrolyte system (minimum at 443°C.), a permeable membrane for the cathode would be a possible choice.

The most distinct advantage given by the permeable membrane is its ready solution to the assorted problems that have long plagued porous, metal-gas electrodes. As the permeability studies indicate, however, the choice of metal for this application is limited to iron and vanadium. Iron has a low hydrogen permeation rate, and vanadium requires pretreatment before it is suitable for use. It should be emphasized that in utilizing a permeable membrane, the temperature of the cell operation must be above about 350°C. (considering a 0.002 in.-thick vanadium diaphragm). Only at this temperature and above can the hydrogen permeation rates through the cathode metal support reasonable current densities.

The quantity of hydrogen diffusing through a metal diaphragm is proportional to the difference in the square roots of the hydrogen pressures on each side. The quantity diffusing through a 0.010 in.-thick vanadium diaphragm at 500°C. is $0.50 \ (\sqrt{P_a} - \sqrt{P_b})$, where P_a and P_b are the hydrogen pressure in atmospheres on each side of the diaphragm. The voltage loss is $\Delta E = -\dfrac{RT}{nF} \ln \dfrac{\sqrt{P_a}}{\sqrt{P_b} - I/A}$, where I is the cell current density in amp./sq. cm. of diaphragm area, and A is related to the theoretical current density (in amp./sq. cm.) for a permeable diaphragm and is equal to 0.05 for $T = 773°K$. With this equation, it can be shown that cell voltage losses may be as great as 0.1 volt for operating a cell at one-half atmosphere hydrogen pressure and 100 ma./sq. cm. current density. For a high output voltage in the cell, it is necessary to operate the cathode as close to one atmosphere as possible; hence, with a regeneration pressure of about 100 mm., pumps will be needed to bring the hydrogen pressure up to one atmosphere or above. Such P-V work could be a real drain on the efficiency, with roughly 50% of the cell voltage conceivably being used for pumping.

In choosing the LiH-LiCl-LiI electrolyte system (ternary eutectic melting at 325°C.), one gains a number of advantages because the cell can now operate at much lower temperatures. Cell voltages will be significantly higher. This electrolyte is at or near saturation with respect to the lithium hydride component. At saturation, the cell voltage is 0.45 volt. Regeneration pressures can be significantly increased by sending to the regenerator a mixture very rich in lithium hydride (90-95 m/o LiH). Such a mixture can be obtained by precipitating lithium hydride as a pure component from this electrolyte near cell-operating temperatures.

As presently visualized, the lithium hydride cell should function at the lowest temperature possible in order to take advantage of the higher voltages obtained. Operation at this temperature may require investigations of cathodes made of porous materials. The apparent success attained by using porous electrodes in the hydrogen-oxygen cells indicates a possible solution to this problem and highlights remarkable advances made recently in porous gas electrode development.

Literature Cited

(1) Carlton, S. S., "Electrode Development Program," ASD-TDR-62-241, Prepared by TAPCO, A Division of Thompson Ramo Wooldridge, Inc., Cleveland, Ohio, 1962.

(2) Ciarlariello, T. A., Werner, R. C., *Chem. Eng. Progr.* **57**, 42 (1961).

(3) Foster, M. S., Johnson, C. E., Crouthamel, C. E., "Helium Purification Unit for High Purity Inert Atmosphere Boxes," USAEC-ANL-6652, December 1962.

(4) Fuscoe, J. M., Carlton, S. S., Laverty, D. P., "Regenerative Fuel Cell System Investigation," WADD-60-442, Thompson Ramo Wooldridge, Inc., Cleveland, Ohio, 1960.

(5) Gunn, S. R., Green, L. G., *J. Am. Chem. Soc.* **80**, 4782 (1958).

(6) Heinrich, R. E., Johnson, C. E., Crouthamel, C. E., *J. Electrochem. Soc.* **112**, 1067 (1965).

(7) Heinrich, R. E., Johnson, C. E., Crouthamel, C. E., *J. Electrochem. Soc.* **112**, 1071 (1965).

(8) Johnson, C. E., Wood, S. E., Crouthamel, C. E., *Inorg. Chem.* **3**, 1487 (1964).

(9) Johnson, C. E., Wood, S. E., Crouthamel, C. E., *J. Chem. Phys.* **44**, 884 (1966).

(10) Johnson, C. E., Hathaway, E., Crouthamel, C. E., *J. Chem. Eng. Data* **11**, 372 (1966).

(11) Kelly, K. K., King, E. G., *U. S. Bur. Mines Bull.* **592** (1961).

(12) Knighton, J., private communication.

(13) Laitinen, H. A., Ferguson, W. S., Osteryoung, R. A., *J. Electrochem. Soc.* **104**, 516 (1957).

(14) Maricle, D. L., Hume, D. N., *J. Electrochem. Soc.* **107**, 354 (1960).

(15) Messer, C. E., "A Survey Report on Lithium Hydride," USAEC-NYO-9470, October 1960.

(16) Messer, C. E., Fasolino, L. G., Thalmayer, C. E., *J. Am. Chem. Soc.* **77**, 4524 (1955).

(17) Messer, C. E., Mellor, J., *J. Phys. Chem.* **64**, 503 (1960).

(18) Moers, K., *Z. Anorg. Allegem. Chem.* **113**, 179 (1920).

(19) Plambeck, J. A., Elder, J. P., Laitinen, H. A., *J. Electrochem. Soc.* **113**, 931 (1966).

(20) Rudd, R. W., Vose, D. W., Johnson, S., *J. Phys. Chem.* **66**, 351 (1962).

(21) Schwartz, H. J., Carlton, S. S., Fuscoe, J. M., "Regenerative Fuel Cell System," ASD-TDR-62-18, Thompson Ramo Wooldridge, Inc., Cleveland, Ohio, 1962.

(22) Shearer, R. E., "Study of Energy Conversion Devices," Progress Reports to U. S. Army Signal Research and Development Laboratory, Ft. Monmouth, N. J., Report 1, MSAR-59-119, 1959.

(23) *Ibid.*, Report 2, MSAR-60-12, 1960.

(24) *Ibid.*, Report 3, MSAR-60-56, 1960.

(25) *Ibid.*, Report 4, MSAR-60-110, 1960.

(26) *Ibid.*, Report 7, MSAR-61-99, 1961.

(27) Snoke, D. R., "Zero Gravity Separator Development for Regenerative Fuel Cell," ASD-TDR-62-240, Prepared by TAPCO, A Division of Thompson Ramo Wooldridge, Inc., Cleveland, Ohio, 1962.

(28) Werner, R. C., Shearer, R. E., U. S. Patent **3,031,518** (April 24, 1962).

RECEIVED November 10, 1965.

Phase Diagram Considerations for the Regenerative Bimetallic Cell

ALBERT K. FISCHER

Argonne National Laboratory, Argonne, Ill.

General relationships which are useful in selecting and operating a bimetallic regenerative cell may be deduced from the phase diagram of the system. The equilibrium pressure of the cell system is effectively fixed by the condensation temperature in the regenerator. This pressure will fix the applicable temperature-composition phase diagram and will determine whether there is the necessary separation of the liquid-vapor loop from the liquid-solid regions. The composition of material to be returned to the cathode will dictate the regeneration temperature. The melting point of any compound formed should not be so high that separating the vapor-liquid and liquid-solid regions cannot be achieved at a practical operating pressure. Additional pressure conditions may be imposed if azeotropy is present and is to be eliminated.

Many of the factors involved in selecting a bimetallic system for a regenerative cell are implicit in the phase diagram of the system. Certain conditions of operation, such as temperatures, pressure, and compositions of materials circulating to and from the anode and cathode, are also evident from a careful consideration of the system's phase diagram. Often the relationships among these factors can be more easily perceived with the pictorial aid of a phase diagram than from analytical thermodynamic expressions. Admittedly, the actual cell operation will not be carried out as an equilibrium process so that an equilibrium diagram will not most accurately represent all conditions in a cell; there is also the difficulty that the needed phase diagrams are not completely known. But these facts do not preclude drawing, from phase diagram considerations and from some reasonable assumptions, certain conclusions which are generally valid and helpful in system evaluation and in predicting operating conditions.

A variety of approaches to the design of a regenerative emf cell is open as a result of various combinations of types of electrodes and methods of regeneration. The particular type of regenerative cell to be discussed here is the bimetallic cell—bimetallic because both electrochemically active electrode components are metals. The mode of regeneration being considered is thermal decomposition of the cell reaction product coupled with distillative separation into the cell reactants. Some of the ideas involved in such a cell have been outlined by Agruss (1). Because a high emf would be favored by selecting the most highly electropositive metals for the anode, the emphasis for the present is on those combinations of metals in which the anode is an alkali metal. This situation has, to an extent, influenced certain features of the discussion which follows.

Attention will be given to two-component, phase diagram considerations as they pertain to compound formation, to the relationship between the liquid-vapor equilibrium loop and solid phase regions, to the bearing of the phase diagram relationships on the regeneration operation, and to the possibility and implications of the occurrence of an azeotrope in the liquid-vapor loop.

Voltage Criterion and Compound Formation

Perhaps the first consideration in selecting a bimetallic system is the voltage which the cell may be expected to deliver. At this point, the working assumption is made that, for a cell to generate an acceptable voltage, strong chemical interaction of the two metallic components is needed to avoid reliance on concentration cell potentials which may be shown to be inadequate. For example, if a cell were to be a concentration cell operating at 700°K. with pure component A as anode and a 1 atom% solution of A in C as cathode, where the activity of A is taken as 0.01, the voltage would be

$$E = -\frac{RT}{nF} \ln \frac{a_C}{a_A} = -\frac{(2)}{(1)} \frac{(700°K.)}{(23 \times 10^3)} (2.3) \log \frac{10^{-2}}{1} = 0.28 \text{ volt}$$

If the cell reaction is one involving an electron change such that $n > 1$, the voltage would be less. Also, running the cell to build up only 1 atom% A in C may be impractical; if a 10-fold concentration increase is allowed, 10 atom% A in C, which is perhaps a more likely practical situation, the voltage indicated above would be halved to 0.14 volt. It is seen that voltages obtained from simple concentration cell operation are rather low, even before they are reduced further by various inefficiencies and by the operating load.

The most effective means to increase the voltage is to decrease a_C in the expression $\ln \frac{a_C}{a_A}$. Because decreasing a_C by decreasing the concentration of A in C alone is impractical, decreasing a_C by virtue of a small value for the activity coefficient is the only alternative. One criterion for the existence of an interaction of A and C so as to provide such a lowering of activity is the existence of a compound(s) of A and C in the phase diagram. As a rough rule for survey purposes, the interaction free energy is taken to be larger the higher the melting point of the compound or, stated differently, the higher the melting point the larger the voltage to be expected from the cell. This approximation, which has some empirical substantiation (*2*), is adopted to serve as a guide among bimetallic systems even though it is recognized that a melting point bears no necessary relationship to a free energy change and hence to an emf. If any justification for the rule is necessary, the operational argument might be made that, in a regenerative cell, the higher the m.p. of the cell product the higher is the temperature that must be reached to break the product up in the regeneration step. Because regeneration must overcome the forces holding cell product together and, since the cell emf itself reflects these forces in their operation to form the cell product, then the more strenuous the necessary regeneration conditions the higher the cell emf. There are limitations, however, on how high the melting point of the compound can be in a practical regenerative galvanic system; the significance of the relationship of the compound hump in the phase diagram to the rest of the diagram will be discussed later. So far, the first phase diagram criteria for selecting a bimetallic system are that the diagram should show compound formation between A and C, and preferably that the melting point of the compound should be reasonably high.

Cell Operating Cycle and Phase Diagram

Let us first consider the course of the cell operation as it may be traced on the constant pressure phase diagram which we take to be one like Figure 1. The cell system is considered to be sealed so that for the present analysis the system pressure may be regarded as uniform. In an actual cell, of course, where fluid flow through tubes must be taken into account, some pressure drops may occur.

The cell operating temperature is T_1, the temperature of the electrodes and the electrolyte separating them. For the time being, let the anode be pure A, and let the cathode be a solution of A in C of overall composition somewhere between x_3 and x_2 on the diagram. In the current-generating reaction, A will oxidize at the anode and go into the electrolyte fused-salt solution, migrate toward the cathode, interact with and go into the liquid cathode, changing the cathode alloy composition in the A-enriching direction, all at T_1. Let us say that the cathode, by this means, reaches composition x_3. Now some of the cathode alloy of the composition x_3 is removed, sent to the regenerator, and heated to the regenerator temperature, T_2. We are now in the liquid-vapor region of the phase diagram, and in the

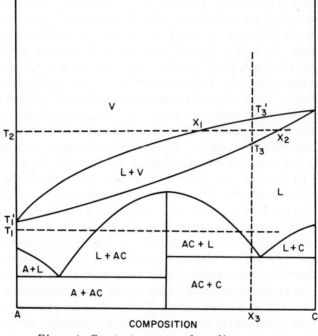

Figure 1. Constant pressure phase diagram

regenerator is formed some vapor richer in A, represented by point x_1. Also, a liquid residue richer in C, represented by point x_2, is formed. The liquid residue x_2 in the regenerator is recirculated to the cathode, after being cooled to T_1.

The course of the vapor, x_1, from this point depends on the shape of the vaporus and on the desired anode composition. Basically, two courses are open. In the first case, if the vaporus bulges far enough to the A side to permit condensation at T_1' to yield a liquid rich enough in A so that it can be returned directly to the anode, this would be the simplest method of operation. In the second case, the vaporus may not bulge far to the A side, and it may be much like the curve in Figure 1. In this case, the vapor x_1 would, most likely, be considered insufficiently rich in A to be condensed and returned directly to the anode. Fractionation would be necessary, and we would trace out a series of steps in the liquid-vapor loop corresponding to the theoretical plates required to reach the desired degree of enrichment in respect to A. In an actual operation, a steady state would be reached which corresponds to operation of a distillation column at a certain reflux ratio. For either case, without or with fractionation, the final temperature at which vapor is condensed is termed the condensation temperature and is labeled T_1'. The liquid formed at this temperature will then be cooled to the cell-operating temperature, T_1, and returned to the anode. T_1' and T_1, of course, may be close together or even equal.

Liquid-Vapor Relationships

Inter-condensed-phase relationships are relatively insensitive to pressure changes, so that the effect of pressure is of minor importance in considering compound formation. Phase relationships involving the vapor phase, however, are decidedly pressure sensitive. Because the method of regeneration involves distillation, the vapor-liquid relationships of the phase diagram will be important. These relationships are represented on the three-dimensional (pressure, composition, temperature) phase diagram, Figure 2.

In Figure 2, the compound is taken to be congruently melting. A cross section at a given pressure gives the temperature-composition diagram. Two such cross sections are indicated here—one at a low pressure and one at a high pressure. Over the pressure range covered, the melting points of A, the anode material, C, the cathode material, and AC, the compound formed between A and C, are shown essentially unchanged.

For initial simplicity, the vapor-liquid region will be assumed to be of the simple ascendant, loop variety. It will be noted that the b.p. of A (anode material) is taken to be lower than that of C (cathode material) because the binary combinations under consideration involve a low b.p. alkali-metal anode. An additional criterion for cell selection is obvious—

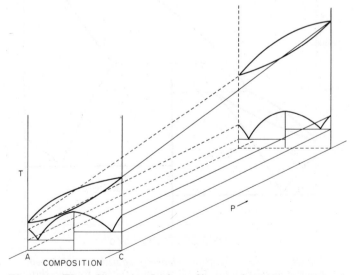

Figure 2. Three-dimensional phase diagram for a two-component system

a large separation between b.p.'s of A and C is desirable to facilitate distillation regeneration.

The height of the liquid-vapor loop relative to the solid-liquid regions will be seen to be different in the two isobaric sections drawn in the figure. Always, the position of the loop on the temperature scale will drop as the pressure is lowered. Thus, sectioning at even lower pressures would eventually reveal contact and overlap of the loop and hump and would result in a phase diagram which conceivably would look like Figure 3. The important feature in Figure 3 is that an additional kind of equilibrium, which is an equilibrium between vapor and solid in the V + AC region, has been introduced.

Implications of Low Pressure

In terms of Figure 3, vapor generated in the upper V + L area has to be condensed in order to be returned to the anode. Regardless of whether

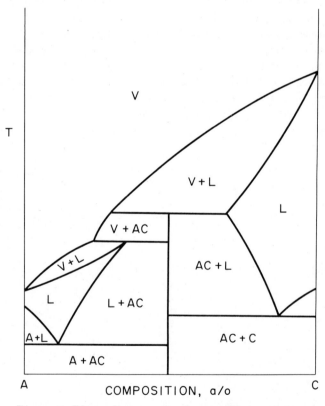

Figure 3. Phase diagram showing equilibrium between vapor and solid in the V-AC region resulting from overlap of V-L and L-AC regions

or not the regeneration involves reflux, there will always be a temperature gradient in the regenerator between T_2 and T_1 or T_1'. If anode material of purity greater than that at a in Figure 3 is to be regenerated, the phase diagram must be traversed into the lower V + L region and, in the process, somewhere in the temperature gradient the V + AC region will be traversed. For the no-reflux case, vapor quenched through the temperature range covering the V + AC region can be expected to deposit at least some solid AC even though the situation is a nonequilibrium one. Hence, in both modes of regeneration, if the system pressure is low enough, there is a point in the regenerator cycle where it is possible for solid AC to deposit. Such solid deposition leading to blockage of the regenerator poses a threat to the operation of the cell. If it is necessary to operate the cell at a pressure such that a phase diagram of the type in Figure 3 pertains, then means must be adopted to cope with build-up of solid. This would probably be an engineering design problem.

The important point of the foregoing is that a phase diagram of the type discussed in Figure 3 applies only if the system pressure is lower than a certain value. The transition from a Figure 3 diagram to a Figure 1 diagram can be achieved simply by an increase in pressure; in other words, deposition of solid in either mode of operation can be avoided by operating at a suitably higher pressure so that the L + V and the L + AC areas clear each other.

The means for achieving the proper pressure deserves discussion. The pressure of the desired temperature-composition phase diagram (Figure 1) is fixed at the value of the vapor pressure of pure A at temperature T_1' or by the summed partial pressures over particular compositions on the liquidus at their respective temperatures on the diagram. In other words, for a given composition of material to be returned to the anode, the condensation temperature will control the pressure and must be high enough to get the required pressure. Conceivably, the regeneration temperature, T_2, could be high enough to cause a higher pressure, but this would not be an equilibrium situation which is what is under consideration here. We are making an idealized analysis, neglecting pressure drops which may occur in an actual cyclic system.

Another method of separating the V-L loop from the L-AC region is sometimes proposed. It usually arises with the question: "Can the separation be accomplished also by pressurizing the system with an inert gas?" To answer this, let us consider a regeneration tube without inert gas present, and in which the pressure is low enough so that there is indeed a point where the temperature is such that solid AC deposits. Now, keeping all temperatures constant, let us introduce inert gas so that the total pressure is higher. Over the solid AC, the partial pressures of A and C (and maybe of AC if it is volatile to any extent) remain virtually the same as before because there has been no temperature change. In fact, over the liquid in the regenerator, the same partial pressures exist as before. (It can be shown that total pressure changes have only an insignificant effect on vapor pressure.) In other words, introducing the inert gas does not produce a change in the activities of A and C, and the driving force for forming AC does not change; therefore, the inert gas has no effect in suppressing the formation of solid AC. Furthermore, from a practical standpoint, the presence of inert gas would have a retarding effect on the regeneration process because it would serve as a diffusion barrier through which the molecules of A would have to pass on their way to the condensation site.

Regeneration and Condensation Temperature Relationships

If the condensation temperature and the composition of regenerated A-rich alloy which is to condense at that temperature have been established so that the phase diagram is like Figure 1, we can consider some further temperature-composition relationships at T_2. On one hand, if for some reason such as limitations of construction materials in the regenerator there is an upper limit to the regeneration temperature, T_2, then this temperature will establish the most C-rich cathode material obtainable from the regenerator, composition x_2. On the other hand, if it is decided that the maximum build-up of A in the cathode shall correspond to cathode composition, x_3, and if this composition is fed to the regenerator, then the *minimum* regenerator temperature is T_3 (the bubble point). Because C-richer material is to be returned to the cathode, a temperature between T_3 and T_3' must be selected. Since the temperature-composition diagram (constant pressure) to represent the system has already been established, the pressure is not changed by this choice. In other words, specifying the composition of material sent to the regenerator permits a range of regeneration temperatures. The maximum temperature is T_3' because any higher temperature would cause complete vaporization and would not produce C-enriched liquid. But, if the composition of material to be returned to the cathode is specified, then a unique regeneration temperature is established.

It should be noted that any increase in temperature above T_3 implies that a concentration gradient in the regenerator exists. That is to say, in an actual cell, material of composition x_3 will be fed to the regenerator, but material of composition x_2 will be returned to the cathode. Composition x_2 will have to exist at the surface of the liquid in the regenerator from where it will be returned to the cell. Composition x_3 will be fed to the bulk of the regenerator liquid somewhere else than at the vapor-liquid interface. At the temperature T_2, the lever principal will indicate (if the L-V loop is known) the relative amounts produced of vapor rich in A and liquid enriched in C for the case of no fractionation. This information, combined with the maximum rate of distillation of A-rich material, is directly related to the current-generating capacity of the cell. That is to say, the rate of circulation of A (and of C), expressed in terms of equivalents of A (and of C), is directly related to the rate at which coulombs of electricity are generated (or to the current density).

Another aspect of a real situation which should be recognized is that there is no such thing as a perfectly nonvolatile material, and C, having a small vapor pressure, would always be present to some extent in regenerated A, even in the most favorable systems. If there is no mechanism for removal of C from the anode, then it would be only a matter of time until the concentration of C in the anode would build up to the value corresponding to the intersection of the T_1 isotherm with the L-AC solidus curve. This build-up would cause solid AC to be deposited in the anode liquid. Two consequences follow—e.g., (1) while C is accumulating, the activity of A in the anode would be decreasing and, therefore, cell voltage would be dropping, and (2) actual deposition of solid AC within the anode could physically block the flow of anode liquid and stop cell operation. It would be a consideration in the cell design, then, to provide an anode of sufficient capacity so that the time needed to plug it would exceed the needed cell lifetime or to design a cell with means of purging the anode of accumulated AC.

It may be useful to see what the numbers might be for some real systems. For the systems with alkali-metal anodes (except Li), the b.p. of A would fall in the range 670 to 880°C.; the b.p. of C may be in the "teen hundreds." For such a system, in order to separate the L-V loop from the L-AC region, and, because it can be judged qualitatively that the slope of the liquidus is probably not very steep close to the A-rich side, then the permissible condensation temperature in the regenerator is unlikely to be lower than perhaps 50-100°C. below the m.p. of AC. As far as the phase diagram is concerned, how low the condensation temperature may be fixed will depend on the steepness of the liquidus (to graze past the AC hump) and on the particular composition of regenerated A-rich material which one wishes to collect. If the m.p. of AC is relatively low and the b.p. of A is relatively high, there will be a wide choice for selecting T_1'. If the AC m.p. and the A b.p. are fairly close, permissible values of T_1' will fall in a more restricted range. An example is the sodium-bismuth system in which Na_3Bi has a m.p. of 838°C., while sodium has a b.p. of 880°C. In such a case, to avoid the solid region in regeneration, it is likely that the cell reaction will not be conducted at the condensation temperature—i.e., $T_1 \neq T_1'$, and regenerated A-rich material will have to be cooled from T_1' to T_1. It may be noted that for an assumed constant pressure system, setting $T_1 > T_1'$ would not be permissible because regenerated anode material would vaporize. If, however, there is a pressure gradient as from a hydrostatic head (pressure increasing from regenerator to cell), then T_1 may be somewhat higher than T_1'.

Azeotropes and Their Significance

The discussion of the liquid-vapor relationships has been based on the assumption that the L-V loop is of the simple ascendant, loop variety. It has been shown above that a desirable feature for a bimetallic regenerative cell is that the two components have widely separated boiling points and that they interact strongly, leading to strong negative deviations from ideality, and thereby favoring a large emf. Such a situation, because of the deviation from ideality, presents the possibility of maximum boiling point azeotrope formation if the negative deviation is not offset by a large enough difference in boiling points. As an example, for the sodium-bismuth system, some of our work at Argonne has shown that sodium has an activity coefficient of about 10^{-4} on the bismuth-rich side of Na_3Bi, but liquid-vapor equilibrium studies have not revealed a maximum boiling point. The difference between the sodium and bismuth boiling points is 680°. Presumably this difference sufficiently overcomes the tendency toward azeotropy. On the other hand, in the Li-Bi system there is strong interaction, as evidenced by the compound Li_3Bi, which melts at 1145°C. Li boils at 1336°C. and Bi boils at 1560°C., the difference being 224°. It would not be surprising if there were a maximum boiling point in the Li-Bi system.

Should a maximum boiling-point azeotrope arise, it is desirable to examine briefly the consequences in a cell system. The phase diagram would have the general features seen in Figure 4. Depending on where the composition of material removed from the cathode, x_c, happens to fall in relation to the maximum, three cases may be considered. First, if the cathode composition falls exactly at the maximum, no regeneration would be possible. The vapor composition would be the same as the liquid composition. Second, if the cathode composition falls to the right of the maximum, regeneration would cause relatively pure C, which could be returned to the cathode, to distill, but the most A-rich residue would have the composition of the azeotrope. This would represent the limiting anode composition and, if the difference in concentration of A between anode and cathode is not great enough, the cell voltage may be too low. Another bad feature is that, because the concentration of C in the cathode product is greater than that of A and, because C is the more volatile component in the regenerator under these circumstances, then the regeneration process consists of removing the major component rather than the minor component through the vapor phase. This is an inefficient situation.

The third case is the one in which the cathode composition falls to the left of the azeotrope. Here, the most C-rich residue obtainable from a distillation would have the composition of the azeotrope. Thus, in regeneration, the cathode this time would have its composition eventually set by the azeotrope. As far as the anode is concerned, in principle, pure A

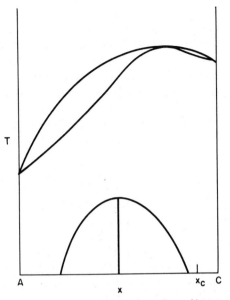

*Figure 4. General features of phase diagram
should maximum boiling point azeotropy arise*

could be obtained by distillation, so that the anode situation would be
essentially equivalent to that of the simple nonazeotropic system.

If an azeotrope does occur in a practical system, it appears that the
best condition is the last one, with the composition of the azeotrope as far
to the C side as possible. What would be compromised is the degree of
C-richness of the cathode, which, of course, translates into a compromise
in the cell voltage. For these maximum boiling point azeotrope systems,
the relative heights of the L-V loop and L-AC regions are still important
in problems which might arise from overlap and resultant V-AC regions.

Of course, the best approach would be to attempt to break up the
azeotrope so that its interference would be impossible. Most simply, without introducing a third component, this could be accomplished by a suitable choice of pressure (*3*). For a maximum boiling azeotrope, the total
pressure of the system for compositions at and near the azeotrope is less
than the vapor pressure of either pure component. Thus, if log P vs. $\frac{1}{T}$ is
plotted for both pure components and for a given composition in the
region of the azeotropic composition, a plot like Figure 5 will result. The
line for the mixture falls below both curves A and C in the temperature
and pressure range on the left of point *d* in this diagram. Only one such
curve is drawn here, although a family of curves, one for each composition
selected, could be drawn. Wherever a curve falls below both the A and C
curves, azeotropic behavior for this composition may be expected in the

pressure and temperature range which falls below A and C. If the line is extended to the right, then in the region between the A and C lines azeotropic behavior will not be found. Thus, to get rid of the azeotrope problem, pressure and temperature conditions must be selected from the portion of the total pressure curves falling between the A and C lines. At the pressure represented by point a, all compositions whose total pressure curves fall in the range spanned by points b and c will behave nonazeotropically. From the standpoint of overall cell operation, one would choose a system pressure which would be determined by the condensation temperature and composition at the condensation site, as discussed earlier; then one would observe whether or not the log P $vs.$ $\frac{1}{T}$ plot indicated freedom from azeotropes at the selected pressure for the whole range of composition involved in the cell operation.

In another aspect, earlier in the discussion it was shown that a minimum system pressure had to be established in order to separate the V-L loop from the AC-L region. Now, it can be seen that in those systems where maximum-boiling azeotropy occurs there are two different ways a total pressure curve can cross the C curve. It can cross with a slope greater or less than that of the C curve. Which occurs would depend on the interactions in the particular system. In the situation shown in Figure 5, there

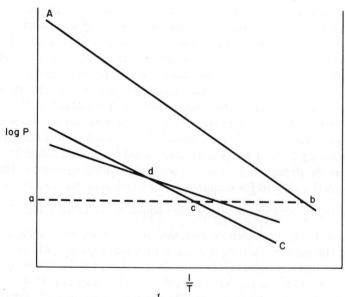

Figure 5. Plot of log P *vs.* $\frac{1}{T}$ *for both pure components and for a*

given composition in the region of the azeotropic composition

is no azeotropy to the right of point d or, in other words, at pressures lower than that which corresponds to point d. This means that, in addition to a minimum pressure requirement to avoid overlap of the L-V loop with the L-AC region, there may be, if azeotropy occurs as described by this plot, also a requirement of a maximum pressure to avoid azeotropes. On the other hand, it is possible that the A, C, and mixture lines have slopes so that pressures higher than those which correspond to point d result in the absence of azeotropy. For a cell in which this condition prevails there will be two minimum pressure requirements—one to avoid the V-L and L-AC overlap and one to avoid azeotropy. The higher pressure would be selected as the minimum one to avoid both problems.

Electrolyte as Source of Additional Components

The discussion has been idealized to the extent that we have considered only two-component systems. Because an actual cell will be operated with a fused-salt electrolyte in addition to the two electrochemically active components, some degree of mutual solubility of each of the three components would result. In particular, the electrolyte is expected to be slightly soluble in the cathode and therefore will appear in the regenerator. Once in the regenerator, it may also be expected to transport to the anode *via* the regenerative process. Of course, it will also be in the anode by virtue of direct contact with and dissolution in A.

One sees immediately that a comprehensive discussion of phase diagram interrelationships is going to involve at least three components. Because a pure salt will most likely not be used as the electrolyte, but rather a lower melting mixture such as a ternary salt eutectic, the full discussion would involve five components. This becomes an extremely complicated situation. For a full analysis, the binary systems will be the important units. In the preliminary stages, the binary A-C systems, despite constituting a somewhat simplified representation of a regenerative galvanic system, will afford guideposts for system selection and establishment of operating conditions.

Summary

The salient points in the preceding discussion are the following:

(1) Interaction between A and C, shown by compound formation at T_1, is desired as an indication of a favorable cell voltage.

(2) Relatively high melting point of this compound, AC, is desirable to indicate an acceptably high cell voltage.

(3) The L-V loop must be separated from the AC-L region at the cell-operating pressure to avoid depositing solid in the regenerator; therefore, in compromise with point 2, the m.p. of AC should not be so high as to make separation of the AC-L region from the L-V region impractical.

(4) Separation of the AC-L region from the V-L region can be accomplished by setting the condensation temperature T_1' high enough for a selected value of composition of material to be returned to anode.

(5) Cell reactions can generally be carried out at $T_1 < T_1'$ but not at $T_1 > T_1'$ unless a pressure gradient exists between the condensation region and the cell proper.

(6) Having fixed T_1' and the composition of anode material at T_1' a unique phase diagram is thereby selected. Setting the composition of material to be *returned to* (not taken from) the cathode then fixes T_2, the regeneration temperature.

(7) For a unique phase diagram, fixing the composition of the cathode product to be removed from the cathode and to be sent to the regenerator (as distinguished from fixing composition of purified material) establishes a minimum value for T_2 (the bubble point) and also a maximum value (the dew point).

(8) For a selected diagram, setting a maximum value for T_2 sets a maximum magnitude of C-enrichment for material returned to the cathode but diminishes the relative quantity of this material to a minimum (zero). The purity of A-rich vapor is also dependent on the choice of T_2, thereby influencing the need and the extent of fractionation.

(9) Large separation of b.p.'s of A and C is desirable.

(10) Accumulation of C in A must be anticipated and means must be provided for its removal so that eventual plugging of anode with AC or too great diminution of voltage do not occur.

(11) The negative deviations implied by AC compound formation may lead to a maximum boiling point azeotrope.

(12) Under some conditions, an azeotrope may not adversely influence cell operation. This might be the case where the azeotropic composition, under a given set of temperature and pressure conditions, falls close to pure A or pure C.

(13) If the azeotrope problem exists and is to be eliminated, pressure limits may be imposed which are, in addition to the minimum pressure, needed to separate the L-V loop from L-AC regions.

(14) Finally, the complications which would be introduced by the electrolyte must be borne in mind.

Acknowledgment

The author is indebted to M. S. Foster, C. E. Johnson, C. E. Crouthamel, and Scott E. Wood for discussions which have aided in the formulation of the ideas presented here.

Literature Cited

(1) Agruss, B., *J. Electrochem. Soc.* **110,** 1097 (1963).
(2) Foster, M. S., unpublished data.
(3) Nutting, H. S., Horsley, L. H., *Ind. Eng. Chem., Anal. Ed.* **19,** 602 (1947).

RECEIVED November 10, 1965.

11

Laboratory Studies of Intermetallic Cells

MELVIN S. FOSTER

Argonne National Laboratory, Argonne, Ill.

The choice of components for laboratory studies of regenerative, intermetallic cell systems is based on the desire to have total liquidity in the cell, a high cell voltage, ability to separate the more base metal used as the anode by distillation or electrolytic regeneration, and negligible corrosive character of the metals and alloys. Several advantages and disadvantages for these cells exist. Concentration cells without transference have been useful in the study of the thermodynamic properties of alloys. The solubility of the anode metal in the fused salt electrolyte, a mixture of halides of the same metal, results in a nonelectrochemical transfer in the cell. Intermetallic compounds may be extracted from the cathode alloy into the fused salt electrolyte which is thermodynamically stable in the cell environment. The solubilities of several intermetallic compounds in fused salts are relatively large.

The primary voltage source of one type of regenerative, galvanic system under consideration is an intermetallic cell. Laboratory investigations of intermetallic cells have been carried out at Argonne National Laboratory and elsewhere (discussions of the work at Allison Division of General Motors and North American Aviation are found elsewhere in this volume). For reasons to be discussed later, the primary emphasis of this chapter will be on cells with a liquid anode metal, a liquid binary alloy cathode, and a molten salt electrolyte. One of the two components of the liquid alloy cathode is a metal identical with the anode metal—hence the name "bimetallic cell." Most of the studies reported here have been of the basic physicochemical properties of binary alloys.

Design of Practical Systems

Although a complete enunciation of the principles of design for a practical system is beyond the scope of this chapter, we may cite some of the considerations involved in order to show the relevancy of the basic

136

studies. Figure 1 is a schematic representation of a regenerative, inter-metallic cell system.

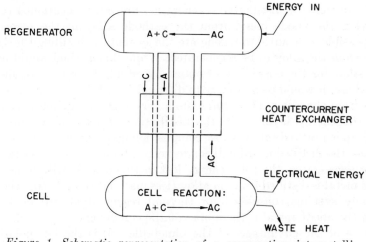

Figure 1. Schematic representation of a regenerative, intermetallic cell system

In the figure, the anode metal, A, is transferred electrochemically through the electrolyte and combined with a cathode metal, C, to form a binary alloy, AC. The cathode metal is the more noble metal. Electrical energy and waste heat are generated in the cell which is ideally a concentration cell without transference. The cathode alloy formed is transferred to a second container and regenerated by removing the anode metal—e.g., by distillation or by electrolysis in a second cell. This separation is accomplished with some expenditure of energy (thermal, electrical, or other). The regenerated cathode alloy and anode metal are returned separately to their respective cell compartments for reuse.

While relatively pure anode metal, A, is removed from the cathode during regeneration, the cathode alloy need not be entirely depleted of A. The energetics for the total removal of A from the cathode alloy would be expected to be unfavorable when compared with a process in which only a small change in the concentration of anode metal, A, in the cathode was effected. If the cyclic process is not isothermal, it can be shown that the efficiency may not exceed Carnot efficiency.

The approach to Carnot efficiency is indeed tortuous. Among the requirements are not only a) that the cycle be operated in a reversible manner, but b) if the anode material is separated from the cathode alloy by distillation, a complete separation must be effected without refluxing, c) ideal heat exchange must take place between the streams from the cell and regenerator, and d) $(C_{products} - C_{reactants}) = 0$, where C is the heat capacity. This implies strongly that all of the anode material vaporized in the regenerator must be (reversibly) condensed at the regenerator temperature without any expenditure of energy, a patently impossible situation.

Note that the distillative regeneration procedure mentioned calls for removing the anode metal from the cathode alloy in the regenerator. It is possible, of course, to regenerate the system by distilling the cathode metal from the alloy to be regenerated. While this method would in principle allow for the possibility of obtaining essentially pure cathode metal for cell use, it would be necessary to distill all, or almost all, of the cathode metal from the alloy. This represents a very high energy input compared with the energy involved in the distillation of reasonably pure anode metal from a cathode alloy whose composition need not be greatly changed. Because the distilled metal will condense at a temperature lower than that of the regenerator, the total energy lost in this process will be less if the anode metal is distilled from an alloy (less material is involved); therefore, the only systems considered for thermal regeneration will be those in which the anode metal is the more volatile component.

One of the advantages of the bimetallic cell is the low polarization at high current densities. This effect is due to the high exchange currents which exist between liquid metal electrodes and molten salts (*see* Reference *29*). Our study thus will be restricted to electrodes which are a single liquid phase. Many anode-cathode combinations are possible. From approximately 66 metals and metalloids may come 2145, $\dfrac{66!}{64!\,2}$, non-degenerate, binary systems; even without intrafamily pairs, the number is still very large—1998. If we restrict our view to those metallic elements which are liquid in the pure state at reasonable cell temperatures (taken arbitrarily as $<1000°K.$), we are confined to the 20 elements shown in Figure 2. This figure shows the melting point immediately below, and the normal boiling point just above the chemical symbol for the element. The electronegativity (*33*) of the element is noted in parentheses; temperatures are given in degrees Kelvin.

Of these elements, divided into two groups according to their electronegativities and their position in the periodic table, those on the left constitute the possible anode metals to be considered. Estimating the strengths of possible interaction solely on the basis of electronegativity differences, one postulates that Cs-Se might be the best combination.

The vapor pressures of these elements (*32*) are compared in Figure 3. If there is to be eventual distillation of the anode metal from the cathode alloy at the regenerator in one step, without refluxing, the least contamination of the anode metal by the more noble cathode metal would be expected in systems where the difference in vapor pressures of the two metals is a maximum. With their vapor pressure curves, Cs and Se make an undesir-

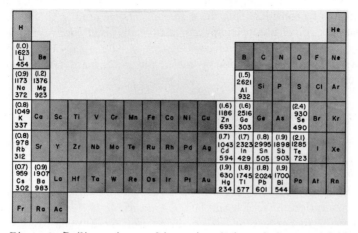

Figure 2. Boiling points, melting points (32), and electronegativities (33) of elements of interest for use in forming binary, intermetallic cells

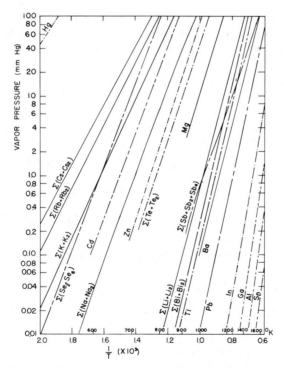

Figure 3. Vapor pressure of the elements of interest (32)

able pair from a regeneration standpoint; the vapor pressure of cesium will be reduced by its low activity coefficient in the alloy, and pure cesium will not be effectively separated. There are, however, 90 other binary combinations to consider. One must make a choice among them, comparing separation of elemental vapor pressures required for regeneration of the anode metal, corrosive characteristics of the elements and alloys, cell voltage produced, the binary metal phase diagram (*see* Chapter 10 this volume), etc.

Characteristics of Regenerative, Intermetallic Cell Systems

The advantages and some of the disadvantages of using regenerative intermetallic cell systems are outlined in the sequences below.

Advantages include the following:

1) These systems are capable of either thermal (distillative) or electrical regeneration, of which the latter is desirable if the cell is used as a secondary (or rechargeable) battery in an isothermal cycle. In a nonisothermal cycle, the regenerator may be electrically operated as an electrolytic cell using some of the power from the cell in a thermal-electrical regeneration cycle.

2) Because most schemes for using these cells involve the conversion of thermal energy to electrical energy, large quantities of heat must be transferred, a process simplified greatly when using flowing metallic systems.

3) If the flowing stream can be maintained in thermal loops (or "harps"), then a simplicity of construction may be achieved.

4) The high conductivity of the molten salts may be utilized to its maximum beneficial effect in reducing voltage loss (ohmic loss) in the cell.

5) The energy required for distillative, thermal regeneration may be obtained from any of several sources: solar, geothermal, fossil fuel, or nuclear.

To prevent over-optimism, nevertheless, the following disadvantages must be acknowledged:

1) Because these systems require operation at elevated temperatures for fluidity maintenance and for distillative thermal regeneration, the corrosion problem must receive careful attention (*see* Chapter 12 by Shimotake and Hesson).

2) The pronounced tendency for the active anode metals to dissolve in their own molten salts (*1, 2, 3, 14, 27*) gives rise to a mechanism for the phenomenon, "irreversible transfer," in which the anode metal is transferred to the cathode without producing any external electrical current.

3) The high temperatures needed for regenerating some of these systems are not readily achieved in presently available, economic, thermal energy sources.

4) A tendency toward electronic as well as ionic conductivity may exist in melts containing appreciable amounts of dissolved anode metal

(*4, 5, 6, 13*). This will lower the cell voltage available (but may increase the power output) (*28, 36*).

5) Although high values of the absolute temperature coefficient, $\left|\left(\dfrac{\partial E}{\partial T}\right)\right|$, are desired in theory, low values are commonly found in practice.

Polarization of the cell voltage may occur for several reasons. The usual resistance to ionic mobility leads to an IR drop of voltage which is much more obvious for solid than for liquid electrolytes. The polarization is normally quite low, but it is possible to minimize this loss by selecting systems with high conductivity. At constant temperature, a size effect would be expected—i.e., the IR drop in a Li^+ (X^-) electrolyte should be less than for Na^+ (X^-), owing to the smaller Li^+ ion.

Because the bimetallic cell is a concentration cell, the voltage may be reduced because of an increased concentration of anode metal in the layer of cathode alloy contiguous with the catholyte. This increased concentration results from the deposition of anode metal ions and metal atoms from the catholyte. To offset the loss, it may be possible to provide mechanical agitation in order to increase the rate of homogenization of the cathode alloy. The kinetics of this process without mechanical or thermal agitation will depend on the diffusion coefficient of A in C. Size effects must again be considered, but in this case the sizes may be those of clusters in solution in C which are not simply related to the atomic size of A.

The solubility of the anode metal in the electrolyte and its subsequent transfer to the cathode alloy without producing any external electrical current cause an additional voltage drop of the cell, with time, as the concentration of the cathode changes. This effect may be minimized by preventing thermal convection in the electrolyte, thus forcing the neutral metal atoms to transfer only by ordinary diffusion. Another way of decreasing the rate of irreversible transfer is lowering the temperature of the cell. This decreases the solubility of the anode metal in the electrolyte which, in turn, leads to a lower concentration gradient of anode metal in the electrolyte and a lesser transfer rate. (Again, the elimination of thermal convection currents is important if the minimum irreversible metal transfer is to be approached.)

The "activation polarization" often encountered in ordinary, low-temperature fuel cells is unimportant in bimetallic cells because of the increased temperature and high exchange currents between liquid-liquid interface of the metal electrodes and molten salt electrolytes.

Intermetallic alloys show solubilities from traces to total miscibility in fused salts. The anode may become contaminated by the extraction of bimetallic compounds or related species from the electrolyte solution. Not only will the activity of the anode metal be lowered, thus reducing the cell potential, but also it will be difficult to provide for removing the cathode metal which so appears in the anode. (Obviously, the removal must be accomplished in a regenerative, closed-cycle system designed for long-term operations.) As previously noted, eliminating thermal convection in the electrolyte will help solve the problem. Inserting porous, inert barriers may also help reduce both diffusion rates and thermal convection, although at a cost of increased ohmic polarization of the cell. Of course, in both cases, one may seek an electrolyte with reduced solubility for anode metal and intermetallic species from the cathode. One of the mitigating facts about the solubility of intermetallic species in the anode is that, apparently, ideal solutions are formed initially with the appearance of the cathode metal in anode metal as solvent. The result is that the voltage reduction of the cell is minimal. The more formidable problem is the cumulative effect of the build-up of cathode metal in the anode, which eventually must be met with special regeneration techniques such as periodically "dumping" the complete anode inventory into the cathode or continuously removing a fraction of the anode and combining it with the cathode alloy sent to the regenerator. The difficulty is compounded if pure A cannot be returned to the cell from the regenerator but, instead, an alloy rich in A must be returned to it.

Experimental Techniques for Intermetallic Cell Studies

Many reports have been written concerning thermodynamic studies of various binary alloys (25). In general, it is most profitable to establish the partial, molal-free energy of the binary alloy as a function of alloy composition and temperature. From this data, it is possible to calculate the open-circuit voltage of the cell, the free energy change at the regenerator temperature, the other thermodynamic properties, and vapor pressures. This information has been commonly obtained by emf cells similar to the ones which are visualized for use in a regenerative, intermetallic cell system. Cells in a regenerative system must be capable of delivering large amounts of electrical power, but the cells used in thermodynamic studies are operated under virtually open-circuit conditions. Potentiometers or electronic voltmeters, such as electrometers, are used to obtain the cell voltage. Cells for laboratory studies, therefore, may have very high, internal resistance and still yield useful data, while the same cells would be useless as power-producing devices.

The galvanic systems in the regenerative, bimetallic cell program use fused salts and liquid metals which are not compatible with an ordinary atmosphere. Experiments at Argonne National Laboratory have been conducted in glove boxes filled with helium. In order to maintain the integrity of the helium atmosphere against minor air leaks, diffusion of water through the gloves, etc., the helium is continuously recirculated through a purification system. The basic purification step in this system is an activated charcoal trap held under boiling nitrogen (*17*). The atmosphere in the box normally contains less than 1 p.p.m. water vapor by volume and less than 5 p.p.m. each of nitrogen and oxygen. Experimental furnace wells have been attached to the metal floor of the glove boxes by means of water-cooled, O-ring seals. These wells can be isolated from the rest of the glove box system by a second O-ring-sealed interior coverplate. The resistance furnaces used to heat the wells are on the outside of the box and thus do not introduce contaminants into the box atmosphere by outgassing.

In the study of bimetallic cells, it is necessary to avoid electrolytes containing components which are not thermodynamically stable in the cell environment. As pointed out by Wagner and Werner (*37*), a lowering of the observed cell voltage will occur if displacement reactions take place at the metal electrodes because of mixed electrolytes. This behavior was noted in the studies shown in Figure 4. The cells used for the lower curve, containing LiCl-KCl electrolyte, yielded voltages which fluctuated markedly and decreased rapidly when the operating temperature was raised above 773°K. The disparity in voltages occurs because, at the elevated temperatures, KCl is reduced by Li at the anode to form K metal which is at least partially volatilized from the cell. This study shows that at

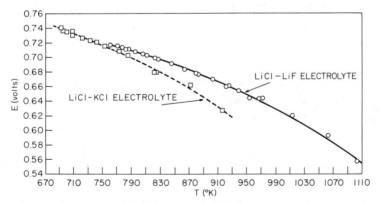

Figure 4. Voltage-temperature properties for different electrolytes in the cell Li(l)/LiCl-LiF or LiCl-KCl/Bi(l) saturated with Li₃Bi(s)

temperatures above 773°K., KCl in the eutectic mixture of LiCl-KCl is not thermodynamically stable in cells containing Li metal. In later studies, electrolytes have been restricted to molten mixtures of the halides of the alkali metal used. Some experiments are currently being made with pure solid NaCl as the electrolyte in cells involving Na as the alkali metal.

Using lithium as an anode metal, the system Li-Bi (*18*) has been studied. The molten electrolyte consisted of the eutectic composition 30 mole% LiF-70 mole% LiCl. The melting point of this mixture is 775°K.

(19). Porous BeO crucibles were used as diffusion barriers and as containers of one of the alloy electrodes. Solidification of the electrolyte in its pores broke the BeO crucible; therefore, cells were operated only at temperatures above 775°K. Figure 5 shows the typical cell construction. This cell yielded stable and reproducible cell voltage data (±3 mv. or less) at temperatures up to approximately 1100°K. The reference electrode of a Bi-rich liquid alloy saturated with $Li_3Bi(s)$ was contained in the bottom of the tantalum crucible. Electrical contact to this electrode was made with a tantalum tube which was welded closed at the bottom. The tube also contained the thermocouple used to monitor the cell temperature. The potential of the reference electrode with respect to pure lithium was measured independently *(18)* as:

$$E = 0.5303 + 7.3272 \times 10^{-4}\,T - 6.4317 \times 10^{-7}\,T^2 \text{ (volts)},$$

where $T = 760°\text{K}. - 1100°\text{K}.$ Using this reference potential, it was possible to convert observed cell voltages to those for the cell containing a pure Li anode.

In addition to being used to calculate the thermodynamic properties of these alloys, the data may also be used to calculate the standard-free energies of formation of solid compounds occurring in the system. The stability of these compounds may be seen from the highly negative values of the free energy of formation, which range from −50.5 kcal./mole at 800°K. to −44.0 kcal./mole at 1100°K. for $Li_3Bi(s)$.

Intermetallic Compounds in Solution

Erich Heymann and co-workers *(21, 22, 23, 24, 31)* conducted what appear to be the first investigations of intermetallic compound solubility in fused salts. These were distribution studies of Na between molten NaBr

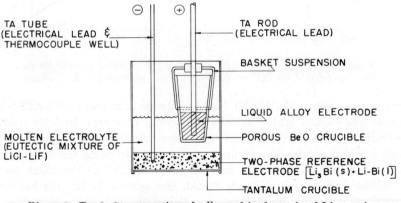

Figure 5. Typical construction of cells used in the study of Li-containing alloys

or NaI and a molten metal phase of Cd, Pb, Tl, Sn, Bi, Sb, or Au. They found that, at a temperature of 1043°K., Na compounds with Tl, Cd, and Pb were not soluble in the salt phase, although Na was apparently extracted from the metal phase. Intermetallic compounds of Na with Sn, Bi, Sb, and Au were extracted into the salt phase. Heymann attributed the insolubility of Pb from mixtures to compound dissociation in the alloy at the high experimental temperature, which was 400° above the melting point of the highest melting compound in the Na-Pb system (*20*).

The results of solubility determinations of intermetallic compounds in molten salts are shown in Figure 6.

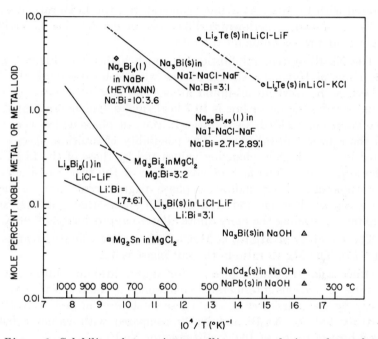

Figure 6. Solubility of some intermetallic compounds in molten salts

In the Li-Bi studies, the Li-Bi ratio in the salt phase was shown to be 3.0 when solid Li_3Bi was present in the metal phase. In view of the lack of other data, a heat of solution, ΔH_f, of the compound, Li_3Bi, in the molten salt was calculated from the solubility data making certain standard assumptions. First, it was assumed that the solution sampled and analyzed was in equilibrium with the pure solid intermetallic compound at the experimental temperature. Secondly, it was assumed that the species in the solid was the monomer, Li_3Bi. Thirdly, it was assumed that these solutions were ideal to the extent that it was permissible to use the expression:

$$\left(\frac{\partial \ln X}{\partial \frac{1}{T}}\right)_P = -\frac{\Delta H_f}{R}$$

where X is the atom fraction of Li_3Bi in the molten salt, T the absolute temperature, and R the gas constant.

Using these assumptions, the heat of solution for Li_3Bi calculated from the solubility data is 18.8 kcal./mole (listed in error in Reference 16 as 9.4 kcal./mole).

In a liquid 50 atom% alloy of Li and Bi, the solubility of Bi is equal to that from $Li_3Bi(s)$ at low temperatures where the 50% alloy becomes saturated with $Li_3Bi(s)$. At higher temperatures, the Li:Bi ratio decreases sharply, as shown; experimental difficulties in determining Li precluded fixing a more precise value for the ratio.

The Na-Bi system solubilities are much higher (see Figure 6). The single point of Heymann should be low when compared with the upper line because he used an all-liquid alloy. The heat of solution of Na_3Bi calculated from the upper line is 10.7 kcal./moles. The nonsaturated alloy in the lower line yielded Na:Bi ratios in the salt phase which were higher than those in the metal phase. The possibility of multiple species is indicated by these higher, changing values and by those of the Li:Bi ratios in the lower curve. The lack of intersection of the two Na-Bi curves at lower temperatures may indicate a phase diagram error because the diagram given by Hanson and Anderko (20) shows that $Na_3Bi(s)$ should precipitate on cooling the more dilute alloy to approximately 798°K.

The solubility of Mg_3Bi_2 in $MgCl_2$ is shown for a limited temperature range (15). The Mg:Bi ratio in the salt phase is 3:2.

Other isolated points shown are for Mg_2Sn, lithium telluride, and the solubilities of various intermetallic compounds in molten NaOH reported recently by Delimarskii et al. (9). These solubilities in molten NaOH are reportedly low for Na_3Bi and NaPb compared with values calculated using a heat of fusion of 16.6 kcal./mole for Na_3Bi.

It is obvious that either the heats of solution of Li_3Bi and Na_3Bi are not very constant with temperature (or these solutions in fused salts are not very ideal). For example, the melting point of Li_3Bi obtained from the extrapolated solubility curve is 2610°C., compared with the literature value (20) of only 1145°C. Further, the curve for Na_3Bi yields a value of 10.7 kcal./mole for the heat of solution compared with a heat of fusion of 16.6 kcal./mole used by Delimarskii et al. (9). The melting point found by extrapolation is again > 2000°C., while the literature value (20) is only 775°C. A knowledge of the phase diagram of some of these intermetallic compound-alkali metal halide systems would aid in resolving this difficulty.

Electrochemical studies of Na_3Bi in molten salts by Delimarskii, Pavlenko, and co-workers (*7, 8, 10, 11, 34*) apparently indicate the presence of Bi^{-3} ions in solution. These studies complement Argonne National Laboratory studies (*26*) of the freezing point depression of Na_3Bi in various alkali metal halides. These studies indicate that all three Na atoms are ionized (or at least replaceable) in dilute solutions of Na_3Bi in LiCl, and that the Bi exists in a species which is monoatomic in Bi in dilute solutions of Na_3Bi in NaI.

In addition to solubility determinations, limited initial studies of the spectra of intermetallic compounds in molten salts have been made. The spectrum of a LiCl-LiF solution of Li_3Bi in a sapphire cell at 798°K. was reported to be characterized by an intense absorption band, with a long wavelength edge located at 615 mμ (*16*).

Other qualitative observations have shown that Li_7Sn_2, $Li_{10}Pb_3$, and LiCd also form colored solutions in molten salts. These studies indicate that the phenomenon of intermetallic compound solubility may be associated with many of the binary metal systems of interest for application in regenerative, galvanic cells. One exception is the amalgams which show very low (8.6×10^{-5} mole%) solubility of Hg-containing, intermetallic species in fused LiCl-LiF mixtures up to about 773°K.

Further Studies

Many basic phenomena relating to both molten salts and alloys remain to be studied before the theoretical and practical behavior of a given intermetallic cell may be predicted. Studies of molecular spectra, conductivity (*30*), calorimetry, vapor pressure, viscosity, electromigration and polarography (*35*) diffusion, and nuclear magnetic resonance (*12*) have barely been initiated, if at all, for many of the binary metallic systems, electrolytes, and solutions of interest.

Literature Cited

(1) Bredig, M. A., Bronstein, H. R., *J. Phys. Chem.* **64,** 64 (1960).
(2) Bredig, M. A., Bronstein, H. R., Smith, W. T., Jr., *J. Am. Chem. Soc.* **77,** 1454 (1955).
(3) Bredig, M. A., Johnson, J. W., *J. Phys. Chem.* **64,** 1899 (1960).
(4) Bronstein, H. R., Bredig, M. A., *J. Am. Chem. Soc.* **80,** 2077 (1958).
(5) Bronstein, H. R., Bredig, M. A., *J. Phys. Chem.* **65,** 1220 (1961).
(6) Bronstein, H. R., Dworkin, A. S., Bredig, M. A., *J. Chem. Phys.* **34,** 1843 (1961).
(7) Delimarskii, Yu. K., Pavlenko, I. G., Zarubitskii, O. G., Oleinik, V. A., *Zh. Prikl. Khim.* **38,** 816 (1965) (in Russian).
(8) Delimarskii, Yu. K., Zarubitskii, O. G., *Dopovidi Akad. Nauk RSR* **1965,** 619 (in Russian).
(9) Delimarskii, Yu. K., Zarubitskii, O. G., Pavlenko, I. G., *Ukr. Khim. Zh.* **30,** 1289 (1964) (in Russian).

(10) Delimarskii, Yu. K., Zarubitskii, O. G., Pavlenko, I. G., *Ukr. Khim. Zh.* **31,** 469 (1965) (in Russian).
(11) Delimarskii, Yu. K., Zarubitskii, O. G., Pavlenko, I. G., *Ukr. Khim. Zh.* **31,** 573 (1965) (in Russian).
(12) Dharmatti, S. S., Vijayaraghavan, R., *Current Science* **33,** 449 (1964).
(13) Dworkin, A. S., Bronstein, H. R., Bredig, M. A., *Disc. Faraday Soc.* No. **32,** 188 (1962).
(14) Dworkin, A. S., Bronstein, H. R., Bredig, M. A., *J. Phys. Chem.* **66,** 572 (1962).
(15) Fischer, J., Argonne National Laboratory, Argonne, Ill., private communication.
(16) Foster, M. S., Crouthamel, C. E., Gruen, D. M., McBeth, R. L., *J. Phys. Chem.* **68,** 980 (1964).
(17) Foster, M. S., Johnson, C. E., Crouthamel, C. E., "Helium Purification Unit for High-Purity Inert-Atmosphere Boxes," USAEC Report ANL-6652 (December, 1962).
(18) Foster, M. S., Wood, S. E., Crouthamel, C. E., *Inorg. Chem.* **3,** 1428 (1964).
(19) Haendler, H. M., Sennett, P. S., Wheeler, C. M., Jr., *J. Electrochem. Soc.* **106,** 264 (1959).
(20) Hansen, M., Anderko, K., "Constitution of Binary Alloys," McGraw-Hill Book Co., New York, N. Y., 1958.
(21) Heymann, E., *Australian Chem. Ins. J. Proc.* **4,** 38 (1937).
(22) Heymann, E., Martin, R. J. L., Mulcahy, M. F. R., *J. Phys. Chem.* **47,** 473 (1943).
(23) Heymann, E., Weber, H. P., *Nature* **141,** 1059 (1938).
(24) Heymann, E., Weber, H. P., *Trans. Faraday Soc.* **34,** 1492 (1938).
(25) Hultgren, R., Orr, R. L., Anderson, P. D., Kelley, K. K., "Selected Values of Thermodynamic Properties of Metals and Alloys," John Wiley and Sons, New York, 1963.
(26) Johnson, C. E., Foster, M. S., unpublished results.
(27) Johnson, J. W., Bredig, M. A., *J. Phys. Chem.* **62,** 604 (1958).
(28) Karpachev, S. V., Pal'gnev, S. F., *Trans. Inst. Electrochem.* **1,** 63 (1961).
(29) Laitinen, H. A., Osteryoung, R. A., "Fused Salts," B. R. Sundheim, ed., McGraw-Hill Book Co., New York, 1964.
(30) Mooser, E., Pearson, W. P., *Phys. Rev.* **101,** 1608 (1956).
(31) Mulcahy, M. F. R., Heymann, E., *J. Phys. Chem.* **47,** 485 (1943).
(32) Nesmeyanov, An. N., "Vapour Pressure of the Elements," Academic Press, New York, 1963.
(33) Pauling, L., "The Nature of the Chemical Bond," 3rd ed., p. 93, Cornell University Press, Ithaca, N. Y., 1960.
(34) Pavlenko, I. G., Zarubitskii, O. G., Oleinik, V. A., *Dopovidi Akad. Nauk Ukr. RSR* **1963,** 1222 (in Russian).
(35) Reddy, T. B., *Electrochem. Technol.* **1,** 325 (1963).
(36) Wagner, C., "Proceedings of the Seventh Meeting of the International Committee of Electrochemical Thermodynamics and Kinetics," p. 361, Butterworths, London, 1957.
(37) Wagner, C., Werner, A., *J. Electrochem. Soc.* **110,** 326 (1963).

RECEIVED November 10, 1965.

Corrosion by Fused Salts and Heavy Liquid Metals—A Survey

HIROSHI SHIMOTAKE and JAMES C. HESSON

Argonne National Laboratory, Argonne, Ill.

A literature survey of corrosion by fused salts and heavy liquid metals is presented. The paper is divided into two sections. The first section covers corrosion of steel, 300- and 400-series stainless steels, nickel, various nickel alloys, tungsten, molybdenum, tantalum, refractory metal alloys, miscellaneous alloys, alumina, and other refractories by fused salt fluorides, chlorides, and hydroxides. The temperature range extends to 1000°C. Seventy literature references are listed. The second section covers corrosion of steel, 300- and 400-series stainless steels, nickel, chromium, vanadium, beryllium, titanium, tungsten, niobium, tantalum, rhenium, refractory metal alloys, miscellaneous alloys, graphite, alumina, magnesia, zirconia, and other refractories by liquid bismuth, liquid lead, and liquid tin. The temperature range extends to 1400°C. One hundred thirteen literature references are listed.

Thermally regenerative emf cell systems of the bimetallic types commonly use mixed fused salt electrolytes and liquid metal electrodes at elevated temperatures. The mixed fused salt electrolytes usually include fluoride, chloride, iodide, bromide, or hydroxide salts and the molten metal electrodes may consist of bismuth, lead, tin, or mercury cathodes and lithium, sodium, or potassium anodes. In the cell proper, temperatures up to 600°C., and in the regenerator, temperatures considerably above 800°C., may be encountered.

Problems of corrosion of construction materials by fused salts and liquid metals are encountered in cell and regenerator operation. In addition to the usual chemical corrosion, mass transfer corrosion can occur because the liquid metals are circulated between the cell at a relatively low temperature and the regenerator at considerably higher temperature. Also,

149

both fused salt (electrolyte) and liquid metals (electrodes) and their vapors are in contact in the cell under conditions of electrochemical reactions. In the regenerator the anode metal is evaporated from the cathode metal and the vapor is condensed for return to the cell. Thus, the corrosion problems include those due to the following: liquid metals, liquid metal alloys, and fused salts under flow conditions and temperature differences; liquid metal-vapor metal interfaces; condensing metal vapors; liquid metal-fused salt interfaces; and electrochemical reactions.

Publications on corrosion by fused salts and liquid metals at elevated temperatures are much less extensive than those on corrosion by aqueous solutions and liquids at low temperatures; nevertheless, there is a fair amount of literature dealing with fused salts and molten metals. Much of the information on corrosion by molten metals was obtained at temperatures below the 800°C. to 1000°C. range generally being considered for regenerative bimetallic cells. Although relatively little information is available on corrosion by mixed molten alloys and fused salts at elevated temperatures, a literature survey on corrosion by fused salts and liquid metals is essential when considering regenerative bimetallic cells.

A literature survey has been made to April 1965 of corrosion problems in regenerative bimetallic cell systems which use fused salt electrolytes, molten sodium or lithium anodes, and cathodes of molten bismuth, lead, or tin. One section of the survey deals with corrosion by fluoride, chloride, and hydroxide fused salts. The other section is devoted to liquid metal corrosion by bismuth, lead, and tin. Each of the two sections has its own bibliography. In the text, the salt mixture compositions, liquid metal alloy compositions, and the compositions of construction material are expressed in mole per cent (m/o), atomic per cent (a/o), and weight per cent (w/o), respectively, unless indicated otherwise.

Section I: Corrosion by Fused Salts

Corrosion of materials by fused salts has long been an important problem of electrochemical, metallurgical, and other industries. Yet only a limited amount of data had been available in the open literature until fused salts began to receive attention as nuclear fuel carriers and reprocessing media. In the 1950's, several long-range research programs were organized to seek materials which would be compatible with fused salts. One of these investigations was concerned with a mixture of fluorides which had been selected as a nuclear fuel carrier. In other programs, chlorides were studied as nuclear fuel reprocessing media, and alkali-metal hydroxides and phosphates were studied as moderators, moderator-coolants, and moderator fuel carriers. Less extensive but equally important were the chloride researches conducted by investigators in the metallurgical industries.

In bimetallic, regenerative emf cells, a molten alkali metal is used as the anode (negative electrode). The alkali metal ions resulting from oxidation at the anode transfer through a fused salt electrolyte to the cathode (positive electrode) which consists of a molten heavy metal. For this reason, the fused salt electrolyte must contain ions of the anode alkali metal. The electrolyte must also be chemically stable at high temperatures ($\sim 500°$C.). A single salt or a mixture of salts with a low melting point is desirable as an electrolyte. Another important requirement for the electrolyte is a low solubility of the alkali metal, cathode heavy metal, and their intermetallic compounds. A high solubility of these metals in the electrolyte results in a high nonfaradic transfer of the anode alkali metal. At Argonne National Laboratory, mixtures of alkali halides have been used as electrolytes.

In view of the vastness and complexities of corrosion research activities, this literature survey emphasizes the alkali-metal fluorides, chlorides, and hydroxides with which the regenerative emf cells are concerned. Other salt systems will be treated only briefly.

Corrosion by Fused Fluorides

As nuclear fuel carriers, fluorides have many advantages, such as low thermal neutron cross sections, low vapor pressures, thermal and radiation stabilities, and high solubilities for U and Th. For these reasons, the Molten Salt Reactor Experiment and the Aircraft Nuclear Propulsion Program (*47, 48, 49, 50, 69*) using fluorides as nuclear fuel carriers were organized at Oak Ridge National Laboratory in the 1950's. Extensive corrosion studies have subsequently been made with Ni, Cr, and Fe alloys (*1, 40, 41*). Of these metals, Cr is considerably more electropositive than Fe or Ni and is thus preferentially leached from the surface of the alloys by fused fluoride salts. In such studies, the salt is found to contain a higher concentration of Cr than Fe or Ni. In addition to its selective removal from the metal surface, Cr is found to diffuse from subsurface regions (*5*), because the temperatures used are high enough for this diffusion process to occur in the alloy. In such alloys, Cr diffusion is more rapid along the grain boundaries and Cr is selectively lost in the grain boundary regions. This grain boundary effect penetrates into the metal to depths that are many times that of the simple surface corrosion by the fused salt. Also in Ni, Cr, and Fe alloys, the Cr diffuses out more rapidly than the other constituents can diffuse in to replace it. As a result, voids form in the metal below its surface. Test methods used for investigation at Oak Ridge National Laboratory have been discussed elsewhere (*68*).

The chemical mechanism of aforementioned removal of chromium from the surface by fluoride mixtures may be shown as follows (*19, 50*):

1. *Impurities in the melt:*
   Example:

$$FeF_2 + Cr \rightarrow CrF_2 + Fe \qquad (1)$$

Other impurities which participate in similar reactions are: NiF_2, CrF_3, CrF_4, FeF_3, HF, and UF_5.

2. *Oxide films on metal surfaces:*
   Example:

$$2Fe_2O_3 + 3CrF_4 \rightarrow 3CrO_2 + 4FeF_3 \qquad (2)$$

Importance:

FeF_3 now reacts with Cr as indicated under 1.

3. *Constituents in the Fuel:*
   Example:

$$Cr + 2UF_4 \rightarrow 2UF_3 + CrF_2 \qquad (3)$$

The time dependence of void formation in Ni-Cr-Fe alloys observed in both thermal- and forced-convection systems indicates that attack was initially quite rapid, but then decreased until a straight line relationship existed between depth of void formation and time. This effect is explained in terms of the corrosion reactions discussed above. The initial rapid attack shown for both types of loops stems from the reaction of chromium with impurities in the melt (1) and (2) and with the UF_4 constituent of the salt (3) to establish quasi-equilibrium amounts of CrF_2 in the salt. At this point, attack proceeds linearly with time and occurs by a mass transfer mechanism. This mass transfer is caused by the fact that at low temperatures the equilibrium is shifted to the left in Equation 3. As a result, Cr precipitates in the cooler regions. In liquid metals, the driving force for mass transfer is the difference in solubility of solid-metal constituents in the liquid metal at the different temperature levels, whereas in fused fluoride systems the driving force for mass transfer results from a temperature dependence of the equilibrium constant for the chemical reaction.

In addition to time, the significant parameters affecting the corrosion of Ni-Cr-Fe alloys by fused fluorides were the operating temperature levels and the surface area-to-salt volume ratio of the system (*1, 40, 41*). Flow rate was significant only for those salt systems where the temperature dependence of the reaction between chromium and UF_4 was sufficient to cause nucleation and growth of pure chromium crystals in colder regions.

The controlling temperature in the case of Ni-Cr-Fe alloy systems was observed to be the maximum fluid-metal interface temperature (*1, 40, 41*). In loops in which the temperature gradient and flow rate remained constant, each 10° increase in wall temperature over the range from 850°C. to 950°C. produced a corresponding increase in attack of from 1 to 2 mils in 1000 hrs. If the maximum operating temperature is decreased to 670°C., the rate of chromium mass transfer in Ni-Cr-Fe alloy systems containing mixtures of NaF-ZrF$_4$-UF$_4$ drops to an almost insignificant value. Under such conditions, it has been possible to attain corrosion rates of less than 2 mils/yr. in both thermal- and forced-circulation systems. In examining loops, severe attack was found in areas relatively close to the point of maximum wall temperature. The depth of attack varies in a manner identical with the variation of wall temperature through the loop. When the ratio of the hot-zone surface area to the volume of fused salt is decreased, a given region of the hot zone must supply more chromium to establish steady-state conditions; thus, the depth of attack is increased (*1, 40, 41*). Similarly, the depth of hot-zone attack is determined by the relative areas of hot and cold zones. Because an increase in cold-zone area results in an increased rate of transfer of chromium, a greater depth of corrosion will be seen in systems with a high ratio of cold-zone area to hot-zone area.

Following successful operation of the Aircraft Reactor Experiments (*4*) of 1954, there began an extensive alloy-development program to provide an improved container material for a circulating fluoride-fueled reactor. As a result, a Ni-Cr-Mo alloy designated INOR-8 was developed; its composition limits are listed in Table I.

Long-time, aging studies on INOR-8 in the temperature range 650°C.– 815°C. have shown that no embrittlement occurs (*41*). Thermal-convection loop tests of INOR-8 operated for periods up to 1000 hrs. show very little attack with mixtures of NaF-LiF-KF-UF$_4$ (11.2–46.0–41.3–2.5 m/o) at temperatures up to 900°C. (The figures, as given in the Reference (*41*), add up to 101.0 m/o.) Further, no cold-zone deposits were observed in these loops. Attack occurs primarily in the form of shallow surface roughening (*41*). The most severe surface attack found in a 20,000-hr. test at

Table I. Specifications for INOR-8

Element	Composition, %
Ni	Remainder
Mo	15–18.00
Cr	6–8.00
Fe	5.00 max.
C	0.04–0.08 max.
Si	1.00 max.
Mn	1.00 max.
Ti + Al	0.50 max.
B	0.010 max.
S	0.020 max.
P	0.015 max.
W	0.50 max.
Cu	0.35 max.
Co	0.20 max.

700°C. reached a maximum depth of 2 mils and contained subsurface voids (50). The mechanical properties of INOR-8 have been summarized elsewhere (67). Forced-convection loops of INOR-8 were also designed (38) and built. When their maximum temperature was increased from 700°C. to 760°C., the results did not vary. In loops with 810°C. maximum temperature, however, surface attack was manifested by subsurface voids appearing to a depth of 4 mils, but the surface was not visibly attacked. The corrosion data for INOR-8, exposed in the pumped loops, indicated that corrosion reactions with fluoride salts at MSRE temperatures are essentially complete within the first 5000 hrs. of operation, do not generally exceed 1 mil even after 20,000 hrs., and are probably associated only with impurity reactions (50). Temperature increase causes no significant corrosion increase until 810°C. is reached, at which point noticeable depletion of Cr occurs, as indicated by subsurface voids; the corrosion mechanism associated with components of the salt is probably effective. INOR-8 was used in the Aircraft Nuclear Propulsion Program (50) in which molten fluorides circulated at 810°C. and proved to be satisfactory. DeVan (10) has also observed very little corrosion (< 2 mg./sq. cm.) of INOR-8 forced-circulation loops containing a salt mixture of $LiF-BeF_2-UF_4$ (62-37-1 m/o) and operated at a hot leg temperature of 700°C. with a temperature differential of 200°C. In the 15,000-hr. test, corrosion reaction was completed after 5000 hrs. of operation.

A centrifugal pump of a Ni-Cr-Fe alloy for handling $NaF-ZrF_4-UF_4$ (50–46–4 m/o) was built and tested at ORNL (9, 58) for 3550 hrs. at 2700 r.p.m., 645 g.p.m., and 40 ft. total head, and at temperatures varying from 590°C. to 760°C. The NPSH (net positive suction head) was 14.1–14.8 ft. Examination of the impeller revealed that, while the working faces of the vanes and shrouds were in good condition, the antiworking face of the front shroud had suffered cavitation damage. Another pump operated for 25,000 hrs. at 2700 r.p.m., 645 g.p.m., and 40 ft. total head, with a positive static suction head of 21 ft., while its temperature was maintained at 650°C. In this test, the impeller suffered considerable cavitation damage. Complete penetration of a vane occurred.

Hoffman et al. (22) evaluated the corrosion resistance of various high-temperature brazing alloys against Na, NaOH, and fluorides. The binary alloy 88Ni-12P possessed good resistance to fluoride attack.

An extensive corrosion study relating to the fluoride volatility process was made at Oak Ridge National Laboratory (33, 34). The compatibility of Ni-alloys with molten $NaF-LiF-ZrF_4$ salts at 500°C. to 600°C., in which HF or F_2 gas is present (33, 34), was studied. A corrosion rate of 20 to 40 mils/month has been reported.

In support of the fused fluoride fuel reprocessing program, compatibility of INOR-8 with fluorides was determined at Battelle Memorial Institute (3). During a 240-hr. exposure to $NaF-LiF-ZrF_4$ (33.5–33.5–33 m/o) at 500°C. to 600°C. Ni-Mo-Cr alloys were corroded at the rate of 3 mils/month in the vapor phase as compared with 18 mils/month for pure Ni.

In connection with the Fluoride Volatility Separation Process Program at Argonne National Laboratory (2), the evaluation of Ni and Ni alloys in fluorinated ZrF_4 was made. Monel and A-Nickel specimens were in contact with molten ZrF_4 in a fluorine atmosphere. With Ni at 600°C. and 675°C., the maximum dimensional reductions were 1.5 and 4 mils, respectively, after 70 hrs. of run. Maximum intergranular attacks of 5.9 mils occurred at both temperatures. The Monel specimens were severely dissolved.

Meyer *et al.* (42) have reviewed the compatibility of graphite with molten fluorides.

Corrosion by Fused Chlorides

Fused chloride systems are perhaps the most widely used of all; they have been studied by many people of varied backgrounds. A number of fundamental studies have been conducted with these salts.

Littlewood, of the United Kingdom, has published a series of papers on an electrochemical analysis of metal corrosion in fused salts.

With Edeleanu (11), he presented a determining factor in the extent of metal corrosion in fused chlorides. It has been shown that for a given combination of metal and fused chlorides, the initial aggressiveness of the melt depends upon its redox potential. This in turn is governed by the soluble and insoluble impurities in the system and, of these, the ones associated with water are particularly important because removing the last traces of moisture from a chloride melt is very difficult. Detailed study of the effect of water showed that at a given level of contamination, the redox potential can vary over a wide range and is, in fact, determined not by the water activity, but by the activity of its hydrolysis and dissociation products, H^+, O^{2-}, H_2, and O_2. These are fixed in a given system by equilibria with oxides and with partial pressures of gases in the atmosphere over the melt. In Littlewood's work, a reference electrode based on the $Ag \rightleftarrows AgCl$ reaction was developed (35) and used. Platinum was chosen as the redox electrode (36) because the experimental results indicated that it was sufficiently inert and reproducible.

Littlewood *et al.* (37) further demonstrated that, in a system containing Ni and NaCl-KCl, the redox potential of the melt at the platinum electrode and the Nernst potential of the nickel metal electrode approach each other. Under normal conditions, where slight contamination by water and oxygen is present, the redox potential of a NaCl-KCl melt is high (about −600 to −500 mv. on the standard chlorine electrode scale at 700°C.); only with very noble metals, such as Pt, Ir, and Pd, would immunity be possible under these conditions. In melts containing relatively small amounts of impurities, the redox potential can be reduced to a value very near to the Nernst potential of the metal without undue corrosion, provided that the metal is relatively noble (e.g., Ni, Fe) and that there are no compounds present in the melt which prevent the redox potential of the melt from falling. Even the traces of silicates introduced by fusing the melt in silica are sufficient to give some poisoning action; traces of other oxides, for example, from ceramics, would have a similar effect (37). In addition to purifying the melt, passivity can be used to nullify the corrosive properties of chloride melts. It is possible that the oxides of metals such as Fe or Ni, which have low solubility products in fused NaCl-KCl, form film on metals. Experiments have indicated, however, that a sufficiently stable passivity is unlikely.

Kochergin of the USSR has presented a series of papers on Fe corrosion in fused chlorides.

The corrosion of Fe in a mixture of $MgCl_2$-KCl (50-50 m/o) at temperatures up to 900°C. was examined (27). Based on the experimental data, the conclusion was that the corrosion of Fe in fused $MgCl_2$-KCl depends upon an electrochemical process, leading eventually to the liberation of gaseous hydrogen. The solution rate of Fe in LiCl-KCl mixtures and also in eutectic mixtures of alkali and alkaline earth metals at 700°C. was studied (30). The Fe dissolved most rapidly in LiCl-KCl and least rapidly in a low melting mixture of $BaCl_2$-KCl; however, adding Mg prevented Fe from dissolving almost completely. The Fe corrosion rate in chloride mixed salts increased in the order of $MgCl_2$-KCl, $MgCl_2$-NaCl, $MgCl_2$-$BaCl_2$, $MgCl_2$-$CaCl_2$, $ZnCl_2$-KCl, and $ZnCl_2$-NaCl at temperatures up to 700°C. (28).

Similarly, the rate of Fe corrosion increased in the order of LiCl-K_2SO_4, LiCl-Na_2SO_4, LiCl-$CaSO_4$, LiCl-$MgSO_4$, and LiCl-$ZnSO_4$ (25). In the nondehydrated mixtures, $ZnCl_2$-KCl, $ZnCl_2$-NaCl, $CdCl_2$-KCl, and $CdCl_2$-NaCl, at 500°C. iron corrosion accompanied the substitution of H^+ and in the last two salt mixtures, both H^+ and Cd^{++} were replaced by iron (29). The rate of Fe corrosion increased in the order of $MgCl_2$-KCl, $ZnCl_2$-KCl, $ZnCl_2$-NaCl, $CdCl_2$-KCl, and $CdCl_2$-NaCl.

In molten $NaNO_3$-$MgCl_2$, $NaNO_3$-$ZnCl_2$, $NaNO_3$-LiCl, $NaNO_3$-KCl, $Ca(NO_3)_2$-NaCl, $Sr(NO_3)_2$-NaCl, $Ba(NO_3)_2$-NaCl, and KNO_3-NaCl, corrosion rates of Fe increased with increasing chloride content in the melt (26). Removing residual H_2O at high vacuum at 400°C. resulted in a lower corrosion rate.

In the series of papers on Kochergin's work, one could notice that the salt mixtures used for his work were apparently not very pure, especially with respect to water (26, 29). In the halide melts water acts like hydrogen halide and readily oxidizes most construction metals with the liberation of hydrogen.

Smirnov *et al.* (*55*) showed that thermodynamic equilibrium can exist at high temperatures between a metal and its corrosion product. The steady potential ϕ_{st} of a metal and its steady state corrosion rate (amp./ sq. cm.) can be expressed in terms of the oxidation-reduction potential $E°$ (ox/red) and the diffusion constants D(ox) and D(red) as follows:

$$\text{potential } \phi_{st} = E°_{ox/red} + \frac{RT}{nF} \log_e \left(\frac{nFD_{red}}{\delta i_{cor}} \frac{d_{kx}}{M_{kx}} [ox] - \frac{D_{red}}{D_{ox}} \right) \quad (4)$$

Equation 4 is given in Reference (*55*) incorrectly as:

$$\left(\frac{nFD_{red}}{\delta i_{cor}} \frac{M_{kx}}{d_{kx}} [ox] - \frac{D_{red}}{D_{ox}} \right)$$

M_{kx} and d_{kx} are the molecular weight and density of the fused salt, F is Faraday's constant, i_{cor} is the corrosion current in amp./sq. cm., [ox] is the oxidizer concentration in the fused salt system in mole fractions, and δ is the thickness of the electrode-adjacent layer.

The steady potential of metallic Zr in an equimolar salt mixture of NaCl-KCl in an argon atmosphere was measured at 700°C., 800°C., and 900°C. The result fits

$$-\phi_{st} = 2.47 - 2.2 \times 10^{-4} \, T \text{ volts.} \quad (5)$$

where T is in °K. In the original reference (*55*), the negative sign before ϕ_{st} in the equation was omitted. The corrosion rate was 3.3, 6.0, and 8.0×10^{-4} grams/sq. cm. hr. at 700°C., 800°C., and 900°C., respectively. An analogous behavior was observed for Be, Ti, Hf, and U.

Copson (*6*) studied corrosion of heating electrodes in a molten NaCl-KCl bath, selecting as electrode material a Ni-Cr-Fe alloy composed of the following weight per cents: 77.51 Ni, 14.4 Cr, 7.4 Fe, 0.08 C, 0.10 Si, 0.16 Mn, 0.009 S, and 0.23 Cu. The temperature ranged from 730°C. to 900°C. Under certain conditions, the electrodes wasted away or "pencilled." This pencilling was caused by the metal being dissolved during the anodic part of the A-C cycle and its plating back as a nonadherent powder during the cathodic part of the cycle. No pencilling of the electrodes occurred in experiments starting with fresh salt despite variations in temperature and current density, but the fused chloride gradually reacted with moisture and CO_2 from the air to form oxides and carbonates. To simulate the decomposition, small amounts of NaOH were added. Under this condition, the electrodes pencilled. Corrosion increased rapidly with alkaline content up to 0.58 to 0.77%. When large amounts of alkali were added, there was no attack of the electrodes whatsoever. In such cases the salt acquired a yellow color and was found to have become high in chromate. Copson suggested that the pencilling of the electrodes could be controlled by the presence or absence of a protective oxide coating.

Jackson *et al.* (*23*) determined the corrosion rate of cast Fe-Ni-Cr alloys in static $BaCl_2$-KCl-NaCl (55–25–20 m/o) at 870°C. Intergranular or interdendritic corrosion along carbide networks was far more severe than metal loss by solution. In some cases penetration attack was reduced when the carbon content of the alloys was reduced from 0.45 or 0.5 to about 0.08 w/o.

Gill *et al.* (*13*) reported that Ti was severely attacked when immersed in a molten alkali chloride bath in the presence of air. The most severe corrosion of this metal was observed in molten NaCl-NaF mixtures; samples disintegrated completely at temperatures of 850°C. in less than 3 hrs. Progressively less corrosion occurred in KCl, NaCl, and LiCl. In many cases, salt fumes were more corrosive than the molten salt itself because of the better access of oxygen to the Ti surface. The chief corrosion products were dispersion of metallic Ti in the molten salt, mixed with some titanium oxides. If Cu or Fe was immersed in the salt in close proximity to Ti sheet, the Ti pyrosol transferred and deposited on the Cu or Fe surface (*53*).

Jansen (*24*) found Ni mass transfer in a NaCl-MgCl$_2$-UCl$_3$ (50.0–33.3–16.7 m/o) at 980°C. after a 100-hr. test, whereas no Ni mass transfer was found in a 500-hr. test at 730°C. A Ni-Cr-Fe alloy showed some attack and mass transfer under these conditions. The tests were conducted in a rocking furnace apparatus.

In connection with the Liquid Metal Fuel Reactor Program, a continuous reprocessing method for spent nuclear fuel was developed at Brookhaven National Laboratory. By this method, an important group of fission products may be extracted from the partially spent liquid U-Bi alloy fuel by contacting it with a mixture of fused chlorides, KCl-LiCl and KCl-LiCl-MgCl$_2$, at 450°C. to 500°C.

Susskind *et al.* (*65, 66*) summarized the corrosion studies and Raseman *et al.* (*52*) the engineering experience at Brookhaven National Laboratory. In the tests, a liquid metal solution of Bi-U (1000 p.p.m.) was added to the NaCl-KCl-MgCl$_2$ eutectic. The Bi wetted the surface of capsule container preferentially and the salt was never found at the Bi-container interface. Therefore, the characteristics of corrosion by the ternary salt and the Bi-U were similar to those produced by the Bi-U mixture alone. AISI 1020 mild steel, $2\frac{1}{4}$-1 Mo alloy steel, and Mo showed good resistance.

When 5 w/o of BiCl$_3$ was added to the salt as oxidizer, corrosion increased by a factor of 10 to 15.

In the dynamic tests without BiCl$_3$ the mass transfer was sufficient to plug several loops; however, corrosion rates remained small. Maximum attacks on the loops made of 347-, 410-stainless steel and $2\frac{1}{4}$Cr–1Mo alloy steel were found to be less than 3 mils/yr. for the maximum temperature of 550°C. with a temperature differential of 150°C.

In connection with EBR-II Reactor Fuel Cycle Development Program at Argonne National Laboratory, liquid Zn and Zn-rich alloys together with molten chloride salts are used as solvent media for recovering and purifying reactor fuel materials. This process requires materials which, at 800°C., withstand the corrosive attack of Zn containing 0 to 15% U and 0 to 10% Mg, and a salt consisting of $MgCl_2$-MgF_2-LiCl or $CaCl_2$ (47.5–5–47.5 m/o). In some cases, up to 5 w/o of $ZnCl_2$, an oxidizing agent, is required in the salt. Nelson *et al.* (*46*) enclosed Ta and Ta-10W coupons in Ta capsules with solvent metal and salt. The capsules were tested at 850°C. in a 30 cycle/hr. rocking furnace. In 100-hr. tests, Ta showed less than 8 mils intergranular corrosion attack by the salt mixtures, but when Zn-5Mg was added to the salt, corrosion became much more severe. Ta-10W showed no attack by Zn-5Mg with the salt mixture, but later in an equipment test the metal was found to have become brittle. Pressed-and-sintered W, sintered-and-rolled W sheet, cast-and-swaged Mo-30W, and W-0.8 Fe-0.4 Ni were tested at 800°C. in an open Al_2O_3 crucible containing LiCl-$MgCl_2$-MgF_2-$ZnCl_2$ (46.6–46.6–4.8–2.0 m/o) under Ar atmosphere. The W-Fe-Ni alloy was severely attacked. Pressed-and-sintered W (95% dense) showed essentially no attack; Mo-30W showed a 4 to 8 mil attack and preferential leaching of Mo from the parent metal.

Corrosion by Fused Hydroxides

Some of the fused alkali-metal hydroxides are of potential interest in reactor technology as moderators, moderator-coolants, and possibly moderator fuel carriers. Their heat-transfer properties are adequate for many industrial uses. In addition, one of them, NaOH, is both inexpensive and abundantly available. For these reasons, it has been the object of considerable research.

For regenerative fuel cell electrolytes, the low melting points of hydroxides are attractive. However, high nonfaradic transfer rates and chemical instability of the salts must be overcome for use in a practical cell application.

Friend (*51*) summarized corrosion reactions of metals in NaOH at 800°C. to 1000°C.

The high-temperature decomposition

$$2NaOH = Na_2O + H_2O \qquad \text{(a)}$$

is followed by

$$Na_2O + M = MO + 2Na \qquad \text{(b)}$$

and

$$Na_2O + MO = Na_2MO_2. \qquad \text{(c)}$$

Also

$$H_2O + M = MO + H_2. \qquad \text{(d)}$$

The overall reaction of (a), (c), and (d) would be

$$2NaOH + M = Na_2MO_2 + H_2.$$

Because of this reaction, Friend suggested that any additives which increase the hydrogen overvoltage or the difficulty with which hydrogen is evolved should retard the corrosion process. This mechanism has been supported by other investigators (*8, 44, 56, 57, 64, 70*). Some (*8, 44, 70*) have shown Ni corrosion to be inhibited in fused NaOH by using a hydrogen atmosphere.

Microstructures of corrosion-product layers investigated by Smith *et al.* (*59*) were formed by the action of fused NaOH at 815°C. on 304- and 347-stainless steel, as well as on four high-purity Fe-Cr-Ni alloys with nominal compositions in weight per cents of 80Fe–20Cr; 80Fe–10Cr–10Ni; 74Fe–18Cr–8Ni; and 60Fe–20Cr–20Ni. Each corrosion-product layer consisted of a nonmetallic network threading through a metallic matrix and resembled similar layers formed by the action of NaOH melts on Inconel.

A compilation of data on static corrosion by NaOH was made by Roben (*51*), Gregory *et al.* (*18*), Craighead *et al.* (*7*), Smith *et al.* (*60, 61, 62*), and Gurowich (*20*). The corrosion rates of Ni in NaOH have been reported to be 0.645 and 1.20 mg./sq. in./day at temperatures of 580°C. (*18*) and 800°C. (*51*), respectively. The Ni base alloys, Inconel (Ni-Cr-Fe) and Hastelloy D (Ni-Si-Cu), showed slightly higher corrosion rates than commercial Ni (*18*). In tests conducted on Inconel at temperatures of 450°C. to 815°C., Fe and Cr were selectively leached (*62*). Certain Ni alloys containing Mo were found to be more resistant to fused NaOH in tests at 850°C. than the ones without Mo (*60, 61*). In comparing corrosiveness of LiOH, NaOH, and KOH at 250–600°C., the corrosion rates of Ni, Cu, Armco Iron, and Kh18N9T (similar to 321-stainless steel) have increased in the order of increasing atomic radii, Li < Na < K. In testing various ceramics in NaOH at 538°C., no corrosion was observed on Al_2O_3 and ZrO_2 (*8*).

In dynamic tests, both thermal and forced convection loops have been commonly adopted, although other methods have also been tried (*12, 32, 45, 51, 63*).

Manly (*39*) operated a thermal convection loop made of a $\frac{1}{2}$-in. Ni tube containing dehydrated NaOH. The loop was run for 316 hrs. with the hot leg temperature at 705°C. and the cold at 465°C. Although the loop was still functioning at the end of the run, a considerable amount of mass transfer of loop material occurred. Ni was deposited in the form of dendritic and polyhedral crystals.

Simons *et al.* (*43, 54*) ran Ni thermal and forced convection loops in which hydrogen-blanketed NaOH was circulated at peak temperatures of 650°C. to 815°C., with temperature differentials in the range of 55°C. to 110°C. Plugs by Ni deposition formed in times ranging from less than 10 to 200 hrs. In 480°C. and 566°C. peak-temperature experiments, with Ni pumped-loop systems, much better results were obtained. For example, after 2000 hrs. of operation, a 480°C.–350°C. loop system displayed a cold-zone metal transfer of only 5 mils.

Gregory *et al.* (*17*) also ran thermal convection loops containing NaOH. Under inert gas atmosphere at temperatures above 600°C., mass transfer of Ni completely obstructed the flow in a few weeks, whereas at 500°C., blocking occurred after about 200 days. In these cases, the mass transfer deposit was a higher oxide of Ni whose composition was complex, but approximated that of Ni_2O_3. Under a hydrogen atmosphere, loops were slower to plug than those operated under an inert atmosphere at the same temperatures, and here the deposit was found to be pure Ni.

Corrosion by Other Fused Salts

Recent attention has focused on sodium polyphosphate as a nuclear fuel carrier. Ginell *et al.* (*14, 15, 16, 21*) tested Fe alloys in sodium polyphosphate ($Na_2O/P_2O_5 = 1.12$) at 700°C. The corrosion rate increased with increased Fe concentration of Fe alloys containing varying amounts of Cr, Ni, and Mo. Among the nonferrous metals, Pt, Mo, W, V, and Ag were not attacked within the limits of detection (< 4 mils/yr.). The experimental evidences suggested that diffusion of reactants through a phosphide film is an important rate-determining step in the corrosion.

Kristal (*31*), studying $ZnSO_4$-K_2SO_4-Na_2SO_4, found that the corrosion rate of Armco Iron and low carbon steel at 450°C.–500°C. in the salts is ≤ 0.83 mm./yr. In salts containing much Fe, the rate is 1.5 mm./yr. The corrosion rate of steel in salt baths decreases with increases in the Cr content of the steel beyond 12%.

Section II: Corrosion by Heavy Liquid Metals

Thermally regenerative, bimetallic cells employ a heavy metal as a cathode (positive electrode) and an alkali metal as an anode (negative electrode). During cell operation the alkali metal is transferred as ions through the electrolyte to the cathode where it forms an alloy with the heavy metal. On regeneration, the alkali metal is separated from this alloy and returned to the anode. Although a considerable amount of information has been accumulated on corrosion by alkali metals in work related to fast reactors and space projects, the amount of information available on corrosion by heavy metals is relatively limited. In this work, liquid metals were used mostly as heat transfer media. In the case of Bi, the metal was further studied as a potential nuclear fuel carrier. As cathode metals for thermally regenerative, bimetallic cells, Bi, Pb, and Sn are attractive among heavy metals because of their high and stable emf-producing characteristics and their very low vapor pressures at high temperatures which permit regeneration by evaporating the alkali metals from the alloy. When Hg is used as a cathode metal, evaporating Hg rather than the alkali metal is required because Hg has a higher vapor pressure than alkali metals. This is a disadvantage of Hg since, to obtain a high voltage in a bimetallic cell, the alkali metal at the anode must be relatively pure, whereas the heavy metal at the cathode may contain considerable alkali metal. Under these conditions of regeneration, it requires less heat to separate an alkali metal from a heavy metal by evaporating a volatile alkali metal than by evaporating a larger amount of a more volatile heavy metal. For these reasons, Bi, Pb, and Sn have been studied at Argonne National Laboratory as potential electrode metals.

This survey is limited to unclassified reports and published literature concerning corrosion by liquid Bi, Pb, Sn, and their alloys. Because the corrosion and solubility data on liquid metals prior to 1950 have already been compiled by Hansen *et al.* (*60*), which is supplemented by Elliott (*49*), Kelman *et al.* (*73*), and Lyon (*77*), they are not covered in this survey. In this survey, the compositions of liquid metals are expressed in atomic per cents, while those of construction metal alloys are expressed in weight per cents.

Static Corrosion by Bismuth

Bismuth and bismuth-base alloys became, in the 1950's, a subject of intensive study in a nuclear reactor development program when the solubility of uranium in bismuth was found to be sufficient for fueling a thermal reactor.

The Liquid Metal Fuel Reactor (LMFR) project was initiated in 1947 at Brookhaven National Laboratory. The project included corrosion studies to establish material suitable for use at about 550°C. in liquid Bi (*56, 57*) and was followed by an extensive liquid metal investigation at Brookhaven National Laboratory. Cordovi (*36*) has reported the results of the preliminary static corrosion study on various steels in Bi, Bi-Pb, and Bi-Pb-Sn eutectics at 550°C. The $2\frac{1}{4}$Cr–1Mo and 5Cr–$\frac{1}{2}$Mo–1.5Si steels showed the greatest promise of success. Subsequent test results were reported elsewhere (*12-24*).

In the course of the study, effects of various additives including Mg, Ti, and Zr as inhibitors were studied. It was reported (*14*) that pure iron immersed in Bi saturated with Zr at 550°C. to 750°C. does not corrode. Small amounts of Zr and Mg added to the Bi made corrosion of intermediate Cr steel negligible (*5, 6, 7*). Zr and Ti additions to the liquid metals inhibit corrosion of steels by Pb, Bi, and Hg by reacting with C and/or N in the steel to form surface deposits of carbides and/or nitrides which are a barrier to dissolution. It was further demonstrated (*71*) that, in Bi and Hg, Zr and Ti adsorb on the surface of the steels and subsequently react with nitrogen and possibly carbon from the steels to form inert adherent surface layers of ZrN, TiN, or TiN + TiC; the results are lower rates of Fe dissolution into Bi, and a higher supersaturation for Fe precipitation from Bi.

Weeks *et al.* (*108*) have discussed the formation of the inhibiting ZrN and/or ZrC films as controlled by the activity and distribution of N and C in the steel. Minor constituents that influence the activity and distribution of the N and C may also affect the corrosion resistance of the steel. Localized attack is accompanied by Zr deposition, possibly resulting from interaction between the dissolved Zr and carbide particles in the steel. ZrN films may spall but can re-form in the spalled and corroded areas.

Weeks *et al.* (*103, 107*) have discussed liquid metal corrosion mechanisms. They postulated that an atom of a solid metal dissolves in a liquid metal by breaking its bonds with its neighboring solid atoms and forming new ones with liquid atoms. This process depends upon the structure at the solid-liquid interface. The dissolved atom then migrates, perhaps with its "solvation sheath," through the relatively quiet liquid adjacent to the solid metal into the main body of coolant. This migration is a function of the liquid flow.

Weeks (*16, 106*) also presented interesting examples of isothermal mass transfer in liquid Bi. Fe was contacted with Fe-saturated Bi for 235 hrs. at 689°C. Within this sample, mass transfer of Fe from a grain boundary to local Fe surfaces took place. Next, a 410-stainless steel was kept in liquid Bi at 600°C. For the first 10 hrs., Fe in the stainless steel leached out at a rate faster than the Cr and nearly saturated the Bi. Cr dissolved slowly in the Bi, however, and being more soluble (150 p.p.m.) than Fe (50 p.p.m.), remained in solution, reducing the Fe solubility. After 350 hrs., concentrations of both Fe and Cr in Bi became the same (25 p.p.m.). This presents an important difference of static tests from dynamic tests where Fe and Cr continue to dissolve at the rate observed in the first hours.

Electrolysis of Fe-Bi and Cr-Bi melts (*110*) and a possible correlation between thermoelectric potentials and liquid metal corrosion (*105*) have been discussed in connection with the liquid metal corrosion study.

The Bi corrosion work at Brookhaven National Laboratory was published in their progress reports (*12-24*) until the curtailment of LMFR project in 1959. A review of material study for the LMFR at Brookhaven National Laboratory has been summarized elsewhere (*74, 104, 109*).

Investigations on corrosion by liquid Bi were also conducted by many other investigators outside Brookhaven National Laboratory. Collins (*33*) made an experimental survey of the solubilities of Armco Iron, Mo, Nb, Ta, W, Ni, 309-, 310-, 316-, 321-, 347-, and 446-stainless steels, Ni-Cr-Fe alloy and low-carbon steel in bismuth covering a temperature range of 480°C. to 1200°C., by using liquid Bi in capsules made of the test materials. Types 309- and 310-stainless steels showed the greatest solubility, < 3600 p.p.m. at 700°C., and 316- and 347-stainless steels were only slightly better, < 2000 p.p.m. at 800°C. Type 446- stainless steel showed the lowest solubility, < 500 p.p.m. at 800°C. Of the pure metals tested, Mo showed the lowest solubility, < 110 p.p.m. at 1000°C., followed closely by Nb, Fe, and Ta, < 230 p.p.m. at 1000°C. However, these data should be treated with caution because the refractory metal specimens were contained in stainless steel crucibles during tests.

Pray et al. (89) evaluated the corrosion resistance of some 50 materials, mostly steels and high temperature alloys, at 750°C. and 850°C. in liquid bismuth. Armco Iron, low-carbon steels, and chromium plate were severely attacked, while the low-chromium alloys, high-chromium steels, stainless steels, and heat-resistant alloys were wet by the bismuth and moderately attacked. The most severe corrosion appeared at or near the liquid-vapor interface. The 2.9% Si transformer steels were attacked to the extent of only 0.75 mil in 38 days at 850°C. Duriron (14.5 Si-Fe) exhibited no visible attack after 11 days at 850°C. The method used Vycor as the test containers.

Wilkinson (111) investigated corrosion by Bi-Pb-Sn eutectic at temperatures up to 800°C. Mo was not attacked by the eutectic at 800°C. and Be was not attacked at 500°C. The presence of oxygen accelerates or increases the attack on Fe, carbon steel, and Al, but limited amounts of oxygen are protective to chromium steels. Increasing the chromium content does not increase resistance to attack unless oxygen is present and may increase the solubility of the steel in the melt. Anodizing Al and maintaining it as an anode help to protect it. Unprotected aluminum is readily attacked by diffusion reaction. Fe is nearly insoluble in Bi-Pb-Sn alloy at 500°C., but transgranular attack, intergranular attack, and localized attack occur on Armco Iron and carbon steel. The reaction with austenitic stainless steel at temperatures up to 500°C. appears to depend on the condition of the steel.

Imai et al. (65, 66, 67, 68) confirmed the following points by their tests on carbon steels and chromium steels at 600°C.–950°C.: (1) The presence of oxygen in liquid Bi or in an overlying atmosphere accelerates the corrosion of carbon steels but retards the corrosion of Fe-Cr alloys. (2) In uninhibited Bi, severe corrosion occurs along grain boundaries, in addition to uniform dissolution. (3) When Zr is added, the corrosion becomes very slight. The inhibiting action is due to forming of a ZrC film, the growing rate of which is controlled by the diffusion of C in steel. (4) The corrosion loss increases with increasing Cr content. (5) The growth rate of ZrC film at the steel surface is retarded by increasing the amount of Cr in steel.

Agrawal (1) tested polished 18-8 stainless steel in liquid Bi, in air atmosphere, at temperatures of 400°C., 500°C., 600°C., and 700°C. Although no corrosion was observed at 400°C., 0.159 mm./yr. at 500°C., 0.337 mm./yr. at 600°C., and 1.120 mm./yr. at 700°C. of corrosion were found. In all cases, the specimens were wet.

Lloyd (*76*) reported that Ta and Mo showed no penetration in Bi-U solutions after 1000 hr. at temperatures up to 800°C. Nb showed an average penetration of 0.002 in. in pure Bi after 500 hr. at 1000°C.

Parry *et al.* (*87*) studied the compatibility of Nb in Bi at 1000°C. After 170 hr. the Nb was found to be intergranularly corroded. Examination of the surrounding bismuth revealed large segregates of Nb dendrites.

Buttinelli *et al.* (*25*) conducted tests on Al and sintered Al powder of various oxide contents in Bi at 550°C. for 400 hrs.

Nikitin (*83*) of USSR has noted, based mostly on U. S. literature, that the corrosion factors for Bi and Pb depend on the rates of simple diffusion of dissolved metals in the liquid metal, while for Na and K, corrosion depends mostly on the amount of oxygen present.

In connection with the regenerative, bimetallic emf cell program at Argonne National Laboratory (*3, 95*), a series of static corrosion tests in Bi was made. The results are presented in Table II.

Coultas (*37*) made tests on several refractory materials in Bi at 980°C. Graphite, Al_2O_3, ZrO_2, ThO_2, mullite (high purity $3Al_2O_3 \cdot 2SiO_2$ from Morgan), Vycor, TaC, MgO, $MoSi_2$, Re, W, Mo, and K-138A (WTiC$_2$ from Kennametal) showed no apparent attack after approximately 167 hr. Ta, Metamic LT-1 (Cr bonded Al_2O_3), and 303-stainless steel with Mo flame-sprayed coatings were severely corroded. Vycor capsules were used to contain the liquid Bi and specimens for the tests.

Reed (*90*) listed Mo, W, Ta, Re, Kennametal (WTiC$_2$), Al_2O_3, MgO, ZrO_2, $MoSi_2$, ThO_2, TaC, and Vycor up to 1000°C., and graphite and Morganite (high purity Al_2O_3 from Morgan) up to 1400°C. as having good resistance to attack by liquid Bi.

Eldred (*46*) conducted tests on Cr and ferrous and nonferrous alloys at temperatures up to 550°C. Richards (*84*) studied the use of V as a container for molten Bi. The solubility of V in Bi was found to vary linearly from 110 p.p.m. at 600°C. to 750 p.p.m. at 1000°C. V suffered severe intergranular attack at temperatures above 900°C.

Eatherly *et al.* (*44*) evaluated a number of graphites by measuring their absorption of liquid Bi. The absorption varied from 3-4 gr. Bi/cc. graphite for large-pore AGOT graphite or its equivalent to less than 0.1 gram/cc. for graphites with smaller pores. It was found that the degree of uptake is a function of the surface tension of Bi. The addition of Zr (250 p.p.m.) in Bi increased its surface tension.

Kamemoto *et al.* (*70*) applied a thermal cycle of heating (550°C. or 700°C.) and cooling (solidification) on impermeable graphite in Bi. Crack formation in the graphite samples was observed and attributed to the volume expansion when Bi which had penetrated the graphite pores had solidified. No cracks were observed in graphite immersed in 58% Bi-Pb. The effects of Bi_2O_3 were also studied. The weight loss of samples im-

Table II. Static Corrosion of Refractory Metals,

Bismuth

Test Materials	Temp. (°C.)	Time (Hrs.)	Results
Molybdenum	1000	97	No corrosion.
Niobium	1000	64	Dissolution, 30 μm. thickness. Intergranular, <50 μm.
Tantalum	1000	95	No apparent attack.
Tungsten	1000	24	No apparent attack.
Mo-30W	1000	97	No corrosion.
	~1000	>1100	No visible attack. Intermetallic, ~100 μm. thickness.
Mo-50Re	1000	91	No apparent attack. Intermetallic, <12 μm.
Nb-1Zr	1000	167	Severe intergranular attack, <250 μm. depth. Specimen became brittle.
Nb-10W-2.5 Zr	1000	71.5	Slight dissolution and pittings.
Armco Iron	850	24	Slight attack.
	1000	50	Complete dissolution.
1040 Steel	1000	22	Intermetallic layer, <80 μm. thick. Cr preferentially segregated.
304-Stainless Steel	850	97	Intergranular, <100 μm. depth. No attacks found in vapor phase.
316-Stainless Steel	700	97	Slight dissolution. Decarburization, <5 μm. depth including vapor phase.
High Purity Alumina	600	99	No attack. No wetting.
	850	52	Partly wetted and greyed.
	1000	72	Partly wetted and greyed, not electrically conducting.

mersed in Bi_2O_3-added Bi was 0.51%, compared with 0.28% for pure Bi at 550°C. in a 210 hr. test.

Meyer et al. (80) reviewed the compatibility of graphite with Bi, Pb, Sn, and their alloys.

Manzone et al. (79) and Nair et al. (82) have compiled data on corrosion resistance of Mo and Mo-base alloys to Bi and its alloys.

A review on Bi corrosion to 1962 has been made by Thamer (97).

Corrosion studies on Bi and Pb at Harwell, England have been reviewed by Finniston (50).

The Nernst equation has been applied by Ward et al. (100, 101) to correlate dissolution rates of solid Cu in liquid Bi and Pb at the temperature range 360°C.-460°C. obtained by rotating a specimen in the liquid metal. The dissolution rate was expressed in the following form.

Steels, and Alumina by Bismuth and Tin

Tin

Temp. (°C.)	Time (Hrs.)	Results
1000	26	Penetration, <15 μm. depth.
1000	24	Slight dissolution. Intermetallic with dendrites, <20 μm. thickness.
1000	96	Penetration, <20 μm. depth.
1000	96	Penetration, <5 μm.
1000	67	No corrosion.
~1000	>850	No visible deterioration. Intermetallic, ~100 μm. thickness.
1000	63.5	No apparent attack.
1000	160	Intergranular attack, <100 μm. depth.
1000	87.5	Slight dissolution and pittings.
—	—	In view of high solubility of Fe, no test was made.
—	—	In view of high solubility of Fe, no test was made.
—	—	In view of high solubility of Ni, no test was made.
—	—	In view of high solubility of Ni, no test was made.
600	77.5	No attack. No wetting.
850	29	Slightly wetted.
1000	74	Completely wetted. Slightly conducting.

$$N_t = N_o(1 - e^{-Kt(S/V)})$$

where

N_t = solute concentration at time t

N_o = saturation concentration at a fixed temperature

K = solution-rate constant

S = surface area of solid exposed

V = volume of solvent

The activation energy estimated from the results for the Cu-Pb system, 3500 cal./mole, agrees well with that predicted from viscosity data for diffusion of Cu in Pb, 3950 cal./mole and suggests that the rate determining step is the diffusion of dissolved material through the liquid layer. However, the calculated activation energy for the Cu-Bi system, 6400 cal./mole, is too large to account for solution rate control by liquid phase diffusion alone. A similar analysis on a Cu-Pb loop has been made by Forgeng (52).

Covington et al. (38) have shown that isothermal mass transfer with an alloy layer formation on an insoluble metal occurs in the systems: Al → Mo, Al → Fe, Ni → Fe, Al → Cr, Co → Nb, and Co → Ta in liquid Bi at 500°C. They pointed out that the layer formation may not take place at the surface if the solubility of the "insoluble" metal is increased by adding the soluble metal to the liquid metal. Reaction products may then be precipitated in the liquid metal as in the case of two soluble compound-forming metals. The formation of compounds of the soluble metal with the liquid metal may prevent the formation of intermetallic compound layers.

An extensive study of the solubilities of elements in liquid Bi has been conducted at Brookhaven National Laboratory (74, 92, 102) by equilibrating Bi with the solute for 18–66 hrs. in an "inert" (graphite, fused SiO_2, or Ta) crucible and taking a filtered sample of the melt at each of several temperatures. The resulting solubility equations are presented in Table III. Some earlier work was conducted in England (53, 64) on Nb, Pd, Sr, Rh, Ru, Fe, and Be.

Shepard et al. (94) studied dissolution of 405- and 410-stainless steels at up to 800°C. by Bi in Vycor capsules. The ultimate solubility of Fe in Bi was obtained in less than 5 hrs. for temperatures below 800°C., while the amount of Cr dissolved in Bi was still increasing after 70 hrs. At 730°C. the solubility of Fe was 117 p.p.m. and that of Cr, 119 p.p.m.

Parry et al. (87) reported that the solubility of Nb in oxygen-free Bi is approximately 100 p.p.m. at 600°C., but that it is approximately 200 p.p.m. at 600°C. in Bi containing 0.01% of O_2. Because of this solubility, they deduced that Nb loops in nonisothermal systems would probably suffer more serious mass transfer effects than systems constructed from low-alloy steels.

Dynamic Corrosion by Bismuth

An intensive study was conducted at the Nuclear Engineering Dept. of Brookhaven National Laboratory in connection with the LMFR project (12-24). Both thermal convection loops and forced circulation loops were constructed. Various materials and additives were studied. The maximum reported temperature of the tests never exceeded 650°C., however, and most of the work was conducted below 550°C. (12-24, 91). Romano et al. (91) summarized the dynamic corrosion of ferritic materials by Bi as follows:

1. Zr is the most effective inhibitor of mass transfer of low alloy steels by Bi, U-Bi, and Pb-Bi eutectic. A minimum concentration of 100

Table III. Solubilities of Elements in Bismuth

Solubility Equation

$$log_{10}\,(p.p.m.\;Solute) = A - \frac{B}{T^0K.}$$

Elements	A	B	Temperature Range (ℑC.)	Source Literature
Be	2.50	2750	600-800	*102*
C	—	—	—	*102*
Mg	7.46	2210	300-550	*102*
Al	6.40	1992	350-620	*102*
Si	—	—	650-850	*102*
Ca	10.34	4.365	320-440	*102*
Ti	6.046	2230	310-630	*102*
V	4.54	2520	400-800	*102*
Cr	6.26	3580	400-700	*74*
Mn	7.804	2177	<446	*102*
Mn	6.214	1030	446-560	*102*
Fe	5.69	3490	425-725	74
Co	4.376	1520	340-600	*102*
Co	5.433	2440	600-900	*102*
Ni	6.496	1465	480-630	*74*
Ge	6.78	2566	270-500	*92*
Sr	8.43	2760	310-440	*92*
Y	6.00	2690	320-730	*92*
Zr	6.69	2780	330-700	*92*
Nb	4.12	2158	400-650	*102*
Mo	insoluble		-800	*92*
Ru	3.12	808	300-560	*92*
Rh	7.90	2460	280-490	*92*
Pd	6.864	1280	260-450	*92*
Ba	7.01	1590	280-370	*92*
La	6.75	2330	280-720	*92*
Hf	6.098	2000	320-700	*102*
Ta	insoluble		-788	*102*
W	insoluble		-798	*102*
Re	insoluble		-800	*102*
Os	insoluble		-800	*102*
Ir	—	—	-1450	*102*
Pt	6.987	1654	280-450	*102*

p.p.m. Zr is required, and higher concentrations are more effective. Adding Mg is essential to protect both Zr and U from oxidizing, but Mg concentrations of > 1000 p.p.m. seem to be detrimental. Ti, Th, and Te are far less effective than Zr as inhibitors; similarly, Ca and Th are less effective than Mg as oxygen getters.

2. Generally, difficulties such as inability to maintain the additive concentration level and enhanced corrosion or deposition arise in loop operation when fission products and corrosion products are added rather

than the nominal concentrations of Zr, Mg, and U. High concentrations of Zr and Mg cause similar difficulties due to solubility limitations.

3. Corrosion in dynamic systems increases with increasing maximum temperature and temperature differential. Very high Zr concentrations seem to offset the effect of raising the maximum temperature to 650°C. and the temperature differential to 150°C. in carbon steel loops.

4. Corrosion in dynamic systems in the presence of Zr and Mg inhibitors increases with the Cr content of a steel; carbon steels are the most resistant, low alloy steels ($< 2\frac{1}{4}\%$ Cr) are moderately corrosion resistant, and high Cr steels ($> 2\frac{1}{4}\%$ Cr) are least resistant, being subject to gross attack.

5. Corrosion increases with decreasing C content in $2\frac{1}{4}$Cr–1Mo steel and with decreasing N/Al ratio in all ferritic steels.

6. In general, $1\frac{1}{4}$Cr–$\frac{1}{2}$Mo steel welds are selectively attacked in $1\frac{1}{4}$ Cr–$\frac{1}{2}$Mo steel loops because of lower N/Al ratios and a lower C content in the weld rod; conversely, $2\frac{1}{4}$Cr–1Mo steel welds are more resistant to attack than $2\frac{1}{4}$Cr–1Mo steel.

7. Nitrided $2\frac{1}{4}$Cr–1Mo steel is more corrosion resistant than the "as received" material. Heat-treating $2\frac{1}{4}$Cr–1Mo steel seems to enhance attack by Bi, probably because of the effect on the N and C activity of the steel.

8. Low temperature and long-time preconditioning runs (pretreatment with Zr) are effective in retarding corrosion of low alloy steels and carbon steels, whereas high temperature preconditioning is detrimental.

The Pb-Bi eutectic and unalloyed Pb are less aggressive fluids than Bi or U-Bi. Both Ti and Zr when protected by Mg are effective inhibitors for Pb-Bi in $1\frac{1}{4}$Cr–$\frac{1}{2}$Mo steel and carbon steel loops. Uninhibited Pb-Bi can be circulated for nearly 10,000 hrs. without appreciable corrosion so long as the maximum temperature does not exceed 400°C., even at a temperature differential of 200°C.

To study the effect of velocity on corrosion and mass transfer several pumped high velocity loops were constructed of $2\frac{1}{4}$Cr steel (*12–24*). The maximum bulk Bi temperature was 520°C. and the temperature gradient was 108°C. The flow was 1.2 g.p.m., and the highest velocity reached was 8 ft./sec. Electromagnetic pumps circulated the Bi, and the flow measurement was made with a submerged orifice. No quantitative information is available from this experiment. Waide *et al.* (*99*) discussed an in-pile corrosion test loop made of $2\frac{1}{4}$Cr–1Mo steel operating at temperatures of 500°C. and 425°C.

In connection with the feasibility study of the Liquid Metal Fuel Reactor at the Babcock and Wilcox Company (*8*, *43*), $2\frac{1}{4}$Cr–1Mo steel and graphite have been evaluated as possible materials of construction. The loops were operated with centrifugal-type pumps and had a maximum temperature of approximately 500°C. and a temperature differential of approximately 75°C. The corrosion specimens which were placed in the hot leg indicated that the heat treatment used on the specimens affected the corrosion rate.

Prior to the extensive Brookhaven National Laboratory work, Elgert *et al.* (*47*, *48*) and Egan (*45*) conducted thermal convection loops made of 5Cr–0.5Mo steel. Ti + Mg was studied as an inhibitor. A reduction greater than a hundredfold (from 2000 to 20 mils/yr.) in the corrosion rate of 5Cr–0.5Mo steel was caused by adding more than 50 p.p.m. Ti and 350 p.p.m. Mg while the loop was running with hot and cold leg temperatures of 700°C. and 615°C., respectively.

Stephan *et al.* (*96*) reported a study made on a forced circulation liquid Bi loop at a hot leg temperature of 950°C. with a 280°C. temperature gradient. The loop was made of a 347-stainless steel tube. The flow velocity reached 20 ft./sec., and after 100 hrs. of operation, only limited corrosion was found.

Coultas *et al.* (*37*) made a "convection-diffusion tube" in which the mass transfer effects could be induced by reflux of boiling liquid metals. In this device, a tube of the steel test material was sealed with Bi in a Vycor capsule which was then arranged in a furnace with the top protruding so that the bottom of the steel was at a high temperature and the top, at a lower temperature. This method is relatively inexpensive but, because the corrosion is induced from both vapor and liquid in this system, the results must be treated differently from those of loops.

Hallett *et al.* (*58*) found no mass transfer or corrosion in a graphite by bismuth with a hot leg temperature of 1400°C. and a cold leg temperature of 875°C. after 279 hrs.

Because of difficulties in fabrication, only a few loops have been made of refractory metals despite their high corrosion resistance to liquid metals at elevated temperatures.

Fisher *et al.* (*51*) built a Ta loop, 0.030″ × ¾″ O.D., enclosed in an outer envelope of Inconel, in which 5 w/o U-Bi alloy was circulated by an electromagnetic pump. The hot leg temperature was maintained at 950°C., and the cold leg, 850°C. Samples of the liquid metal were taken at the end of 2000, 4000, and 5000 hrs., and the tantalum content was found to be less than 6 p.p.m. at all times. After 5250 hrs., the loop was dissected and no corrosion or erosion of the Ta was noted, but there was evidence of pitting 5 to 6 mils deep at points wherever Inconel contacted the Ta under extreme pressure. The Ta remained shiny and ductile throughout the experiment. Another Ta loop containing an alloy of 10 w/o U-0.5 w/o Mg-Bi was operated with the hot leg temperature at 1160°C. and a temperature differential of 400°C. After 957 hrs., the experiment was interrupted by failure of a weld in the Inconel sheath. No Ta was found in the 800-hr. sample. Still another Ta loop containing 5 w/o U-0.3 w/o Mg-Bi was run with a hot leg temperature of 1050°C. and a temperature differential of 250°C. Samples which were taken during the operation showed that the alloy contained less than 6 p.p.m. Ta. After 4500 hrs., the loop operation was terminated. Metallographic examination showed that one section of the Ta loop contained many inclusions. Consultation with the manufacturer revealed that this particular piece of Ta had been fabricated from reclaimed metal and not from virgin Ta.

Lloyd (76) has shown that Mo exhibits good resistance to dynamic corrosion by Bi at low flow velocities. A thermal convection loop constructed from 1 cm. bore quartz tubing was used. The most successful loop ran continuously for 2500 hrs. with hot and cold leg temperatures of 825°C. and 400°C., respectively. The estimated flow velocity was approximately 0.5 cm./sec.

Horsley et al. (63) studied dynamic corrosion of $2\frac{1}{4}$Cr–1Mo silicon-killed steel tubing in liquid Bi with a maximum hot leg temperature of up to 625°C. and a temperature differential of 150°C. At a fluid velocity of 3 to 4 mm./sec., the corrosion rate was 0.65 in./yr. An addition of 250 to 500 p.p.m. of Zr reduced the corrosion rate to 0.17 in./yr. The Zr film, however, occasionally spalls off the tube wall and is not re-formed. Under this condition, intergranular corrosion of the underlying steel proceeds rapidly. If the steel is heavily plated with ZrN, its corrosion rate is reduced to a maximum of 0.01 in./yr. The film re-forms, if broken, and intergranular penetration is prevented.

The Colburn-Chilton analogy can be applied to mass transfer in liquid metal where the rate-determining process is the diffusion in the boundary layer. The following form of the Colburn-Chilton mass-transport equation has been proposed by Horsley (62) for a circuit with a small thermal gradient ΔT:

$$r = 0.023 \, d^{-0.2} V^{0.8} D^{0.6} \nu^{-0.4} \frac{dS}{dT} \Delta T$$

where

r = corrosion rate
V = velocity of liquid metal
ν = kinematic viscosity
D = diffusion coefficient
d = diameter of pipe
S = solubility of container material

Seifert et al. (93) studied dynamic corrosion effects of liquid Bi on Ta, Mo-0.5 Ti, and Be. The specimens were placed in pumped loops which were fabricated from $2\frac{1}{4}$Cr–1Mo steel pipe. The maximum temperature in the loop was 488°C., and the minimum temperature was 412°C. The corrosion rates of Ta, Mo-0.5 Ti, and Be were 0.004, 0.229, and 0.690 mil/yr., respectively, at a liquid-metal flow velocity of 8 ft./sec.

By measuring weight losses of steel pins after immersion in the hot leg of a thermal convection loop, James *et al.* (*69*) studied the corrosion of several steels in liquid Pb and Bi in the temperature range 600°C. to 900°C. In uninhibited Bi, low alloy steels are more corrosion resistant than 13% Cr–Fe or 18-8 stainless steel. Both Ni and Mg in steels have deteriorative effects on the corrosion resistance of $2\frac{1}{4}$Cr–1Mo steel. Adding 500 p.p.m. of Zr greatly reduces steel corrosion in Bi and are both important in this inhibition process; some protection is afforded by the alloying constituents in the steel, such as W, Cr, and Si which govern the availability of C and N at the Bi-steel interface.

Dawe *et al.* (*41*) studied low carbon steels with varying concentrations of Cr up to 550°C. A 12% Cr steel showed the least mass transfer rate. No mass transfer of the steel was observed after 2500 hrs. of operation.

Yajima *et al.* (*113*) have constructed a loop completely from graphite, including a centrifugal pump, a valve, a liquid level gage, and a flow meter. This system was designed for an operating temperature of 550°C. and a maximum temperature of 700°C. The unit has been run only briefly. Potter *et al.* (*88*) conducted exploratory work on 28 different insulating and refractory materials up to 540°C. in liquid Bi, using a thermal convection loop.

In connection with the regenerative, bimetallic emf cell program at Argonne National Laboratory (*3, 95*), thermal convection loops made of a low carbon steel and 316-stainless steel containing Bi and Na-Bi alloys were operated.

Fluid flow and energy balance of thermal convection loops are discussed by Hamilton *et al.* (*59*) and Cordovi (*36*).

Static Corrosion by Lead

The principal interest in liquid Pb today is directed toward its application as heat-transfer media in nuclear- and conventional-fueled power plants. Pb has two advantages over Bi and Sn as a heat transfer medium: (1) Pb contracts upon freezing, whereas Bi expands and this may cause pipe ruptures, and (2) Pb has less ability to dissolve Fe than Bi or Sn and probably most of the other elements present in engineering materials (i.e., Cr, Ni, and Co base alloys) (*91*). Pb possesses a low absorption cross section for thermal neutrons. A disadvantage as the heat transfer medium is its slightly higher melting point (Pb, 327°C.; Bi, 271°C.; Sn, 231°C.).

In the regenerative emf cell application, Pb has two more advantages over Bi or Sn in addition to the two mentioned above: (1) Pb has slightly lower vapor pressure than Bi, although Sn has the lowest vapor pressure of the three metals (*77*), (2) Pb does not form high melting point intermetallic alloys with alkali metals (*60*). A disadvantage is that it produces a lower emf when coupled with an alkali metal.

Parkman *et al.* (*86*) found by the Vycor capsule method that Mo, W, Ta, and Nb are inert to Pb at 980°C., and 446-stainless steel, Ti, and Zr show poor resistance.

In the work done by Collins *et al.* (*34*) 18-8 stainless steels proved to be inferior to 446-stainless steel in Pb-Bi eutectic up to 760°C. because of selective solubility of Ni.

By spectrographic examination, Grassi *et al.* (*55*) found no dissolution of Nb at 870°C. or of Mo at 1090°C. in Pb after 500 hrs.

Cash *et al.* (26) studied the corrosion of Nb, Ta, Y, and a Ni-Cr-Fe alloy by Pb at temperatures ranging from 600°C. to 1100°C. No penetration was found in Ta which had been kept in Pb at 1100°C. for 1255 hrs. Pb wet Ta slightly at this temperature. Nb which had been immersed in Pb at 1100°C. for 1255 hrs. showed 0.001-in. penetration. The Ni-Cr-Fe alloy showed 0.011-in. penetration at 800°C. after 100 hrs. Y was completely penetrated by Pb at 700°C. after 50 hrs.

Agrawal (*1*) tested polished 18-8 stainless steel in liquid Pb at temperatures of 400, 500, 600, and 700°C. The tests were conducted in air atmosphere. No corrosion was observed at 400°C.; but 0.106 mm./yr. at 500°C., 0.180 mm./yr. at 600°C., and 0.569 mm./yr. at 700°C. of corrosion were observed. In all cases, the specimens were wet by the Pb.

Corrosion resistance of ceramics and cermets engaged the attention of Cook (*35*), who observed that none of the ceramics, including various borides, carbides, nitrides, oxides, and silicides, was attacked in 100-hr. exposure to static Pb at 815°C. Under similar conditions, cermets consisting of 87 $\sim$ 94% WC-13 $\sim$ 6% Co showed no sign of attack.

Brasunas (*10*) reported extensive static corrosion tests on various metals by liquid Pb. Inconel, 309-, and 446-stainless steel were tested in Pb for 100 hrs. up to 700°C. None showed any attack except for Inconel, where 0.5 mil attack was noted. There was almost no interaction of Fe with Pb at 1000°C. Two other metallic elements showing little or no visible reaction in static tests at 1000°C. were W and Zr. Austenitic stainless steels containing Ni (300 series) were attacked intergranularly by Pb. The ferritic stainless steels (400 series) appeared generally to have better corrosion resistance to Pb at 1000°C. than did the 300 series stainless steels. At 815°C., the severity of attack of Ni and Ni-base alloys by Pb remained fairly high, but the attack on Fe-base alloys was considerably reduced. Even the 310- stainless steel, containing 20% Ni, appeared to be unattacked in 100-hr. tests.

Brasunas (*10*) ran 100-hr. static tests by liquid 50 w/o Na-Pb alloy at 815°C. Inconel, 317-, and 446-stainless steels showed no evidence of attack, but 316-stainless steel showed 0.5 mil attack.

Attack of various materials by Pb at 1000°C. was investigated by Wilkinson *et al.* (*112*) BeO, fused silica, Ta, Nb, and a sintered mixture of BeO and urania showed no attack by Pb. AISI 1020 carbon steel, 430-

stainless steel, Cr, 347-stainless steel, 302-stainless steel, Ni-Cr-Fe alloy, Mo, and Armco Iron dissolved in Pb slightly. Ti and Zr were deeply attacked. Cast iron and U underwent complete dissolution.

Eldred (*46*) studied corrosive effects of Pb on Cu, Fe, Ni, C, and steels up to 550°C. for 300 hrs. Very little corrosion was observed for Fe, C, and steels while Ni and Cu were severely attacked.

Research by Covington *et al.* (*38*) has shown the existence of iso-thermal mass transfer of Al → Mo in liquid Pb at 500°C.

In the findings of Imai *et al.* (*65*), it was shown by adding PbO in Pb at 800°C. that the oxygen content in liquid Pb accelerates the corrosion rate of pure iron, carbon steels, and 13 Cr steel. Adding Al and Mg fix oxygen as their oxides and reduce the corrosiveness of Pb; however, excessive amounts of Al diffuse into steel and form intermetallics.

An examination of the resistance of 40 refractory materials by Gangler (*54*) has been published. He rotated the samples in liquid Pb-Bi eutectic at 816°C. and 1100°C. With the exception of ZrC, all the ceramics and cermets resisted attack by the liquid metal at 1100°C. Of the 13 refractory metals listed, only arc-cast Mo showed resistance at 1100°C.

Surveying the literature, Manzone and Briggs (*79*) and Nair and Briggs (*82*) compiled corrosion data on Mo and Mo-base alloys by liquid Pb.

A review on corrosion by Pb on Ta and Nb has been presented by Miller (*81*).

Dynamic Corrosion by Lead

Cathcart and Manly (*27, 28, 29, 30*) have studied dynamic corrosion by Pb of various metals and alloy coupons inserted in a small quartz thermal convection loop. The hot- and cold-leg temperatures were 800°C. and 500°C., respectively. The loop plugged after 86 hrs. of operation. The mass-transferred material had collected in the bend at the bottom of the cold leg. Of the metals tested, only Nb and Mo exhibited a high resistance to mass transfer. Ni and Ni-base alloys were susceptible to mass transfer.

In connection with the Aircraft Nuclear Propulsion Project, a series of investigations has been conducted at Oak Ridge National Laboratory (*61, 85*). Using small quartz thermal convection loops, Ni-Cr-Fe alloy, Nb, Mo, 304-, 347-, 446-stainless steels, and Armco Iron were tested. The hot leg temperature was 800°C. and cold leg temperature was 500°C. Results indicate that alloys with a high Ni content, for example, Ni-Cr-Fe alloy and 347-stainless steel, show little resistance to mass transfer or corrosion. Stainless steels containing no Ni suffer relatively little mass transfer as compared with the Ni-rich alloys. Nb and Mo show no mass transfer.

Zr and Ti as inhibitors of the corrosion and mass transfer of steels by Pb are discussed by Kammerer *et al.* (*71*). In studying various Cr-Ni

176 REGENERATIVE EMF CELLS

alloy steels, James and Trotman (69) measured weight losses of steel pins after immersion in the hot side of a thermal convection loop. The hot leg temperature was kept at 800°C. with a temperature differential of 100°C. For serving as a deoxidant, 2000 p.p.m. of Mg was added to the Pb. The corrosion of the steels in uninhibited Pb was about $\frac{1}{40}$th as much as in uninhibited Bi under similar conditions. Addition of 500 p.p.m. of Ti to the Pb reduced the corrosion substantially.

Romano *et al.* (91) summarized the work on container materials for Bi and Pb alloys at Brookhaven National Laboratory. A $2\frac{1}{4}$Cr–1Mo steel loop containing Pb with 225 p.p.m. Mg in solution was operated at an average temperature differential of 105°C. (550° ∼ 445°C.) for 27,765 hrs. with no corrosion detected and only a slight deposition in the cold leg. Adding Zr into this loop failed due to the low solubility of Zr in Pb. Liquid Pb, Pb-Mg, and Pb-Bi eutectics were found less corrosive than Bi and U-Bi.

Day and Brasunas (42) reported the testing and examination of thermal convection loops operated with Pb.

Two sets of thermal convection loops were compared by Cygan (39, 40). One was made of a low-carbon steel and one of 400-series stainless steel. They contained Pb-Bi eutectic with a hot leg temperature of 450°C. and a temperature differential of 270°C. The low-carbon steel loop operated for 220 hrs., but the stainless steel loop ran for 950 hrs. before stoppage due to plug formations. Chemical analysis of the plugs suggested they were Bi_2O_3, Pb_3O_4, and Fe_3O_4. When a small pocket containing a permanent magnet was attached to the cold leg exit, the low-carbon steel loop was able to operate for over 11,000 hrs. without stopping. A forced circulation loop with a centrifugal pump was also operated. A sizable quantity of oxide dross collected in the pump sump after 500 hrs. of operation.

Clifford (31, 32) built three thermal convection loops, two from 347- and one from 430-stainless steel to circulate a Pb-Bi mixture. They were run with maximum hot leg temperature of 700°C. and maximum temperature gradients of 400°C. All three, with operating durations ranging from 250 hrs. to 4300 hrs., failed because plugs were formed by mass transfer products. A forced circulation loop was also tested, using an experimental diaphragm pump to circulate liquid Pb.

Akutagawa and Ogawa (2) studied 304-, and 316-stainless steel, mild steel, 5Al–Fe, 5Cr–$\frac{1}{2}$Mo–$1\frac{1}{2}$Si steel, Monel, and Ni in Pb-Bi eutectic, using a quartz thermal convection loop. The specimens were kept in the hot leg section of the loop at 800°C. The 304, 316, 5Cr–$\frac{1}{2}$Mo–$1\frac{1}{2}$Si steel and 5Al–Fe alloy showed little corrosion, while other metals were severely attacked.

A dynamic corrosion test method using a rocking apparatus has been proposed (11).

Static Corrosion by Tin

Applying tin as a heat transfer medium has been prohibitive because of its severe corrosiveness. No materials have been found to be resistant in liquid Sn above 300°C. (77, 73) or inert (95). Despite the severe corrosiveness, Sn is an attractive cathode metal in the regenerative emf cell application because the attainable emf is relatively high. Also, its vapor pressure is the lowest of the three heavy metals discussed in this survey and this indicates that, aside from corrosive problems, efficient regeneration of an anode metal from Sn should be achievable. The literature data to date are very limited. Available data are briefly presented below.

The corrosive effects of Sn on Cr and ferrous and nonferrous alloys up to 550°C. for 300 hrs. were examined by Eldred (46) and Woolf (38). Covington has demonstrated the existence of isothermal mass transfer in the systems: Al $\rightarrow$ Mo in liquid Sn at 500°C.

Imai *et al.* (65) studied mild steel, pure iron, and 13 Cr stainless steel at 400°C. While a considerable amount of $FeSn_2$ formation was found with pure iron and mild steel, only a minute amount was found with Cr stainless steel.

The resistance of Mo, W, Nb, Ta, Ti, and some Ni-Mo-Cr alloys were tested by Thwaites (98) in Sn at 300 to 350°C. for 30 hrs. Refractory metals, except Mo and Nb which contained Co binders, showed complete resistance. Other materials showed limited resistance.

Lance and Kemeny (75) tested Mo, Nb, Ta, and W in static Sn at temperatures ranging from 630 to 830°C. for approximately 100 hrs. Ta showed the best resistance (0.00001 mils of corrosion/hr. at 790°C.) followed by W and Mo. Nb showed the highest corrosion rate of 0.000421 mils/hr. at 800°C.

Cash *et al.* (26) tested Nb, Ta, Y, and Inconel at temperatures up to 1100°C. Sn did not wet Ta at 700°C. At temperatures above 900°C., very slight attack and up to 0.001 in. inward diffusion of Sn atoms into Ta were observed. Nb was attacked slightly, but Y and Inconel were attacked severely at 700°C.

Blumenthal *et al.* (9) reported compatibility of 304-stainless steel in Bi-Sn eutectic in connection with their study on the top seal of EBR II. A rotating disk was used. After 70 days' operation at approximately 200°C., a large amount of dross was found over the surface of the eutectic. The analytical data indicated that Sn was preferentially oxidized. In conjunction with the same project, the dissolution kinetics of 304-stainless steel in Bi-Sn eutectic have been under investigation at Argonne National Laboratory (4).

In connection with the regenerative, bimetallic emf cell program, a series of static corrosion tests has been conducted on steel, refractory metals, and alumina in Sn at Argonne National Laboratory (3, 95). The results are presented in Table II.

Coultas (37) tested several refractory materials at 980°C. Listed in decreasing order of resistance to attack, they are graphite, Al_2O_3, Vycor, W, $MoSi_2$, TaC, Kennametal K-138A ($WTiC_2$), Haynes Metamic LT-1 (Cr bonded Al_2O_3), Ta, and Mo. Mo showed pronounced dissolution in Sn. W recrystallized and was attacked slightly. Ta showed a suggestion of solution attack.

MacIntosh (78) presented a literature survey, up to the year 1960, on Sn and its alloys' properties.

Nair and Briggs (82) and Manzone and Briggs (79) have compiled data on the resistance of Mo and its alloys to liquid Sn.

Dynamic Corrosion by Tin

Keen and Cygan (72) circulated liquid Sn in an all-graphite loop for 60 hrs. at temperatures ranging between 850°C. and 1000°C. The graphite was found to be completely intact with no evidence of erosion or corrosion.

No data on dynamic corrosion of metallic material by Sn are available.

Literature Cited: Section I.

(1) Adamson, G. M., Manly, W. D., Crouse, R. S., "Corrosion by Molten Fluorides," ANP Materials Meeting, November 16-18, 1954, ORNL-2685, 127, Oak Ridge National Laboratory (March 26, 1959).
(2) Argonne National Laboratory, Chemical Engineering Division Summary Report July, August, September, 1959, ANL-6068, 107 (1959).
(3) Battelle Memorial Institute, Progress Relating to Civilian Applications During May, 1963, BMI-1632 (May 1963).
(4) Bettes, E. S., Nucl. Sci. Eng. 2, 804 (1957).
(5) Brasunas, A. deS., Metal Progr. 62, (6), 88 (1952).
(6) Copson, H. R., J. Electrochem. Soc. 100, 257 (1953).
(7) Craighead, C. M., Smith, L. A., Jaffee, R. I., "Screening Tests on Metals and Alloys in Contact with Sodium Hydroxide at 1000 and 1500°F." BMI-706, Battelle Memorial Institute (November 6, 1951).
(8) Craighead, C. M., Smith, L. A., Phillips, E. C., Jaffee, R. I., "Continued Studies of Corrosion by Fused Caustic," AECD-3704, Battelle Memorial Institute (December 18, 1952).
(9) DeVan, J. H., "Examinations of Pump Impellers from Sodium and Fused Salt Pump Endurance Tests," ORNL CF-61-4-77, Oak Ridge National Laboratory (April 10, 1961).
(10) DeVan, J. H., Evans, R. B. III., "Corrosion Behavior of Reactor Materials in Fluoride Salt Mixtures," in "Corrosion of Reactor Materials II," Proceedings of the Conference on Corrosion of Reactor Materials held by the International Atomic Energy Agency at Europahaus, Salzburg, Austria, 4-8 June, 1962, 557-580, International Atomic Energy Agency, Vienna (1962).
(11) Edeleanu, C., Littlewood, R., Electrochem. Acta 3, 195 (1960).
(12) Forestieri, A. F., "Effects of Additives on Corrosion and Mass Transfer in Sodium Hydroxide-Nickel Systems Under Free-Convection Conditions," NACA-RM-E54E19, Lewis Flight Propulsion Laboratory (August 2, 1954).

(13) Gill, C. B., Straumanis, M. E., Schlechten, W. B., *J. Electrochem. Soc.* **102,** 42 (1955).

(14) Ginell, W. S., "Molten Phosphate Reactor Fuel, I," NAA-SR-5925, North American Aviation, Inc. (September 30, 1961).

(15) Grantham, L. F., Hiller, M. A., Young, T. L., Ginell, W. S., "Molten Phosphate Reactor Fuel, III., Mass Spectrometric Identification of Gaseous Corrosion Products of Metals in Molten Sodium Polyphosphate," NAA-SR-5927, North American Aviation, Inc. (June 15, 1961).

(16) Grantham, L. F., Young, T. L., Hiller, M. A., Ginell, W. S., "Molten Phosphate Reactor Fuel, IV, In Situ Corrosion Studies of Metals in Molten Sodium Polyphosphate," NAA-SR-5928, North American Aviation, Inc. (August 15, 1961).

(17) Gregory, J. N., Hodge, N., Iredale, J. V. G., "The Corrosion and Erosion of Nickel by Molten Caustic Soda and Sodium Uranate Suspensions Under Dynamic Conditions," British Report AERE-C/M-273 (March 1956).

(18) Gregory, J. N., Hodge, N., Iredale, J. V. G., "The Static Corrosion of Nickel and Other Materials in Molten Caustic Soda," British Report AERE-C/M-272 (1956).

(19) Grimes, W. R., Blankenship, F. F., Keilholtz, G. W., Poppendiek, H. F., Robinson, M. T., "Chemical Aspects of Molten Fluoride Reactors," *Proceedings of the Second United Nations International Conference on Peaceful Uses of Atomic Energy, Geneva, 1958, 28,* 99-111, United Nations, New York, 1958.

(20) Gurowich, E. I., *Zh. Prikl. Khim.* **32,** 817 (1959).

(21) Hiller, M. A., Young, T. L., Grantham, L. F., Ginell, W. S., "Molten Phosphate Reactor Fuel, II, Corrosion of Metals in Molten Sodium Polyphosphate," NAA-SR-5926, North American Aviation, Inc. (August 15, 1961).

(22) Hoffman, E. E., Patriarca, P., Leitten, C. F., Jr., Slaughter, G. M., "An Evaluation of the Corrosion and Oxydation Resistance of High Temperature Brazing Alloys. Period Covered: July 1954-September 1955," ORNL-1934, Oak Ridge National Laboratory (November 7, 1956).

(23) Jackson, J. H., LaChance, M. H., *Trans. Am. Soc. Metals* **46,** 157 (1954).

(24) Jansen, D. H., "Dynamic Corrosion Screening Tests on Inconel and Nickel in NaCl-MgCl₂-UCl₃ Bath," ORNL CF-57-6-72, Oak Ridge National Laboratory (June 19, 1957).

(25) Kochergin, V. P., Bogatereva, N. E., *Nauchn. Dokl. Vysshei Shkoly, Khim. i Khim. Tekhnol.* **1959,** 206.

(26) Kochergin, V. P., Druzhinina, E. P., Men'shenina, G. V., Asanova, E. P., *Zh. Prikl, Khim.* **33,** 1580 (1960).

(27) Kochergin, V. P., Kabirov, A. V., Skornyakova, O. N., *J. Appl. Chem. USSR* **27,** 883 (1954) (English translation).

(28) Kochergin, V. P., Khaibullina, L. G., Potapova, O. G., *Zh. Neorgan. Khim.* **1,** 2617 (1956).

(29) Kochergin, V. P., Potapova, O. G., *Izv. Vysshikh Uchebn. Zavedenii Khim. i Khim. Teknol.* **2,** 406 (1959).

(30) Kochergin, V. P., Stolyarova, G. I., *J. Appl. Chem., USSR* **29,** 789 (1956) (English translation).

(31) Kristal, M. M., *Tr. Vses. Nauchn.-Issled. i. Konstrukt. Inst. Khim. Mashinostr.* **27,** 102 (1959).

(32) Lad, R. A., Simon, S. L., *Corrosion* **10,** 435 (1954).

(33) Litman, A. P., "Corrosion of Volatility Pilot Plant Mark I INOR-8 Hydrofluorinator and Mark III L Nickel Fluorinator After Fourteen Dissolution Runs," ORNL-3253, Oak Ridge National Laboratory (February 26, 1962).

(34) Litman, A. P., Goldman, A. E., "Corrosion Associated with Fluoridation in the Oak Ridge National Laboratory Fluoride Volatility Process," ORNL-2832, Oak Ridge National Laboratory (June 19, 1961).

(35) Littlewood, R., *Electrochim. Acta.* **3,** 270 (1961).

(36) Littlewood, R., Argent, E. J., *Electrochim. Acta.* **4,** 114 (1961).

(37) Littlewood, R., Argent, E. J., *Electrochim. Acta.* **4,** 155 (1961).

(38) McDonald, M. B., Crowley, J. L., Clark, D. L., *Trans. Am. Nucl. Soc.* **2, No. 1,** 174 (June 1959).
(39) Manly, W. D., "Operation of a Ni-NaOH Thermal Convection Loop," ORNL CF-51-11-186, Oak Ridge National Laboratory (November 29, 1951).
(40) Manly, W. D., Adamson, G. M., Jr., Coobs, J. H., DeVan, J. H., Douglas, D. A., Hoffman, E. E., Patriarca, P., "Aircraft Reactor Experiment-Metallurgical Aspects," ORNL-2349, Oak Ridge National Laboratory (January 9, 1958).
(41) Manly, W. D., Coobs, J. H., DeVan, J. H., Douglas, D. A., Inouye, H., Patriarca, P., Roche, T. K., Scott, J. L., "Metallurgical Problems in Molten Fluoride Systems," *Proceedings of the Second United Nations International Conference on Peaceful Uses of Atomic Energy, Geneva, 1958,* **7,** 223, United Nations, New York, 1958.
(42) Meyer, R. A., Bokros, J. C., "Graphite-Metal and Graphite-Molten-Salt Systems," in "Nuclear Graphite" edited by Nightingale, R. E., Academic Press, New York, 1962.
(43) Miller, N. E., Simons, E. M., "Sodium Hydroxide Pump Loops," in *Chem. Eng. Progr. Symp. Ser. No. 19* **52,** 113, American Inst. of Chemical Engineers, 1956.
(44) Miller, R. R., The Thermal Properties of Sodium Hydroxide and Lithium Metal: Fourth Progress Report (For) November 1, 1952 to January 31, 1953, NRL-Memo-130; Progress Report No. 4, Naval Research Laboratory.
(45) Mosher, D. R., Lad, R. A., "Kinetic Study of Mass Transfer by Sodium Hydroxide in Nickel under Free-Convection Conditions," NACA-RM-E53K24, Lewis Flight Propulsion Laboratory (March 10, 1954).
(46) Nelson, P. A., Kyle, M. L., Bennett, G. A., Burris, L. Jr., *Electrochem. Technol.* **3,** 263 (1965).
(47) Oak Ridge National Laboratory, Aircraft Nuclear Propulsion Project Quarterly Progress Report for Period Ending March 31, 1957, ORNL-2274 (July 11, 1957).
(48) Oak Ridge National Laboratory, ANP Materials Meeting, November 16-18, 1954, ORNL-2685 (March 26, 1959).
(49) Oak Ridge National Laboratory, Metallurgy Division Annual Progress Report for Period Ending May 31, 1961, ORNL-3160 (August 17, 1961).
(50) Oak Ridge National Laboratory, Molten-Salt Reactor Program Semiannual Progress Report for Period Ending July 31, 1964, ORNL-3708 (November 1964).
(51) Oak Ridge National Laboratory, Proceedings of the First Information Meeting on Hydroxide and Metal Interaction, ORNLCF-51-11-204 (August 31, 1953).
(52) Raseman, C. J., Susskind, H., Farber, G., McNulty, W. E., Salzano, F. J., "Engineering Experience at Brookhaven National Laboratory in Handling Fused Chloride Salts," BNL-627 (June 1960).
(53) Schlechten, A. W., Straumanis, M. E., Gill, C. B., *J. Electrochem. Soc.* **102,** 81 (1955).
(54) Simmons, E. M., Miller, N. E., Stang, J. H., Weaver, C. V., "Corrosion and Component Studies on Systems Containing Fused NaOH," BMI-1118, Battelle Memorial Institute (July 30, 1956).
(55) Smirnov, M. V., Volodin, V. P., Ozeryanaya, I. N., *Dokl. Akad. Nauk SSSR* **155,** 418 (March 11, 1964).
(56) Smith, G. P., "Corrosion of Materials in Fused Hydroxides," *Am. Inst. Mining Met. Engrs., Inst. Metals Div., Spec. Rept., Ser. No. 2,* **1956,** 71.
(57) Smith, G. P., "Corrosion of Materials in Fused Hydroxides," ORNL-2048, Oak Ridge National Laboratory (March 27, 1956).
(58) Smith, G. P., DeVan, J. H., Grindell, A. G., *J. Basic. Eng.* **85,** 329 (September 1963).
(59) Smith, G. P., Hoffman, E. E, "Corrosion Products Formed in the Reaction Between Fused Sodium Hydroxide and Iron-Rich Alloys of Iron, Chromium, and Nickel," ORNL-2156, Oak Ridge National Laboratory (May 1957).
(60) Smith, G. P., Hoffman, E. E., *Corrosion* **13,** 627t (October 1957).

(61) Smith, G. P., Hoffman, E. E., Steidlitz, M. E., *Corrosion* **13**, 561t (September 1957).
(62) Smith, G. P., Steidlitz, M. E., Hoffman, E. E., *Corrosion* **14**, 47t (1958).
(63) Smith, G. P., Steidlitz, M. E., Hoffman, E. E., "Experimental Procedures Used for the Measurement of Corrosion and Metal Transport in Fused Sodium Hydroxide," ORNL-2125, Oak Ridge National Laboratory (October 11, 1956).
(64) Smothers, W. J., Progress Report for the Period January 1, 1953 through March 31, 1953, AECU-2872, Univ. of Ark. (April 20, 1953).
(65) Susskind, H., Hill, F. B., Green, L., Kalish, S., Kukacka, L., McNulty, W. E., Wirsing, E., Jr., *Chem. Eng. Progr.* **56**, 57 (March 1960).
(66) Susskind, H., Hill, F. B., Green, L., Kalish, S., Kukacka, L. E., McNulty, W. E., Wirsing, E , Jr , "Corrosion Studies for a Fused Salt-Liquid Metal Extraction Process for the Liquid Metal Fuel Reactor," BNL-585, Brookhaven National Laboratory (June 30, 1960).
(67) Taboada, A., Cook, W. H., Patriarca, P., *Trans. Am. Nucl. Soc.* **7**, 438 (November 1964).
(68) Vreeland, D. C., Hoffman, E. E., Manly, W. D., *Nucleonics 11* **No. 11**, 36 (1953).
(69) Weinberg, A. M., *Nucl. Sci. Eng.* **2**, 797 (1957).
(70) Williams, D. D., Ewing, C. T., Thermal and Related Physical Properties of Molten Materials: Progress Report (For) Period February 1, 1953 to May 1, 1953, NRL-Memo-170, Progress Report 5, Naval Research Laboratory (June 1, (1953).

Literature Cited: Section II.

(1) Agrawal, B. C., *Trans. Indian Inst. Metals* **16**, 184 (September 1963).
(2) Akutagawa, T., Ogawa, K., *J. Japan Inst. Metals* **24**, 256 (1960).
(3) Argonne National Laboratory, "Chemical Engineering Division Research High-Lights," May 1964-April 1965 ANL-7020 **1965**, 216.
(4) Argonne National Laboratory, Reactor Development Program Progress Report, ANL-6923, 56 (July 1964).
(5) Atherton, J. E., Jr., Gurinsky, D. H. (to U. S. Atomic Energy Commission) "Inhibition of Corrosion," U. S. Patent **2,840,467** (June 24, 1958).
(6) Atherton, J. E. Jr., Gurinsky, D. H., Kammerer, O. F., Klamut, C., Silberberg, M., Turovlin, B., Weeks, J., "Studies in the Uranium-Bismuth Fuel System," in *Nuclear Engineering, Part II, Chem. Eng. Progr. Symp. Ser. No. 12* **50**, 23 (1956).
(7) Atherton, J. E., Jr., Kammerer, O. F., Klamut, C. J., Sodofsky, J., "Static Corrosion Behavior of Materials in Bi and U-Bi Solution at 550°C.," BNL-395, Brookhaven National Laboratory (August 1954).
(8) Babcock and Wilcox Co., Liquid Metal Fuel Reactor Experiment Quarterly Technical Report (For) July-September 1958, BAW-1125.
(9) Blumenthal, B., Kelman, L. R., Rhude, H. V., "Some Metallurgical Considerations in the Design and Operation of the Top Seal of EBR-II," ANL-6837, Argonne National Laboratory (April 1964).
(10) Brasunas, A. deS., Interim Report on Static Liquid Metal Corrosion, ORNL-1647, Oak Ridge National Laboratory (1954).
(11) Brasunas, A. deS., "A Simplified Apparatus for Making Thermal Gradient Dynamic Corrosion Tests: Seesaw Tests," ORNL-CF-52-3-123, Oak Ridge National Laboratory (1954).
(12) Brookhaven National Laboratory Progress Report Nuclear Engineering Department November 15, 1955-February 15, 1956, BNL-418.
(13) Brookhaven National Laboratory Progress Report Nuclear Engineering Department February 15-December 31, 1956, BNL-434.
(14) Brookhaven National Laboratory Progress Report Nuclear Engineering Department January 3-April 30, 1957, BNL-472.

(15) Brookhaven National Laboratory Progress Report Nuclear Engineering Department May 1-September 30, 1957, BNL-477.
(16) Brookhaven National Laboratory Progress Report Nuclear Engineering Department October 1-December 31, 1957, BNL-491.
(17) Brookhaven National Laboratory Progress Report Nuclear Engineering Department January 1-March 31, 1958, BNL-506.
(18) Brookhaven National Laboratory, Progress Report Nuclear Engineering Department April 1-June 30, 1958, BNL-516.
(19) Brookhaven National Laboratory, Progress Report Nuclear Engineering Department July 1-September 30, 1958, BNL-536.
(20) Brookhaven National Laboratory, Progress Report Nuclear Engineering Department October 1-December 31, 1958, BNL-554.
(21) Brookhaven National Laboratory, Progress Report Nuclear Engineering Department May 1-August 31, 1959, BNL-583.
(22) Brookhaven National Laboratory, Progress Report Nuclear Engineering Department September 1-December 31, 1959, BNL-595.
(23) Brookhaven National Laboratory, Progress Report Nuclear Engineering Department May 1-August 31, 1960, BNL-646.
(24) Brookhaven National Laboratory, Progress Report Nuclear Engineering Department September 1-December 31, 1960, BNL-659.
(25) Buttinelli, D., Gregorio, G. de, Signorelli, G , *Ric. Sci.* (2) **1**, 127 (1961).
(26) Cash, R. J., Fisher, R. M., Core, M. R., "Compatibility Studies of Several Molten Uranium and Thorium Alloys in Niobium, Tantalum, and Yttrium," IS-888, Ames Laboratory (February 1964).
(27) Cathcart, J. V., Manly, W. D., "Corrosion and Mass Transfer in Liquid Lead," ORNL-2685, Oak Ridge National Laboratory (August 19, 1954).
(28) Cathcart, J. V., Manly, W. D., *Corrosion* **12**, 87t (February 1956).
(29) Cathcart, J. V., Manly, W. D., "A Technique for Corrosion Testing in Liquid Lead," ORNL-1737, Oak Ridge National Laboratory (August 19, 1954).
(30) Cathcart, J. V., Manly, W. D., *Corrosion* **10**, 432 (December 1954).
(31) Clifford, J. C., "A Loop for Circulating Liquid Lead-Bismuth Mixtures: Corrosion and Equipment Studies," M.S. Thesis, Iowa State University of Science and Technology, 1958.
(32) Clifford, J. C., "A Loop for Circulating Liquid Lead-Bismuth Mixtures: Corrosion Studies and Operation," Ph.D. Thesis, Iowa State University of Science and Technology, 1960.
(33) Collins, J. F., "Summary Report on the Solubility of Metals and Alloys in Pure Bismuth Eutectic at Temperature up to 2200°F.," NEPA-1800, NEPA Division, Fairchild Engine and Airplane Corporation (April 12, 1951).
(34) Collins, J. F., Stephan, H. R., "The Solubility of Metals and Alloy in Lead-Bismuth Eutectic at Temperatures up to 2200°F.," NEPA-1803, NEPA Division, Fairchild Engine and Airplane Corporation (April 12, 1951).
(35) Cook, W. H., "Corrosion Resistance of Various Ceramics and Cermets to Liquid Metals," ORNL-2391, Oak Ridge National Laboratory (June 15, 1960).
(36) Cordovi, M. A., "Static Corrosion Behavior of Construction Materials in an Environment of Liquid Bismuth Base Metals at 500°C.," BNL-179, Brookhaven National Laboratory (1952).
(37) Coultas, T. A., "Corrosion of Refractories by Tin and Bismuth," NASA-SR-192, North American Aviation, Inc. (September 15, 1952).
(38) Covington, A. K., Woolf, A. A., *J. Nucl. Energy, Pt. B: Reactor Technology* **I**, 35 (1959).
(39) Cygan, R., "Circulation of Pb-Bi Eutectic at Intermediate Temperatures," NAA-SR-253, North American Aviation, Inc. (October 1, 1953).
(40) Cygan, R., "Lead-Bismuth Eutectic Thermal Convection Loop," NAA-SR-1060, North American Aviation, Inc. (October 15, 1954).
(41) Dawe, D. W., Parry, G. W., Wilson, G. W., *J. Brit. Nuclear Energy Conf.* **5**, 24 (January 1960).

(42) Day, R. B., Brasunas, A. deS., "Testing and Examination of Thermal Convection Loops Operated with Lithium and Lead," ORNL Y-F31-4, Oak Ridge National Laboratory (August 20, 1951).

(43) Deville, R. E., Foley, W. R., "Liquid Metal Fuel Reactor Experiment: Liquid Bismuth Dynamic Corrosion Tests," BAW-1253, Babcock and Wilcox Company (June 1960).

(44) Eatherly, W. P., Janes, M., Mansfield, R. L., Bourdeau, R. A., Meyer, R. A., "Physical Properties of Graphite Materials for Special Nuclear Applications," *Proceedings of the Second United Nations International Conference on the Peaceful Uses of Atomic Energy, Geneva, 1958* **7,** 389, United Nations, New York, 1958.

(45) Egan, C. J., "Dynamic Corrosion and Mass Transfer of Chrome Steel by Bismuth," AECD-3733, California Research Corporation (December 14, 1951).

(46) Eldred, V. W., "Interactions Between Solid and Liquid Metals and Alloys," British Report AERE-X/R 1806 (1955).

(47) Elgert, O. J., Egan, C. J., "Dynamic Corrosion of Steel by Liquid Bismuth," CRD-T1-74, California Research and Development Company (August 29, 1952).

(48) Elgert, O. J., Egan, C. J., "Dynamic Corrosion of Steel by Liquid Bismuth," MTA-12, California Research and Development Company (January 6, 1953).

(49) Elliott, R. P., "Constitution of Binary Alloys, First Supplement," McGraw-Hill, Inc., New York (1965).

(50) Finniston, H. M., "Some Studies of Corrosion in Liquid Metal," *Australian Atomic Energy Symposium* **1958,** 189.

(51) Fisher, R. W., Fullhart, C. B., "Feasibility Studies on Molten Metal Reactor Components," *Proceedings of the Second United Nations International Conference on the Peaceful Uses of Atomic Energy, Geneva, 1958* **7,** 216, United Nations, New York, 1958.

(52) Forgeng, W. D., Jr., "Corrosion of Copper by Liquid Lead in An Isothermal Loop," Ph.D. Thesis, Purdue University, 1962.

(53) Frost B. R. T., Addison, C. C., Chitty, A., Geach, G. A., Gross, P., James, J. A., Metcalfe, G. J., Raine, T., Sloman, H. A., "Liquid Metal Fuel Technology," *Proceedings of the Second United Nations International Conference on the Peaceful Uses of Atomic Energy, Geneva, 1958* **7,** 139, United Nations, New York, 1958.

(54) Gangler, J. J., *J. Am. Ceram. Soc.* **37,** 312 (July 1954).

(55) Grassi, R. C., Bainbridge, D. W., Harman, J. W., "Final Report on Metallurgical Investigation of Materials Subjected to Liquid Lead-Bismuth Alloy Environment," AECU-2201, University of California (July 31, 1952).

(56) Gurinsky, D. H., Atherton, J. E., Kammerer, O. F., Klamut, C., Silberberg, M., Turovlin, B., Weeks, J., *Nucleonics 12* **No. 7,** 40 (1954).

(57) Gurinsky, D. H., Kaplan, I., Miles, F. T., Williams C., Winsche, W. E., "Preliminary Study of a U-Bi Liquid Fuel Power Reactor LFR-2," BNL-111, Brookhaven National Laboratory (June 5, 1951).

(58) Hallett, W. J., Coultas, T. A., "Dynamic Corrosion of Graphite by Liquid Bismuth," NAA-SR-188, North American Aviation, Inc. (September 22, 1952).

(59) Hamilton, D. C., Lynch, F. E., Palmer, L. D., "The Nature of the Flow of Ordinary Fluids in a Thermal Convection Harp," ORNL-1624, Oak Ridge National Laboratory (March 16, 1954).

(60) Hansen, M., Anderko, K., "Constitution of Binary Alloys," 2nd ed., McGraw-Hill, Inc., New York, 1958.

(61) Hoffman, E. E., Manly, W. D., "Comparison of Sodium, Lithium, and Lead as Heat-Transfer Media from a Corrosion Standpoint," in "Problems in Nuclear Engineering," **1,** 128, Pergamon Press, New York, 1957.

(62) Horsely, G. W., *J. Nucl. Energy, Part B: Reactor Technology* **1,** 84 (1959).

(63) Horsely, G. W., Maskrey, J. T., *J. Iron Steel Inst. (London), 189* **Part 2,** (June 1958).

(64) Horsely, G W., Maskrey, J. T., *J. Inst. Metals* **86,** 401 (1957/58).

(65) Imai, Y., Ishizaki, T., *Nippon Genshiryoku Gakkaishi* **2,** 96 (1960).

(66) Imai, Y., Ishizaki, T., Nishino, K., Matumoto, T., "Corrosion and Erosion of Ferritic Steels by Liquid Bismuth," in *Corrosion of Reactor Materials* **2**, International Atomic Energy Agency, Vienna, 1962.

(67) Imai, Y., Nishino, K., *Sci. Rept. Res. Inst., Tohoku Univ., Ser. A* **15** (4), 186 (1963).

(68) Imai, Y., Nishino, K., *Sci. Rept. Res. Inst., Tohoku Univ., Ser. A* **15** (4), 197 (1963).

(69) James, J. A., Trotman, J., *J. Iron Steel Inst.* (*London*) **194**, 319 (1960).

(70) Kamemoto, Y., Takahashi, Y., Yamaguchi, S., *Nippon Genshiryoku Gakkaishi* **6**, 71 (February 1964).

(71) Kammerer, O. F., Weeks, J. R., Sadofsky, J., Miller, W. E., Gurinsky, D. H., *Trans. Met. Soc. AIME* **212**, 20 (1958).

(72) Keen, R., Cygan, R., High Temperature Materials Studies Semi-Annual Progress Report, July-December, 1952, NAA-SR-231, North American Aviation, Inc. (May 1953).

(73) Kelman, L. R., Wilkinson, W. D., Yaggee, F. R., "Resistance of Materials to Attack by Liquid Metals," ANL-4417, Argonne National Laboratory (1950).

(74) Klamut, C. J., Schweitzer, D. G., Chow, J. G. Y., Meyer, R. A., Kammerer, O. F., Weeks, J. R., Gurinsky, D. H., "Material and Fuel Technology for a LMFR," *Proceedings of the Second United Nations International Conference on the Peaceful Uses of Atomic Energy, Geneva, 1958* **7**, 173, United Nations, New York, 1958.

(75) Lance, J. R., Kemeny, G. A., *Am. Soc. Metals, Trans. Quart.* **56**, 204 (March 1963).

(76) Lloyd, E. D., *Plansee Proc. 3rd Seminar, Reutte/Tyrol, 1958*, **1959**, 249.

(77) Lyon, R. N., "Liquid-Metals Handbook," NAVEXOS P-733 (Rev), Office of Naval Research, Washington, D. C., 1954.

(78) MacIntosh, R. M., *Ind. Eng. Chem.* **52**, 947 (1960).

(79) Manzone, M. G., Briggs, J. Z., "Less-Common Alloys of Molybdenum," Climax Molybdenum Company, New York, 1962.

(80) Meyer, R. A., Bokros, J. C., "Graphite-Metal and Graphite-Molten Salt Systems," in "Nuclear Graphite" edited by Nightingale, R. E., Academic Press, New York, 1962.

(81) Miller, G. L., "Tantalum and Niobium," Academic Press, New York, 1959.

(82) Nair, F. B., Briggs, J. Z., "Corrosion Resistance of Molybdenum and Molybdenum-base Alloys," Technical Notes, Climax Molybdenum Company, January, 1964.

(83) Nikitin, V. I., *Teploenergetika* **2**, 90 (1962).

(84) Nuclear Metals, Inc., Technical Progress Report for the Period of April-September, 1955, NMI-1139 (February 8, 1956).

(85) Oak Ridge National Laboratory, Aircraft Nuclear Propulsion Project, Quarterly Progress Report for Period Ending June 10, 1953, ORNL-1556 (July 24, 1953).

(86) Parkman, R., Shepard, O. C., "Investigation of Materials for Use in Heat Transfer System Containing Liquid Lead Alloys, Report No. XII, Final Report," ORO-45, Stanford University (June 11, 1951).

(87) Parry, G. W., Graham, L. W., *J. Inst. Metals* **87**, 125 (December 1958).

(88) Potter, R., Wingard, R., Boggild, R., "Preliminary Handling Tests of Liquid Bismuth," NEPA-1482, NEPA Division, Fairchild Engine and Airplane Corporation (June 2, 1950).

(89) Pray, H. A., Peoples, R. S., Boyd, W. K., "Corrosion by Molten Bismuth," BMI-773, Battelle Memorial Institute (October 15, 1952).

(90) Reed, E. L., *J. Amer. Ceramic Soc.* **37**, 146 (1954).

(91) Romano, A. J., Klamut, C. J., Gurinsky, D. H., "The Investigation of Container Materials for Bi and Pb Alloys. Part I. Thermal Convection Loops," BNL-811, Brookhaven National Laboratory (July 1963).

(92) Schweitzer, D. G., Weeks, J. R., *Am. Soc. Metals, Trans. Quart.* **54**, 185 (1961).

(93) Seifert, J. W., Lowe, A. L., Jr., *Corrosion* **17**, 475t (October 1961).

(94) Shepard, O. C., Morgan, J. R., Parkman, R., Keating, K. L., Seibel, R. D., "Investigation of Materials for Use in a Heat Transfer System Containing Liquid Lead or Bismuth, Report 14," AECU-2549, Stanford University (April 1, 1953).

(95) Shimotake, H., Hesson, J. C., *Trans. Am. Nucl. Soc.* **8**, 413 (1965).

(96) Stephan, H. R., Koshuba, W. J., "Circulation of Bismuth at Elevated Temperatures, Progress Report on Project 2-01," NEPA-1675, NEPA Division, Fairchild Engine and Airplane Corporation (December 1950).

(97) Thamer, B. J., *Atomic Energy Review, 1* **No. 2**, 3 (1963).

(98) Thwaites, C. J., *Tin and Its Uses* **No. 59**, 7 (1963).

(99) Waide, C. H., Kukacka, L. E., Meyer, R. A.. Milau, J., Klein, J. H., Chow, J. G. Y., Klamut, C. J., Gurinsky, D. H., "Uranium-Bismuth In-Pile Corrosion Test Loop, Radiation Loop No. 1," BNL-736 (T-265), Brookhaven National Laboratory (May 1961).

(100) Ward, A. G., Taylor, J. W., *J. Inst. Metals* **86**, 36 (1957/58).

(101) Ward, A. G., Taylor, J. W., *J. Inst. Metals* **85**, 145 (1956/57).

(102) Weeks, J. R., *Am. Soc. Metals, Trans. Quart.* **58**, 302 (1965).

(103) Weeks, J. R., "Liquid Metal Corrosion Mechanisms," BNL-7553, Brookhaven National Laboratory (October 2, 1963).

(104) Weeks, J. R., "Metallurgical Studies on Liquid Bismuth and Bismuth Alloys for Reactor Fuels or Coolants," in "Progress in Nuclear Energy" Series IV, 378-408, McGraw-Hill, Inc., 1956.

(105) Weeks, J. R., "Possible Correlation Between Thermoelectric Potentials and Liquid Metal Corrosion," BNL-5574, Brookhaven National Laboratory, 1960.

(106) Weeks, J. R., Gurinsky, D. H., "Solid Metal-Liquid Reactions in Bismuth and Sodium," in "Liquid Metals and Solidification," 106-163, American Society for Metals, Cleveland, 1958.

(107) Weeks, J. R., Klamut, C. J., "Liquid Metal Corrosion Mechanisms," in *Corrosion of Reactor Materials* **1**, 105, International Atomic Energy Agency, Vienna, 1962.

(108) Weeks, J. R., Klamut, C. J., *Nucl. Sci. Eng.* **8**, 133 (August 1960).

(109) Weeks, J. R., Klamut, C. J., Silberberg, M., Miller, W. E., Gurinsky, D. H., "Corrosion Problems with Bismuth Uranium Fuels," *Proceedings of the First United Nations International Conference on the Peaceful Uses of Atomic Energy, Geneva, 1955* **9**, 341, United Nations, New York, 1956.

(110) Weeks, J. R., Odle, R. L., "Electrolysis of Fe-Bi and Cr-Bi Melts," *Proceedings of the 9th Annual AEC Corrosion Symposium, May 10-12, 1960.* NMI-1220.

(111) Wilkinson, W. D., "Attack on Metals by Bismuth-Lead-Tin Alloy at Elevated Temperatures," ANL-5262, Argonne National Laboratory (January 15, 1954).

(112) Wilkinson, W. D., Hoyt, E. W., Rhude, H. V., "Attack on Materials by Pb at 1000°C.," ANL-5449, Argonne National Laboratory (October, 1955).

(113) Yajima, S., Kamemoto, Y., Takahashi, *Nippon Genshiryoku Gakkaishi* **5**, 672, (1963).

RECEIVED November 10, 1965.

13

Design Features and Performance of a Lithium-Chlorine Cell

ROBERT ELIASON, JERRY ADAMS, and JOHN KENNEDY

General Motors Corp., Santa Barbara, Calif.

A fuel cell—i.e., fuel storage external to the power module based on the reactions:

Anode: $Li \rightarrow Li^+ + e^-$
Cathode: $\frac{1}{2}Cl_2 + e^- \rightarrow Cl^-$
Total: $Li(l) + \frac{1}{2}Cl_2(g) \rightarrow LiCl$ (LiCl *electrolyte*, 625°C.)

was constructed and delivered 650 watts (370 amp. at 1.75 volts). Power density was 8000 watts/sq. ft. at maximum power. The cell was self-sustaining under load and, in fact, required cooling when operated at maximum power. Principles of secondary operation of lithium-chlorine batteries have been developed, and laboratory investigation is in progress. The design features necessary to build a cell which does not fail in the presence of these energetic and highly corrosive reactants are given.

In the quest for high energy batteries and fuel cells, it is apparent from any list of oxidation potentials that an alkali metal-halogen couple would be an attractive prospect. Of the many combinations which exist, Li-F, Li-Cl, and Na-F have the highest specific energy (watt-hr./lb.).

Theoretical specific energies for a number of alkali metal-halogen couples are given in Table I.

High-power density (watt/sq. ft.) is another factor necessary for lightweight fuel cells and can only be achieved with low resistance electrolytes. Pure alkali metals cannot be used in the presence of water and, of the many nonaqueous solvents, fused salts offer the lowest resistivities. Resistivities of various electrolytes are given in Table II. In addition to low resistivity, using the corresponding alkali halide as electrolyte has the advantage of invariance—i.e., no change in electrolyte composition during discharge. Thus, a more stable cell voltage would be observed with varying load compared with a similar system using a different electrolyte.

Table I. Theoretical Specific Energy

		Open-Circuit Voltage		
Anode	Cathode	1[a]	2[b]	Watt-Hr./Lb.
Li	F_2	(2.55)	4.85	2263
Li	Cl_2	3.53		1008
Li	Br_2	3.22		449
Li	I_2	2.87		259
Na	F_2	(2.78)	4.53	1834
Na	Cl_2	3.25		673
K	F_2	(2.84)	4.31	900
K	Cl_2	3.40		552

[a] Decomposition potential of the pure halide at the melting point (1).
[b] Calculated from free energy of formation: Li-F, K-F at 1227°C., Na-F extrapolated to melting point (992°C.) (5).

Table II. Electrolyte Resistance

Solvent	Electrolyte	Resistivity (Ohm-Cm.)	
H_2O	35% H_2SO_4	1.4	(4)
NH_3	38% KSCN	2.5	(4)
Nitromethane	$2M$ (LiCl-AlCl_3)	12	(4)
Acetonitrile	$2M$ NaClO_4	16	(4)
Propylene carbonate	$1.2M$ AlCl_3	67	(4)
LiCl	LiCl	0.17	(5)

Finally, the gaseous reactant must be considered in terms of handling, polarization, and diffusion rates. The first consideration, handling, eliminates fluorine from the list of halogens with present technology. Alkali fluorides melt around 1000°C., and at these temperatures fluorine is highly corrosive to all materials. In addition, it is especially corrosive to electronic conductors which could serve as electrode materials. Thus, theoretical voltage would not be obtained. Comparing free energy data shown in Table I (5) with experimental decomposition potentials (1), one can see that fluorine-handling problems have prevented observation of potentials predicted by thermodynamics. The next choice, then, is a lithium-chlorine electrode system having a theoretical, open-circuit voltage of 3.53 volts and a specific energy of 1008 watt-hr./lb. Chlorine electrodes in fused salts have been used as reference electrodes and, on graphite, give reversible potentials (3).

The last limiting factor, diffusion rate, cannot be eliminated, but the solubility of chlorine in molten lithium chloride offers a mechanism by which high current densities may be attained (6). Chlorine travels through pores in the graphite cathode, dissolves in the electrolyte, and picks up electrons at the graphite surface. In this way, the delicate three-phase boundary equilibrium required for hydrogen and oxygen electrodes is not necessary, and a large area is available for the charge-transfer process. Because the solubility increases with pressure, maximum current density will increase with increasing pressure, and future work will be directed toward realizing this performance. Small, experimental cells were constructed to study chlorine electrode polarization and attainable current densities at atmospheric pressure. The results of these experiments were reported previously (8). With proper graphite porosity, chlorine showed little activation polarization, and current densities as high as 8 amp./sq. cm. were observed. The maximum current density calculated for the Li-Cl system with 0.5 cm. electrode spacing is 20 amp./sq. cm., but this value has not been achieved because of electrode and contact resistances and polarization effects. These polarization effects include decreased chlorine activity because of accumulation of impurities (e.g., nitrogen, carbon dioxide) at the cathode surface.

The next step was to design and test a cell capable of producing large amounts of power because performance data with electrodes of 1 sq. cm. can rarely be extrapolated to 1 sq. ft.

Cell Design

Power density is usually limited by gas electrode performance, and for this reason the cell was designed around a given cathode area. In order to study currents in the 200 amp. range, the cathode was assigned a 4-in. diameter (81 sq. cm.). It is reasonable to conclude that performance characteristics with this cell could be achieved with smaller cells and possibly up to 400-500 amp. The cell components for Model A are shown in Figure 1. From left to right are cathode chamber, cathode, electrical insulator, anode-retaining ring, anode, and anode chamber. In the background is an assembled three-cell battery showing how the individual cells can be stacked in series without electrical leads between the cells. Figure 2 is a cut-away drawing illustrating the various components in an assembled, single cell.

The cathode material was 0.25 in.-thick, porous graphite. Various porosities have been tested in the range 1–12 μ pore size, and all function effectively as chlorine electrodes. The cathode was sealed in the cathode chamber with National Carbon C-9 cement. This decreased the active area a small amount around the circumference, and all performance figures are based on 80 sq. cm. The cemented cathode was then cured as prescribed by the manufacturer. An additional treatment with H_2 followed by Cl_2 at 800°C. removed any material which would be liberated during operation.

The cathode chamber consisted of high-density graphite having a low resistivity (0.00027 ohm-in.). The chlorine inlet was machined to fit

Figure 1. Lithium-chlorine power cell, Model A

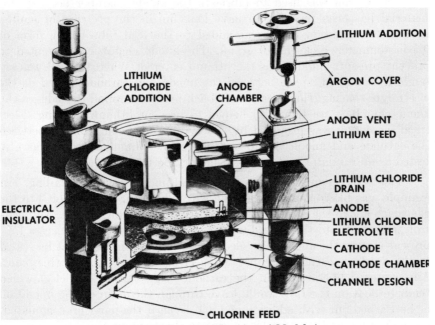

Figure 2. Cut-away drawing of Model A

graphite feed tubes, and the channel design allowed chlorine to reach all portions of the cathode surface. Flow rates in excess of 8 liters/min. at

625°C. (equivalent to 350 amp. at 100% efficiency) were achieved. At these flow rates, it was found necessary to pre-heat the chlorine to avoid thermal shock to the cathode. Pre-heating was accomplished by packing the chlorine feed tube with aluminum oxide chips over the length in the furnace compartment.

Electrical contact with the bottom of the cathode chamber was made with a solder pool (60-40 Pb-Sn) on a steel plate. This method gave cathode resistance as low as 2.5×10^{-4} ohms. The cathode chamber also served as a container for the electrolyte. An inlet for addition of molten LiCl for start-up and an outlet for drainage of molten LiCl as it formed during operation were also provided.

The anode consisted of 0.063 in.-thick metal disks (3.5 in. diameter) of varying densities. A high density sheet (50–60%) was exposed to the electrolyte but was backed by low density material (5–20%) which aided the distribution of molten lithium across the surface of the electrode. Three different materials were found to function well as anodes: nickel, Armco iron, and stainless steel. Performance figures given in this paper were obtained using stainless steel. The anode was secured to the anode chamber with a retaining ring and machine screws.

Armco iron was used to fabricate the anode chamber because this material has been reported to have long life in the presence of molten lithium (2). Lithium metal was added to the feed tube in the form of 0.5 in.-diameter sticks (5–10 gram). The anode chamber was vented to prevent pressure build-up as the lithium entered. When the cell was assembled, a 0.25-in. space between the anode and cathode served as the electrolyte spacing. However, a LiCl back-pressure around the sides of the anode chamber (see Figure 2) helped to prevent lithium shorting. Electrical insulation was provided by a beryllium oxide ring placed between the cathode and anode chambers (Figure 2). Aluminum oxide was also tested as an insulator and gave satisfactory performance.

This cell design allows for certain malfunctions without failing. For example, gas blowout at the cathode will bubble through the LiCl to the gas space above the electrolyte and finally out the LiCl drain. Any electrolyte carried into the drain by gas bubbles was replaced by excess LiCl present around the anode. The electrical insulator ring need not be sealed to the anode or cathode because the electrolyte level is below this point. Any material liberated from the cathode (e.g., carbon particles) which tends to float on the LiCl would leave through the drain during operation or be washed out with addition of LiCl. Even if the particles coagulated, a significant quantity must be present to short-circuit the cell because of the large space between anode and cathode at the electrolyte surface. Lithium shorting (caused by adding too large a quantity at one time) could be handled by reaction with a fast flow of chlorine gas.

Open-circuit voltage offered a means of noting these malfunctions. Partial shorting by carbonaceous materials in the electrolyte caused low voltages. Fluctuating voltages were observed when chlorine bubbled out of the cathode surface. Zero voltage was observed with lithium shorting.

The assembled cell was held together with a set of steel clamps which were electrically insulated from the cell with aluminum oxide. The cell was then mounted in a furnace compartment heated with two, 1-kw. Chromalox ring-heaters (above and below the cell) and packed with Fiberfrax insulation.

A modified design, Model B (Figure 3), has been studied which is 2.5 in. high while still retaining the 4-in., active cathode area. This cell is more compact and incorporates a number of improved features. Ceramic feed tubes bonded to the graphite chamber are used in place of graphite tubes. The ceramic tubes allow parallel chlorine feed without shorting and are considerably smaller and lighter in weight. A second chlorine line has been incorporated to provide an exit for the chlorine. This system is much less sensitive to changes in flow and pressure than "dead-ended" cells and allows impurities to be purged from the cathode chamber without bubbling out into the electrolyte. The purity of chlorine is extremely important and, in addition to the "flow-through" system, the purity of the chlorine supply itself was improved by using Teflon lines and purging large tanks for long periods of time to decrease the amount of air present.

Figure 3. Lithium-chlorine power cell, Model B

The purity of lithium was also improved by purchasing oil-free lithium and casting sticks in a vacuum dry-box which would fit the lithium feed tube. The anode housing was also modified by using 347 stainless steel in place of Armco iron, incorporating the LiCl inlet in the anode instead of the cathode chamber and soldering the top contact to the anode housing similar to the cathode contact. The furnace compartment was sealed to prevent attack of the graphite by traces of air and redesigned to keep the LiCl exit tube sufficiently hot at all times to prevent freezing of salt in the line.

Recent studies have shown that $\frac{1}{8}$ in.-graphite frits give better results than $\frac{1}{4}$ in. (for most grades), and Model B was fabricated to utilize the thinner cathode frits.

Cell Performance

The cell assembly took approximately 1 hr. to reach the operating temperature of 625°C. (1.5–2.0 kwh.). The lowest operating temperature is set by the 613°C. melting point of LiCl. Molten LiCl was added after heating the cell in the dry state. This was followed by replacing argon in the cathode with chlorine. Finally, lithium was added to the anode chamber. Within minutes the voltage rose. Theoretical open-circuit is 3.5 volts (thermodynamic values range between 3.47 and 3.53), and values between 3.45 and 3.50 were observed with Model B. On the other hand, voltages as low as 3.2 volts were observed with Model A, the "dead-ended" chlorine electrode design. This effect may have resulted from low chlorine activities because of inability to flush the pores without blowing out the electrolyte.

Carbon pile resistors or a bank of 400 low voltage light bulbs (1.25 volts or 2.5 volts) served as a load for the cell output. Figure 4 shows voltage-current performance for two of these cells. An apparent cell resistance of 0.0034 ohm was calculated from the initial slope for curve A (Figure 4). The electrolyte contributed 0.0016 ohm while the remaining 0.0018 ohm resulted from electrode resistance, contact resistance, and small polarization effects. This cell remained in operation for 2 hrs. before shutting down. During this time it idled between open circuit and 130 watts and delivered a maximum power of 456 watts for 3 min. A power level of 130 watts was maintained for 1 hr.

Performance for design B is also shown in Figure 4. In this experiment, a maximum power of 650 watts was observed during the 2-hr. run. The straight line discharge curve observed at high current densities reflects the small polarization of the chlorine electrode. The initial slopes for the two runs were nearly identical, which is understandable because the electrolyte, electrolyte spacing and electrode materials were the same for the two experiments. All external heating was turned off during opera-

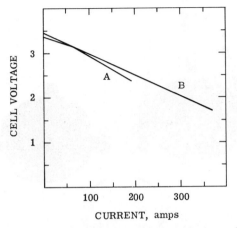

Figure 4. Performance of lithium-chlorine cells

tion. Cell temperature was maintained at the 130-watt level, and insulation was sufficient to allow short periods of time at open circuit. At maximum power, the cell temperature increased as much as 100°C. in 5 min. The cell continued to operate even at 720°C., but no attempt was made to study operation at higher temperatures with Model A. A thermocouple was inserted in the graphite frit in one Model B cell in order to study the temperature rise during operation. The frit temperature was within 10°C. of the graphite chamber wall temperature until powers in excess of 200 watts were drawn. Under these conditions, the frit temperature increased to 850°C. within 10 min. During the same period, the temperature in the wall adjacent to the frit rose to 800°C., while the temperature at the top of the cell rose to 750°C. The performance did not degrade under these conditions, which indicates the wide temperature latitude the cells possess. The heat balance problems will be amplified in the operation of batteries, and for that reason cooling will be provided. For the small, one-cell units, heat balance can be maintained at normal load with proper insulation, and operation at maximum power with resulting temperature increases can be sustained for short periods of time.

Problems associated with liquid lithium control made it necessary to design a modified cell, Model C, which is 2.87-in. high. Photographs of Model C, Figures 5 and 6, were taken after 221 hrs. of operation. A summary of the performance is presented in Table III, and the discharge curve is shown in Figure 7. These data presented are typical of the 40–50 cells that have been operated. Except for the 650 watts, studies are normally conducted at lower power densities, 300 to 500 watts per cell. Also, the normal length of time of cell operation is usually 6 hrs., but in four experiments the cells were operated for more than 50 hrs.

Figure 5. Lithium-chlorine power cell, Model C, after 221 hours operation

Figure 6. Cathode assembly, Model C, after 221 hours operation

Lithium-Chlorine System as a Secondary Battery

Because the lithium-chlorine cell can deliver theoretical open-circuit potential and does not show large polarization effects on discharge, it is a logical, next step to make a secondary battery with this system. In practice, though, the charging cycle is much more difficult to achieve.

There are two general approaches: (1) using the same electrodes for charge and discharge, and (2) using a separate electrode system for charging. The first approach has the advantage in weight and size but creates problems at the chlorine electrode because the gas will normally be generated at the surface. There are two general approaches which can be used

Table III. Summary of Performance, Model C

(Run 1/10/66; Cell 17-6B)

Run Time (Hrs.)	Time-Under Load (Hrs.ᵃ)	Open-Circuit Voltage	Load Voltage	Current (Amps.)	Power (Watts)	Lithium Efficiency		
						Coulombic	Voltage	Overall
0-102	102	3.47	3.45	13.5	47	93.5	99.4	92.9
102-103	1	3.47	3.39	27.2	92	Not meas.	97.7	——
103-168	0	Banked idle						
168-175	7	3.47	3.40	27.5	93	97.0	97.9	95.0
175-192	0	Banked idle						
192-199	7	3.47	3.32	39.8	132	97.4	95.7	93.2
199-216	0	Banked idle						
216-220	4	3.47	2.99	68.0	203	98.9	86.2	85.2
220-221	1	3.44	2.97	67.8	201	Not meas.	85.5	——
221	122							

ᵃ Including periodic open-circuit checks.

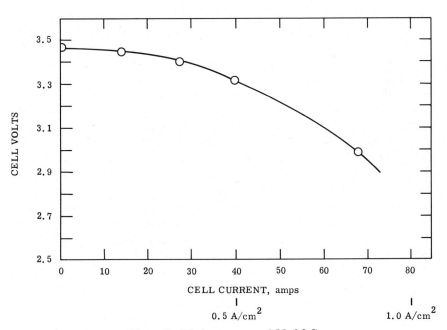

Figure 7. Discharge curve of Model C

to collect the chlorine: (1) allow the gas to remain in the electrolyte and collect at the surface, and (2) force the chlorine back into the feed system used for discharge. The first approach is used by lithium producers where electrode separation is greater than the $\frac{1}{4}$ in. used in the power cells described here. With a small electrode separation, it becomes difficult to prevent low current efficiencies because of direct recombination between chlorine gas and lithium metal. The second approach requires a pressure differential such that chlorine will flow through the porous cathode structure instead of through the electrolyte. In addition, this pressure differential cannot be so high that the cathode is flooded with electrolyte. Theoretically, wetting properties can be used to establish the pressure differential (7), but the choice of materials is severely limited by the environment of chlorine gas and molten lithium chloride containing dissolved lithium at 650°C. Fortunately, lithium chloride does not wet graphite, and fairly large pressures (0.1–0.6 atm. typical) are required to flood the porous graphite cathode. The same problems exist at the lithium electrode, and again a pressure differential must be established to force the liquid metal into the anode chamber. Gravity can be used in some cell designs because lithium floats on molten lithium chloride. Actually, the ideal cell would operate under pressure, and in this case the establishment of pressure differentials would be incidental to high-pressure operation.

It is also known by lithium producers that lithium chloride is not a good medium for electrolysis. Lithium has a definite solubility (0.5–1 mole %) in its own salts, and because the chlorine is in close proximity the resulting current efficiency is poor. The use of a LiCl-KCl eutectic allows high-efficiency operation at a lower temperature (approximately 400°C.) and still produces pure lithium metal. Even with 1- to 2-in. electrode spacing, the operating cell voltage is less than 5 volts. It is reasonable to assume that by decreasing electrode spacing to 0.5 in. or less (as has been done in the discharge cycle in this study) the operating voltage can be reduced to 4.0–4.5 volts. A battery discharging at 2.8 volts and charging at 4.2 volts would have a voltage efficiency of 67%. If the current efficiency were 90%, an overall efficiency of 60% would be achieved. Experiments have shown that these efficiencies can be realized in the laboratory provided the current density during charge is kept low (less than 0.5 amp./sq. cm.). Methods to increase charge acceptance are presently under investigation. The lithium chloride product from discharge would flow into a cell containing sufficient KCl to form a low melting mixture. In the charging cycle, lithium could be deposited and pumped to the discharge cycle reservoir. Chlorine would be collected at the top of the cell and compressed in a tank for future delivery in the discharge cycle. With two sets of electrodes, optimum configurations and active areas for the two operations could be used. Also, if this part of the cycle were at a stationary depot where weight is not a significant factor, large charging electrodes could be used to decrease charge time. The charge/discharge time ratio is often an important consideration, depending on application, and this is one way to circumvent the problem.

In conclusion, technical achievement of two-electrode, lithium-chlorine, secondary battery cells is being pursued by General Motors Corp., (*6, 7*), but there are some applications for which a four-electrode system will be a more practical development.

Literature Cited

(1) Delimarskii, Iu. K., Markov, B. F., "Electrochemistry of Fused Salts," p. 145, Sigma Press, Washington, D. C., 1961.
(2) Hoffman, E. E., "Corrosion of Materials by Lithium at Elevated Temperatures," ORNL-2924, Oct. 1960.
(3) Laitinen, H. A., Liu, C. H., *J. Am. Chem. Soc.* **80**, 1015 (1958).
(4) Murphy, J. J., "New Primary Battery Systems," AIAA Meeting, Philadelphia, Sept. 1964.
(5) Smithells, C. J., "Metals Reference Book," V. II, p. 639, Butterworth, Washington, D. C., 1962.
(6) Swinkels, D. A. J., "Lithium-Chlorine Secondary Battery," Electrochemical Society Meeting, San Francisco, Calif., May 1965.
(7) Weaver, R. D., "Secondary Lithium-Chlorine Batteries," *Proc. 19th Annual Power Sources Conference*, p. 113, May 1965.
(8) Werth, J., Kennedy, J., Weaver, R. D., "Lightweight Lithium-Chlorine Battery," AIAA Meeting, Philadelphia, Pa., Sept. 1964.

RECEIVED November 23, 1965.

14

Regenerative Chloride Systems for Conversion of Heat to Electrical Energy

C. ROLAND McCULLY
Prospect Heights, Ill.

TED M. RYMARZ
IIT Research Institute, Chicago, Ill.

STANLEY B. NICHOLSON
U. S. Naval Ordnance Plant, Forest Park, Ill.

Closed cycle combinations of thermochemical and electrochemical reactions provide a potentially simple and efficient mechanism for conversion of heat to electrical energy. Several chloride systems meet the primary criteria for this cyclic process. Molten tellurium dichloride is ionic and a suitable anode material but is gaseous at the regeneration temperature complicating the separation from chlorine in this step. Antimony trichloride is less ideal as an anode but is easily separated in the regeneration step. Successful operation of the cyclic process in a single device has provided potentials from 0.3 to 0.5 volts. Projected operating efficiencies range to 28% of the accepted heat.

The theoretical principles involved in conversion of heat to electrical energy by thermally regenerative electrochemical systems are well-known and have been discussed in a number of publications (6, 9, 12, 13). In essence, such systems combine an electrochemical process which yields electrical energy with a high temperature regeneration that is a thermal reversal of the electrochemical process.

The study of chloride systems reported herein was part of a more general investigation of most classes of simple inorganic compounds for applicability in the chemical conversion of heat to electrical energy. Compounds capable of undergoing endothermic dissociation or disproportionation reactions were detected by searching the literature and by making computations with thermodynamic and thermochemical data (1, 3, 8, 11). Ultimately, the computations were made by a computer program (16) which supplied family plots of the variations of free energy of formation with temperature. It was found that many chlorides should be susceptible to useful dissociation or disproportionation reactions.

As a class the simple chlorides were interesting also because of the low melting points of many compounds and eutectic mixtures, thereby facilitating materials transport within a device. The molten state also tends to be more ionic, a property important to galvanic cell performance. A combination of these factors, the free energy of formation calculations, some preliminary experimental work, and projections of possible conversion efficiencies led to the selection of the chlorides of antimony and tellurium for the most intensive study. It is these systems that will be primarily discussed herein.

Galvanic Cell Studies

Figure 1 depicts the galvanic cell system used for preliminary studies with most of the chlorides. The system was constructed from borosilicate glass, and care was taken to maintain uniformity in the glass construction, the asbestos plugs, and the electrodes to permit quantitative comparisons between cells. The bottom plug separated the anode and cathode compartments, while the top plug equalized pressure and minimized convective mixing of vapors. These cells were filled with dry powders in a dry box and were usually sealed under vacuum. In some cases, the lower plug was saturated with a molten salt electrolyte before adding the respective anode and cathode chemicals. Potentials and currents were measured with the cells immersed in a temperature-controlled oil bath. The usual operating temperature was approximately 200°C.

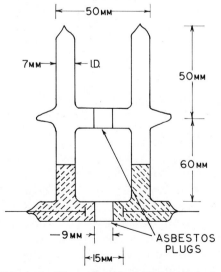

Figure 1. Glass cell with platinum electrodes used for study of molten chlorides

Voltages obtained with tellurium chloride cells are presented in Figure 2. The anodes contained mixtures of divalent and tetravalent tellurium chlorides dissolved in aluminum chloride. The cathodes contained cupric chloride dissolved in aluminum chloride. Data labeled "high Te" were obtained with cells in which the Te/Al mole ratio was greater than 1, while data labeled "low Te" were from cells in which the mole ratio was from 0.02 to 0.35. The experimental slopes of both lines are consistent with the theoretical Nernst-slopes; however, the large effect of the tellurium chloride to aluminum chloride ratio suggests that there is an appreciable interaction between the two chlorides. This is not altogether surprising, since complex chlorides of tellurium and aluminum have been reported (7).

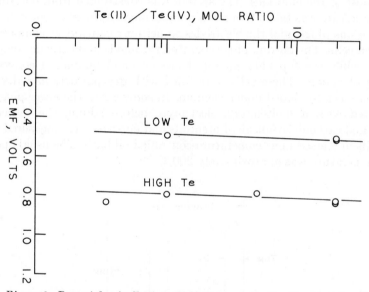

Figure 2. Potentials of tellurium dichloride-cupric chloride galvanic cells at 200°C. in molten aluminum chloride

Discharge curves for tellurium chloride cells are given in Figure 3. In these experiments, the cells were allowed to discharge continuously through either 50 ohm- or 100 ohm-load resistors. At intervals, the voltage under load was recorded, and the circuit interrupted briefly to allow measurement of the open-circuit potential. At the 50-ohm load, 88 mah. of cell current were drawn, compared with 72 mah. at the 100-ohm load. The former figure translates to a current efficiency of more than 75%.

For preliminary tests with cells of the antimony chlorides, $SbCl_5$ and $SbCl_3$, elevated temperatures and pressures were not required. Simple cells were constructed of two concentric glass tubes; the bottom of the

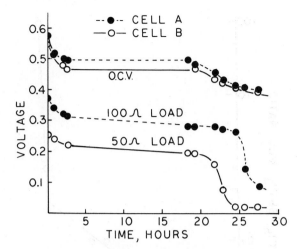

Figure 3. Discharge curves for tellurium dichloride-cupric chloride cells under 50 and 100 ohm loads

outer tube was closed and the bottom of the inner tube was packed with asbestos fibers. Electrodes rested in both the tubes, which were open at the top to a dry nitrogen atmosphere. The anode composition containing the trivalent antimony chloride, sometimes dissolved in arsenic trichloride, was in the outer tube. The cathode composition, rich in pentavalent antimony chloride, also sometimes containing arsenic trichloride, was in the inner tube. As evident from Figure 4, which presents the effects of $SbCl_5/SbCl_3$ mole ratio on the cell potential, these systems do not yield simple concentration cells. It is noteworthy that the ratio changed from 100/1 to less than 1/1 before an appreciable decrease occurred in the cell potential of 0.68 volt.

With both the antimony and tellurium systems, acceptable high-cell potentials are possible. The chief limitation on cell power per unit electrode area has been found to be the ionic conductivity of the cell electrolytes. The antimony chlorides are poor electrolytes, however, additions of arsenic trichloride and smaller amounts of aluminum trichloride made it possible to increase the specific conductivity for these systems to the order of 10^{-3} ohm^{-1}-cm.$^{-1}$ This low conductivity would, of course, require a cell design with a small interelectrode spacing in order to have substantial power to volume ratios.

Because the ionic conductivities in the tellurium chloride cells are of the order 10^{-1} ohm^{-1}-cm.$^{-1}$, high current densities are possible. The electrode reactions at both the anode and the cathode are, nevertheless, limited primarily by ion transport and activation overpotentials are relatively insignificant. For example, limiting currents greater than 1000 ma./sq. cm. are achievable with $TeCl_2$ anodes, and exchange currents of

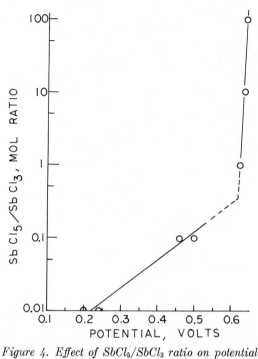

Figure 4. Effect of SbCl₅/SbCl₃ ratio on potential in AsCl₃ solvent

more than 100 ma./sq. cm. have been obtained with anodes comprising only 16 mole% of TeCl₂ in AlCl₃. Cupric chloride cathodes show poorer performance, but current densities of 35 ma./sq. cm. have been achieved at 0.1 volt polarization exclusive of the IR drop.

Regeneration Studies

The regeneration studies required different equipment for each of the chemical systems studied. Dissociation of TeCl₄ to TeCl₂ and Cl₂ was studied in both equilibrium and nonequilibrium conditions. Direct measurements on the equilibrium vapor pressures reported in the literature are concerned with molecular weight measurement (*14, 15*), with the dissociation never more than 10%. As sketched in Figure 5, an apparatus was constructed in which the sickle gage of borosilicate glass served as a null device to determine the total pressure. Samples of TeCl₄ were weighed approximately and sublimed into the gage in the presence of Cl₂. After being evacuated and sealed, the gage was immersed in a Wood's metal bath, and the total pressure was measured at several temperatures. Finally the samples were sublimed out of the gage through a frangible seal and weighed or analyzed.

Figure 6 presents the data obtained on the dissociation of TeCl₄. The data are in the form of plots of pressure on a log scale as a function of reciprocal temperature. There are two slopes, as expected, and the initial slope corresponds well with the data of Simons (*15*).

A successful experiment in separation of $TeCl_2$ and Cl_2 by quenching led to a quantitative measure of the recombination kinetics in an apparatus capable of following very rapid changes in pressure. A weighed amount of $TeCl_2$ was sealed in the thin glass bulb of this apparatus (*see* Figure 7).

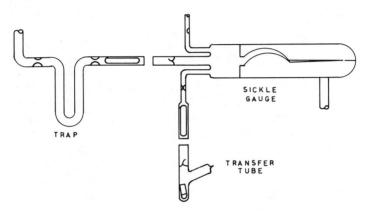

Figure 5. Sickle gage for measurement of equilibrium pressures

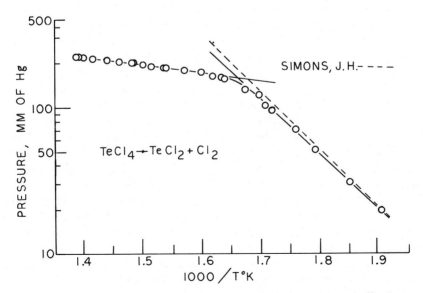

Figure 6. Equilibrium pressures for the thermal decomposition of tellurium tetrachloride

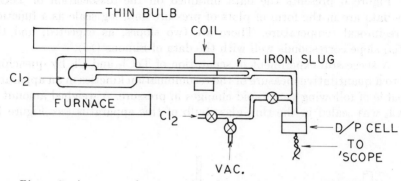

Figure 7. Apparatus for measuring the reaction rate of tellurium di-chloride with chlorine

The surrounding volume was then evacuated, and Cl_2 was admitted to achieve the desired pressure. With the system at the desired temperature, the thin bulb was broken by manipulating the glass encased iron slug with the solenoid. Reductions in pressure, indicating the extent of the recombination reaction, were followed with the pressure transducer-oscilloscope combination, which had been equipped for photographic recording.

Studies with the above apparatus found that the recombination was complete in approximately 20 msec. at a temperature of 500°C. With the $TeCl_2$ in the liquid state at 250°C., the reaction was much slower.

A system for regeneration studies with $SbCl_5$ is sketched in Figure 8. This device permitted operation over a wide range of controlled pressures by the simple means of controlling the temperature of the Cl_2 reservoir. Circulation was obtained with the heating coil, and temperatures were measured with thermocouples. The device was first flushed with Cl_2 gas, the $SbCl_5$ or an $SbCl_5$ rich mixture was then added, and the system was sealed and weighed. The extent of the dissociation was determined by the amount of liquid Cl_2 in the calibrated reservoir.

Data for the dissociation of $SbCl_5$ at various pressures are plotted in Figure 9, giving the Cl_2 recovery as a function of temperature. Total conversion to $SbCl_3$ and Cl_2 corresponds to about 0.46 gram Cl_2. Corrections have been made for the temperature of the liquid Cl_2 collected and for the temperature and pressure of Cl_2 in the gas phase. It was assumed that the Cl_2 extended only to the observed condensate ring of $SbCl_3$ which appeared in the neck of the boiler. Separation of the Cl_2 gas from the $SbCl_3$ liquid and vapor was essentially complete in all of the experiments, and no $SbCl_3$ was detected in the Cl_2 reservoir.

Figure 10 shows a larger system, made primarily of nickel, which was constructed to obtain design information. Its filling system and sight gage were of glass, and the condenser was of copper tubing. Concentric tube construction of the boiler permitted upward circulation in the annular

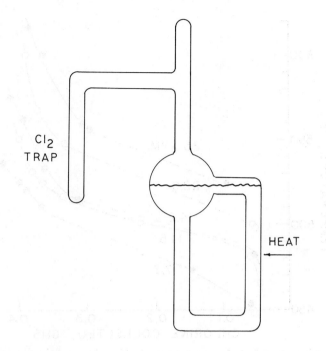

$$SbCl_5 \longrightarrow SbCl_3 + Cl_2$$

Figure 8. Small glass regenerator for decomposition of antimony pentachloride

volume and downward circulation in the center. Filling was accomplished by first evacuating the system. A Cl_2 bottle was available for pressurization. The rate of dissociation was determined by the rate of rise of Cl_2 in the gage glass when the lower valve was closed for a short period.

With this nickel regeneration system, the initial Cl_2 evolution with $SbCl_5$ and a pressure of 120 psig began at 180°C. In the case of a 1:1:1 mole composition of $SbCl_5$, $SbCl_3$, and $AsCl_3$, the temperature for initial Cl_2 evolution was 240°C. The highest rate at which Cl_2 could be generated without having liquid carried over into the outlet tube was 0.8 cc. of liquid Cl_2 per min., which is calculated to be a gas velocity of 0.4 cm./sec.

Regeneration of the antimony chloride system is thus possible with the simplest equipment and proceeds in a straightforward way. The products of the endothermic dissociation reaction are essentially Cl_2 gas and $SbCl_3$ liquid at all of the pressures tested up to 25 atm. Regeneration of the tellurium chloride system is more difficult because, at the dissociation temperature and pressure, $TeCl_2$ is mainly in the gas phase and will recombine rapidly with Cl_2 as the temperature is lowered. Attempts to separate $TeCl_2$ from Cl_2 at high temperatures have led to studies of the

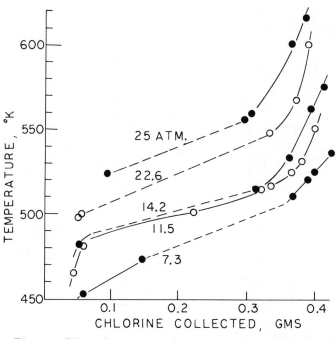

*Figure 9. Effect of pressure on the decomposition temperature of
antimony pentachloride*

solution of $TeCl_2$ in molten salts. Because this work is still in its early
stages, no conclusive results are yet available.

Integral Systems

Integrated systems combining the thermochemical and electrochemical
phases were studied with the antimony chlorides. The galvanic cell of one
such system comprised two recessed nickel flanges separated by an electrolyte membrane, thus providing the anode and cathode compartments.
The anode compartment was an integral part of the circulation path of a
regeneration system of borosilicate glass similar to that of Figure 8. A
glass loop integral with the cathode compartment connected to the Cl_2
reservoir of the regenerator and allowed the Cl_2 gas from the regeneration
process to be continuously absorbed in the cathode liquid. Anode and
cathode sides of the integral system were filled with identical compositions
rich in $SbCl_5$, and the system was then sealed under a Cl_2 pressure of 1 atm.
The system was provided with thermal insulation as required and was
carefully instrumented.

Temperature data for the system disclosed that the regenerator could
not be operated up to the desired maximum temperature without having

the cell temperature and the absorber temperature rising to undesirable levels. A potential of 0.3 volt was achieved and maintained when the initial, filling composition was $SbCl_5$ without additives. When the filling composition contained arsenic trichloride in 1:1 mole ratio to the antimony chlorides, potentials of 0.4 volt and 0.5 volt were attained. The internal resistance was high for all of the experiments, although the addition of the $AsCl_3$, along with 4% by weight of $AlCl_3$, did afford some improvement.

With the help of information and experience gained, a larger device was designed and built. This battery of cells was nominally designed for 500 watts and had 10 cells connected in series, each with electrode areas of 120 sq. in. The interelectrode spacing was 0.125 in., and the anode and cathode compartments were separated by an ionic solid electrolyte of woven glass cloth impregnated with doped lead chloride. For testing this system, filling was with an anode composition of $SbCl_3$-$AsCl_3$ in a molar ratio of 2:1 and a cathode composition of $SbCl_5$-$AsCl_3$ in a molar ratio of 1:4. Both compositions contained 4% by weight of $AlCl_3$ in order to improve further ionic conductivity.

The regenerator of this device was modeled after the smaller system of Figure 10, and a regenerative heat exchanger was placed between the regenerator and the battery of cells.

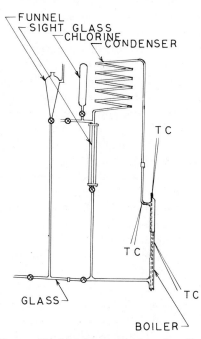

Figure 10. Metal regenerator for the thermal decomposition of antimony pentachloride

Although the regeneration system operated successfully, performance of the cell stack was below expectations. For example, the measured impedance of the stack was 5 ohms. A maximum charging current of 3.5 amp. was attained with an external source of 17 volts, and this current dropped to 2.0 amp., indicating the development of 7.3 volts. The system could be charged to an output potential of only 1.4 volts, which decreased rapidly without appreciable load. It was determined that minute fractures had developed in the ionic solid membranes and did permit mixing of the anode and cathode liquids through slight changes in pressure between the two systems. Tests have not been conducted with other membranes.

Interpretations of Data

Galvanic cell potentials obtained in this study have been higher in most cases than can be reasonably explained from reference to free energy data (1, 3, 8, 11, 16). The couple with the chlorides of tellurium and copper, for example, gives potential the opposite from what was expected. The potential of 0.9 volt for high mole fractions of tellurium chlorides and the potentials of 0.5 volt for low mole fractions indicate free energies of -37 kcal. and -23 kcal., respectively, per mole. Values given in the literature for the standard free energy are about 8 kcal. Without change in activity coefficients, a change in concentration by a factor of 10 results in a change of potential of only $0.10/z$ volt at 200°C. Further, within the respective high and low ranges of mole fraction, the observed potentials are consistent with the molar ratios of $TeCl_2$ to $TeCl_4$. Interpreting the data given in Figure 6 for the experiments on dissociation of $TeCl_4$, it can be stated that the lower portion of the slope corresponds to the vaporization of $TeCl_4$. The slope of the succeeding curve is then determined by increasing temperature and dissociation. A plot of equilibrium constants, on a log scale, vs. reciprocal temperature, $1000/T°K$., has been calculated from the data for the upper segment of the dissociation curve and appears in Figure 11. The heat of dissociation predicted from the slope of the curve is 27.2 kcal./mole. This value is still not large enough to be compatible with the free energy values for the association reaction as indicated by the galvanic cell measurements.

Circumstances similar to those for the tellurium chlorides are encountered in attempting to explain the potentials up to 0.68 volt delivered by galvanic cells embodying anodes based upon $SbCl_3$ and cathodes based upon $SbCl_5$. From Figure 4 it is apparent that an insignificant change in cell potential occurred when the ratio of $SbCl_5$ to $SbCl_3$ in the cathode system was varied from 100/1 to 1/1 with the anode remaining unchanged. The 0.68 volt, furthermore, points to a free energy of reaction of -31 kcal. This cannot be reconciled to the literature of -6 kcal., which corresponds to an anode, half-cell reaction as follows:

$$SbCl_3 + 2Cl^- \rightleftarrows SbCl_5 + 2e$$

It appears that mixtures of antimony and arsenic chlorides can be oxidized by free chlorine to form complex chlorides containing pentavalent arsenic (*10*). The total cell reaction thus may be:

$$SbAsCl_{10} + SbCl_3 \rightarrow 2SbCl_5 + AsCl_3$$

Postulating this sort of reaction would be consistent with the results presented in Figure 4 because it involves different reactions at the anode and cathode, leading to a definite chemical change rather than to changes in concentration.

The data of Figure 9 concerning the dissociation of $SbCl_5$ into Cl_2 and $SbCl_3$ require little interpretation in the intended application. It has been of interest, however, to calculate equilibrium constants from the data. The variability of these values at a fixed temperature and the lack of adherence to a fixed slope in plots of the equilibrium constant as a function of reciprocal temperature indicate that these systems are far from ideal. Values for the heats of dissociation cluster around 20 kcal./mole and 30 kcal./mole; however, the lack of observations in the mid-range of the dissociations and the general precision of the experiments possibly do not justify the calculation of these values.

Discussions of combinations between $TeCl_4$ and $AlCl_3$ appear in the literature (*2, 7*), as do discussions of compounds of the type $AsSbCl_{10}$ (*5,*

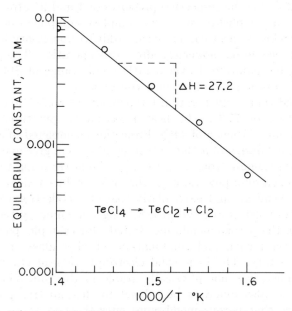

Figure 11. Equilibrium content for thermal decomposition of tellurium tetrachloride

10). There are also numerous suggestions for the existence of such species as $TeCl_3^+$, $AlCl_4^-$, $SbCl_6^-$, and $AsCl_4^-$. At present, insufficient data are available for determining the extent of the influence of such species upon cell potentials, or upon heats of reaction. Such information is of interest for the design of integral systems combining both the thermochemical and electrochemical phases.

Conclusions

This study has explored a number of simple chlorides for applicability in electrochemical systems for converting heat to electrical energy. Several of the chlorides have been found to combine the properties which are necessary to the application; however, only the chlorides of antimony and tellurium were investigated in sufficient detail for inclusion in these discussions.

In the case of the chlorides of antimony, $SbCl_3$ and $SbCl_5$, it has been found possible to convert heat energy to chemical energy in a straightforward fashion by the reaction

$$SbCl_{5(l)} \xrightarrow{\text{Heat}} SbCl_{3(l)} + Cl_{2(g)},$$

where the subscripts l and g refer respectively to liquid and gas, with the dissociations approaching 100% for temperatures that range from about 252°C. to 352°C. for the respective pressures of 1 and 25 atm. Separation of the Cl_2 is accomplished with the simplest equipment and without apparent prejudice to heat conservation. Additives necessary for adequate ionic conductance do not adversely affect this operation. The potential of 0.68 volt can be maintained over a rather wide range of $SbCl_3$ to $SbCl_5$ ratios. Again, this is favorable to heat conservation.

It is noted that a regeneration temperature of 352°C. and a galvanic cell temperature of 77°C., the heat rejection temperature, indicate a Carnot maximum efficiency of 44%. Projections completed in conjunction with the detailed design of a 500 watt integral system give overall conversion efficiencies ranging from 28% to 16%, the latter being the value for operation at maximum power. So far the ionic conductivities of the anode and cathode chemicals and particularly that of the electrolyte membrane are the factors most restrictive in achieving maximum system performance. None of the porous membranes tested—for example, porous Teflon, fiber glass filter media, and combinations of fiber glass and Teflon, is deemed satisfactory. The ionic solid electrolyte of lead chloride cast on woven fiber glass was not physically stable in the thin membranes required and was also found to be subject to thermal transport. Present indications are that porous membranes offer the best route toward improved galvanic cell performance.

Although the operation of integral systems was not accomplished for the tellurium chlorides, $TeCl_2$ and $TeCl_4$, the high ionic conductances observed are favorable to galvanic cell performance. Despite the fact that the tellurium anode regeneration reaction,

$$TeCl_{4(g)} \xrightarrow{\text{Heat}} TeCl_{2(g)} + Cl_{2(g)},$$

does indeed take place at temperatures higher than 577°C., the products, as indicated, are both gases at normal pressures. The products were found to recombine rapidly as the temperature was lowered; for example, the recombination was complete in 20 msec. at 500°C. in the apparatus of Figure 7. It is expected that separation of the $TeCl_2$ and Cl_2 gases can be accomplished by selective retention of the $TeCl_2$ in a melt, perhaps as a complex (2, 7). There is precedent in the literature (4) for such retention of compounds of high vapor pressure. In addition to favorable galvanic cell performance, there are other incentives for proceeding with such efforts. Carnot efficiency for operation between the limits of 597°C. and 147°C. is above 51%, and galvanic cell operation is amenable to temperatures of at least 327°C. for applications in which heat rejection must be at a high temperature.

The conclusion is that both the chlorides of antimony and the chlorides of tellurium are inherently suitable as bases for the development of integral devices for converting heat energy to electrical energy *via* thermochemical and electrochemical reactions. For the chlorides of antimony, attention must be directed toward improved galvanic cell performance. For the chlorides of tellurium, the principal interest should be in improved separation of $TeCl_2$ and Cl_2.

Acknowledgments

The studies reported herein were carried out at IIT Research Institute and received support from the Bureau of Naval Weapons, Department of the Navy, under Contract No. NOw 60-0760-C and Contract No. NOw 63-0512-C. The authors gratefully acknowledge the assistance of J. N. Keith, W. Sumida, D. E. Anthes, and R. J. Dausman who performed certain of the experiments, and of C. K. Hersh, M. J. Klein, and Milton Knight for suggestions during the course of the studies.

Literature Cited

(1) Brewer, L., Bromley, L. A., Giles, P. W., Lofgren, N. L., "The Chemistry and Metallurgy of Miscellaneous Materials," L. L. Quill, ed., McGraw-Hill Book Co., New York, N. Y., 1950.
(2) Gerding, H., Houtgraff, H., *Rec. Trav. Chim.* **73**, 759 (1954).
(3) Glassner, A., Argonne National Laboratory Report 5750, Argonne, Ill., 1959.
(4) Grothe, H., Piel, C. A., *Z. Electrochem.* **54**, 210 (1950).
(5) Gutman, V., *Monatsh.* **82**, 479 (1951).

(6) Hess, F. D., Schieler, L., AD No. 266551, Aerospace Corp.
(7) Houtgraaf, H., Rang, H. J., Vollbracht, L., *Rec. Trav. Chim.* **72,** 978 (1953).
(8) Kelly, K. K., *U. S. Bur. Mines Bull.* **477** (1948).
(9) King, J., Ludwig, F. A., Rowlette, J. J., American Rocket Society, September 27–30, 1960.
(10) Kolditz, *Z. Anorg. Allgem. Chem.* **296,** 188 (1958).
(11) Kubaschewski, O., "Metallurgical Thermochemistry," Pergamon Press, New York, 1958.
(12) Liebhafsky, H. A., *J. Electrochem. Soc.* **106,** 1068 (1959).
(13) McCully, C. R., U. N. Conference·on New Sources of Energy, Rome, Italy, August, 1961.
(14) Michaelis, A., *Ber.* **20,** 1781 (1887).
(15) Simons, J. H., *J. Am. Chem. Soc.* **52,** 3488 (1930).
(16) Snow, R. H., AD No. 265-376 L, IIT Research Institute, Chicago, Ill.

RECEIVED November 10, 1965.

Thermally and Photochemically Regenerative Electrochemical Systems

L. B. ANDERSON, S. A. GREENBERG, and G. B. ADAMS

Lockheed Palo Alto Research Laboratory, 3251 Hanover St., Palo Alto, Calif.

Expressions derived for assessing theoretical performance characteristics are applied to regenerative emf cells with molten salt electrolytes. Predicted efficiencies for systems based on metal iodides range from 15–30%, with power densities of 5–140 milliwatts/sq. cm. Rapid recombination rates severely limit systems regenerable by thermal dissociation, and regeneration by high temperature electrolysis and by thermal dissociation are thermodynamically equivalent processes. Nonisothermal processes suggest that there is little evidence for ionic entropy of transport effects in molten salt electrolytes. For a photoregenerative system, observed conversion efficiencies are below 1% and agree with predictions based on a theoretical model.

Various devices have been developed for converting heat or light into electricity; thermoelectric generators and solar cells are familiar examples. A major disadvantage of such converters is a lack of energy storage capacity. This limitation is removed by coupling the energy converter with a galvanic cell which has the required energy storage capacity. The converter-secondary battery combination remains the most reliable method for accumulating energy from heat or light for conversion to electricity on demand.

An alternate system for conversion and storage of the energy from heat or light is the regenerative electrochemical cell in which favorable energy storage characteristics are combined with thermal or photoregeneration of cell reactants to produce a closed-cycle electrochemical system. A thermally regenerative system of this type is basically an electrochemical heat engine with consequent Carnot limitation on thermal efficiency. Theoretical thermal efficiencies for such systems are often higher than thermoelectric, thermionic, and photovoltaic-secondary battery combinations. In a practical sense, however, potential gains in efficiency for regenerative electrochemical systems must be weighed against added system complexity and serious materials problems in the circulation and containment of highly corrosive substances at high temperature. Hence, it is necessary to compare realistically candidate systems based on a careful analysis of relative advantages and disadvantages of each competing system for the application involved before a proper system choice can be made. The first step in this analysis is to outline the thermodynamic and kinetic performance limits for an idealized model of the system. This analysis, when correctly made, then serves as a foundation for a realistic appraisal of a proposed system.

In the work presented here, two classes of regenerative electrochemical systems are discussed. These comprise systems regenerable by absorption of heat or by absorption of light.

Within the first class, four different types of thermally regenerative cells are analyzed. These are thermocells; galvanic cells used in thermocycles in which regeneration of cell reactants is accomplished by electrolysis at elevated temperatures; galvanic cells which are regenerated by electrolysis at reduced partial pressure of gaseous reactant; and galvanic cells regenerated by thermal dissociation.

General expressions for both theoretical and operational thermal efficiencies are derived for these four types of thermally regenerative cells; these are then applied to selected electrochemical systems. It is shown that the most important factor involved in achieving high overall efficiency is establishing the widest possible operational temperature limits over which the cycle operates. Molten salt electrolytes are selected for use in these systems because long liquid ranges can be obtained and because electrode polarization problems are minimal.

The thermocell represents one approach to a thermally regenerative electrochemical device. The thermocell is analogous to a thermoelectric device and consequently has both advantages and disadvantages when compared with thermogalvanic systems. Advantages of simplicity, reliability, and no moving parts or valves are offset by lack of energy storage capacity and low thermal efficiency owing to direct coupling of thermal and electrical paths. Galvanic systems regenerable by electrolysis have the advantage that separating regenerated materials is inherent to the electrolysis process. In thermally dissociative regenerative systems, product separation can be a major problem because of high back-reaction rates of dissociation products (a necessary consequence of the system chemical reaction kinetics). Thermal regeneration of galvanic systems by electrolysis or by thermal dissociation is a thermodynamically equivalent process. Some of the kinetic limitations on the latter process are discussed in detail.

Photoregenerative electrochemical systems appear at first sight to have advantages of inherent energy storage as well as high limiting thermodynamic efficiencies. Actually, this potentially high photochemical energy conversion efficiency is drastically reduced in practice owing to the absorbed light being degraded into heat *via* recombination mechanisms.

A photoregenerative electrochemical system is discussed in which light enters the cycle by absorption on a dye-coated electrode with concurrent photo-oxidation of one component of an organic redox couple contained in an aqueous electrolyte. Regeneration is accomplished electrically by galvanic discharge in a second cell where the photo-oxidized material is reduced and returned to the photocell. This system is discussed in terms of energy conversion efficiency and the photoelectrochemical reaction kinetics; results are interpreted through using a solid state mechanism by analogy to inorganic semiconducting systems.

Regenerative electrochemical systems of the types discussed here will require a large amount of research and development before they become practicable. The present discussion serves as a guide for meaningful analysis of new thermally or photochemically regenerative electrochemical systems and points out some of their inherent advantages and deficiencies.

Irreversible Thermodynamic Approach to a Generalized Regenerative EMF System Analysis: Application to Molten Salt Thermocells

Irrespective of the detailed mechanisms by which an energy conversion system functions, an important consideration is its overall efficiency—i.e., the work obtainable from a specified net quantity of energy transferred into the system. Energy for which there is no conjugate driving force or energy which is degraded by irreversible processes occurring in the system becomes unavailable for useful work. Through using the entropy function S, a perfectly general method becomes available for assessing the maximum fraction of the energy which is usable. This assessment can be made readily through using methods of irreversible thermodynamics.

For an analysis of the efficiency of a cycle which absorbs energy as heat and produces electrical work, it suffices to know the pertinent coefficients of electromotive force of all electroactive elements within the system and the extent of the dissipative processes—i.e., it is not necessary to know the actual cell voltages themselves. For example, the net emf for an energy conversion cycle which includes electrical regeneration steps at uniform pressure is given by the line integral over temperature of the temperature coefficients of electromotive force in the cycle. The electrically active components in an electrochemical system are the individual electrodes or half cells. In general, the temperature dependence of these half-cell emf's will change with time as thermal diffusion effects (Soret effect) act to alter local concentration ratios among the various species. When the various half-cell reactions in the system take place concurrently in a common pure fused ionic salt, however, the thermal diffusion process is inhibited by the electrical neutrality requirement. Furthermore, it appears that available evidence indicates no large effect of thermal diffusion on the electrical behavior of nonisothermal cells which employ mixed molten salt electrolytes. Developing a theory of temperature coefficients of electrode potentials in fused salt electrolytes is potentially quite useful for estimating ideal efficiencies in generalized regenerative emf cell systems because it allows one to analyze nonisothermal galvanic cell systems.

The molten salt thermocell affords a simple means for studying the temperature coefficient of electrode potential in an experimentally accessible system. In this section, the theory of irreversible thermodynamics will be applied to analyzing simple molten salt thermocells to illustrate the methods. This analysis will clarify the concepts needed for generalized application to regenerative galvanic cell systems—i.e., for systems based on galvanic cells with molten salt electrolytes in the presence of temperature gradients. In the subsequent sections which treat regenerative galvanic systems, however, the methods of irreversible thermodynamics will be replaced by the more familiar thermodynamic methods because normally galvanic cells are experimentally investigated under isothermal conditions.

The theory of irreversible thermodynamics is a phenomenological theory of near-equilibrium systems—i.e., the theory is best suited to systems in which forward and reverse reaction rates are large compared with the drift rate of the perturbed system as it approaches equilibrium. This is the usual situation in electrochemistry when exchange current densities at electrodes are large—which is true in molten salts. The theory assumes that the system can be divided into subsystems which behave as if each were in local thermodynamic equilibrium, despite the gradients which give rise to the irreversibility. Then, for each subsystem, the requisite variations in thermodynamic state variables may be evaluated in the usual way along hypothetical reversible paths. The state function most expedient for analysis of systems in temperature gradients is the entropy function, S.

A change in the entropy of a subsystem may be written as a sum of entropy transferred across the subsystem boundaries and an additional term $dS_{int.}$, the entropy created internally by irreversible processes which take place. In principle, $dS_{int.}$ is evaluated for each subsystem, and the results are summed to give the total internal entropy produced, $S_{int.}$. Miller (37) gives a concise review of these ideas. If the time rate of change of $S_{int.}$/unit volume is denoted by $\dot{S}_{int.}$, then in the irreversible thermodynamic formalism one may always write

$$\dot{S}_{int.} = \sum J_k X_k \tag{1}$$

where the J_k's are flows of matter, or heat, and the X_k's are generalized thermodynamic forces, such as electrical potential gradients or gradients of chemical potential or temperature. The only requirement on the choice of flows and their conjugate forces is that the product must always give the entropy production, $\dot{S}_{int.}$, according to Equation 1.

The theory is a linear one; the flows must be linearly related to the driving forces. For completeness, each flow is given by the linear sum of all the driving forces:

$$J_k = \sum_l L_{kl} X_l \qquad (2)$$

Each constant, L, is a rate constant for the linear response of a particular flow to a particular thermodynamic driving force in the system. If an L is zero, the flow and force related to it are mutually independent.

For purposes of analysis, one may choose a single uniform electrolyte containing two identical immersed electrodes. Such a cell may be represented as $M/MX_\nu/M$ where the liquid electrolyte comprises νX^- ions for each $M^{+\nu}$ ion of the parent metal M. The cell is at true equilibrium only when there are no flows of heat or electricity through it. For temperature and voltage imbalances the system is subject to two fluxes. Following deBethune (13) one takes the flow of current as positive when positive charge flows through the cell from left to right under the influence of a potential difference, $-dV$, supplied by an external potentiometer. The flow of entropy, J, is positive when it flows from high to low temperature (right to left by convention). Equation 1 now becomes:

$$\dot{S}_{int.} = I\left(\frac{-dV}{T}\right) + J\left(\frac{dT}{T}\right) \qquad (3)$$

where $X_I = (-dV/T)$ and $X_J = (dT/T)$.

Equation 2 is expanded as follows:

$$I = L_{II} X_I + L_{IJ} X_J \qquad (4)$$

$$J = L_{JI} X_I + L_{JJ} X_J \qquad (5)$$

The rate constant L_{II} is related to electrical conductivity, the usual proportionality constant between the driving force for current flow—i.e., voltage, and current, I. Likewise, the coefficient L_{JJ} is related to ordinary thermal conductivity. The "cross coupling" constants, L_{IJ} and L_{JI}, are rate constants for current flow produced by a temperature gradient and entropy flow arising from a voltage drop, respectively. According to Onsager's general relation (39):

$$L_{IJ} = L_{JI} \qquad (6)$$

so that there are only three independent rate constants, L, in Equations 4 and 5.

If the electrodes of the cell are maintained at different temperatures (thermocell) and a current is allowed to flow, the question of possible interaction between the current and the temperature gradient arises. This question is easily examined (15). If the parameters X_I and J in Equation 3 are eliminated by means of Equations 4 and 5, the result is:

$$\dot{S}_{int.} = \frac{I^2}{L_{II}} + \left(\frac{L_{JI} - L_{IJ}}{L_{II}}\right)(IX_J) + \left(L_{JJ} - \frac{L_{IJ}L_{JI}}{L_{II}}\right)X_J^2 \qquad (7)$$

Analysis of Equation 4 for current flow under isothermal conditions shows, by Ohm's law, that $L_{II} = T/R$. Thus, the first term in Equation 7 is the entropy production from Joule heating. Through explicit evaluation of the other constants, L, the third term in Equation 7, is found to be the entropy production due to thermal conduction. The second term is the entropy production arising from interaction of the current I with the temperature gradient term X_J. As a consequence of Equation 6, this second term is zero. Thus, for the "cross effect," $\dot{S}_{int.} = 0$, which means that all irreversibility in the system arises from the Joule heating and from the flow of heat necessary to maintain the temperature gradient. The chemical electrode heats associated with production, consumption, and transfer of current-carrying species may be treated separately as reversible quantities.

Application to Thermocells.   One of the most useful connections between half-cell entropy changes and measurable quantities is the relationship between thermoelectric power of a thermocell and its electrode reaction entropy. This relationship is easily derived (12) by eliminating the ratio of rate constants L_{II}/L_{IJ} in Equations 4 and 5. For 1 mole of charge transported through the cell, the result is:

$$\mathfrak{F}\left(\frac{d\epsilon}{dT}\right)_{I=0} = (\Delta S)_{\Delta T=0} \tag{8}$$

where ΔS is the reversible half-cell entropy change for passing one equivalent of charge through the isothermal cell and $(d\epsilon/dT)_{I=0}$ is the thermoelectric power, measured at zero current. The entropy ΔS is transported into the hot electrode region through transport of ions, molecules, and electrons, as a consequence of the half-cell reaction. This entropy is exchanged with the surroundings to keep the half-cell temperature constant.

The fraction of the current carried by each ion in the bulk electrolyte depends on its transference number τ. Thus, the thermoelectric power of the pure ionic thermocell has been found by several investigators (14, 24, 25, 36) to be, in the notation of Agar and Breck (1),

$$\mathfrak{F}\frac{d\epsilon}{dT} = -\sum \frac{S_k^* \tau_k}{Z_k} - S_e^* - \Delta S_{elec.} \tag{9}$$

where S_k^*, S_e^*, τ_k, and Z_k are ionic and electronic "entropy of transfer," transference number, and charge of the kth ion; $\Delta S_{elec.}$ is the appropriate sum of partial molal entropies for the electrode reaction, which involves only the ion to which the electrode is reversible. The terms S^* are included to allow for possible entropy flow arising from interaction of transported species with their environments. The sum of transport numbers for anions and cations is unity, so that for a pure salt, MX_ν, Equation 9 may be written as follows:

$$\mathfrak{F}\frac{d\epsilon}{dT} = \tau_{x^-}\left(\frac{S_{M^{+\nu}}^*}{\nu} + S_{x^-}^*\right) - \frac{S_{M^{+\nu}}^*}{\nu} - S_e^* - \Delta S_{elec.} \tag{10}$$

Pitzer (*41*) asserts that the quantity in parenthesis, which is just the entropy of transport of the salt itself, cannot be finite:

$$S_{M^{+\nu}}^* + \nu S_{x^-}^* = 0 \tag{11}$$

Thus, the thermoelectric power of the pure salt thermocell is independent of transport number, an important and occasionally overlooked result (*17*).

For a thermocell with salt electrolyte MX$_\nu$ and with metal electrodes, M, Equations 10 and 11 combine to give

$$\mathfrak{F}\left(\frac{d\epsilon}{dT}\right)_{\text{M elec.}} = -\frac{S_{M^{+\nu}}^*}{\nu} - S_e^*(M) + S_{M^{+\nu}} - \frac{\overline{S}_{M^{+\nu}}}{\nu} - \overline{S}_e(M) \tag{12}$$

For the corresponding thermocell with gas electrodes G:X$_2$

$$\mathfrak{F}\left(\frac{d\epsilon}{dT}\right)_{\text{G:X}_2} = S_{X^-}^* - S_e^*(G) + \overline{S}_{X^-} - \frac{1}{2}S_{X_2} - \overline{S}_e(G) \tag{13}$$

where G refers to an inert conducting electrode such as graphite. The sum of electronic entropies $S_e^* + \overline{S}_e$ is obtained from the integrated Thomson coefficient of the electronic conductor G or M (*48*). The electronic terms are negligible for most thermocell considerations.

By a straightforward analysis which includes application of Equations 10 and 11 the following general relationship may be derived.

$$\left(\frac{d\epsilon}{dT}\right)_{\text{X}_2:\text{G elec.}} - \left(\frac{d\epsilon}{dT}\right)_{\text{M elec.}} - \left(\frac{d\epsilon}{dT}\right)_{\text{G-M}} = \left(\frac{d\epsilon}{dT}\right)_{\text{galv.}} \tag{14}$$

Mazur (*36*) and Holtan (*24*) have derived similar expressions for particular types of cells, without explicit use of Equation 11. Equation 14 shows how the temperature coefficient of a galvanic cell $(d\epsilon/dT)_{\text{galv.}}$ may be attributed to various thermoelectric powers, which may themselves be expressed in terms of half-cell entropy changes. The first term on the left in Equation 14 is the thermoelectric power of a thermocell with electrodes reversible to the anion of a pure salt. The second term is the thermoelectric power for the corresponding thermocell with electrodes reversible to the cation of the same salt. The third term corresponds to the thermoelectric power for a thermocouple with legs of the parent metal of the salt cation and the inert conducting material used to form the anion-reversible gas electrode.

The entropy of a salt is just the appropriate sum of individual ion entropies, $\overline{S}$. From statistical mechanical considerations, Pitzer (*41*) arrives at a simple method for partitioning the salt entropy between the ions in simple molten salts. Pitzer points out that for a fused salt in which positive and negative ions are identical in every respect, except for the sign of the net electrical charge on each, the measured molal salt entropy may be divided equally between positive and negative ions. If the cation and anion masses differ, then there will be a mass correction effect on translational entropy for each ion. There may be further small correction terms for effects of differences in ion size, shape, charge, and polarizability which would affect the space configurational portion of the liquid phase partition function. Such effects are difficult to assess but are likely to be small in a simple ionic melt. Applying the Pitzer concept to a molten salt, MX_ν, leads to the following expressions for the individual ion entropies.

$$\overline{S}_{M^+} = \frac{1}{\nu + 1} \left(S_{MX_\nu} + \frac{3}{2} R\nu ln \frac{M_M}{M_X} \right) \tag{15}$$

$$\overline{S}_{X^-} = \frac{1}{\nu + 1} \left(S_{MX_\nu} - \frac{3R}{2} ln \frac{M_M}{M_X} \right) \tag{16}$$

In Equations 15 and 16, $\overline{S}_{M^+}$ and $\overline{S}_{X^-}$ are the partial molal entropies of the cation and anion; S_{MX_ν} is the thermodynamic molal entropy of the salt; and M_M and M_X are the gram atomic masses of M and X, respectively.

When Equations 15 and 16 are substituted in Equations 12 and 13 and the ionic entropies of transports, S^*, and electronic terms are ignored, expressions of the type shown in Table I are obtained for various thermocells.

In addition to the type of differential relations shown in Table I, one may derive integral expressions for the electromotive force $\Delta\epsilon$ given by the thermocell for a finite temperature difference ΔT between the electrodes. The integral of entropy over a range of temperature gives the free energy F:

$$\int_{T_1}^{T_2} SdT = -(F_2 - F_1) \tag{17}$$

Thermodynamic data in the literature are conveniently tabulated in terms of "free energy function," here abbreviated as Y.

$$Y = -\frac{F^0 - H_0^0}{T} \tag{18}$$

Thus, one may write

$$\int_{T_1}^{T_2} SdT = T_2 Y_2 - T_1 Y_1 \tag{19}$$

Integration of the expressions in Table I and applying Equation 19 leads to the expressions shown in Table II.

Table I. Application of Pitzer's Method for Specific Types of Molten Salt Thermocells

Cell	$\mathcal{F}\dfrac{d\epsilon}{dT}$
M/MX/M	$S_M - \dfrac{1}{2} S_{MX} - \dfrac{3}{4} R \ln \dfrac{M_M}{M_X}$
M/MX$_2$/M	$\dfrac{1}{2} S_M - \dfrac{1}{6} S_{MX_2} - \dfrac{1}{2} R \ln \dfrac{M_M}{M_X}$
X$_2$/MX/X$_2$	$\dfrac{1}{2} S_{MX} - \dfrac{1}{2} S_{X_2} - \dfrac{3}{4} R \ln \dfrac{M_M}{M_X}$
X$_2$/MX$_2$/X$_2$	$\dfrac{1}{3} S_{MX_2} - \dfrac{1}{2} S_{X_2} - \dfrac{1}{2} R \ln \dfrac{M_M}{M_X}$

Table II. Integral Relations for Specific Thermocells

Cell	$\mathfrak{F} \Delta E$
$T_1,\ M/MX/M,\ T_2$	$(T_2Y_2 - T_1Y_1)_M - \dfrac{1}{2}(T_2Y_2 - T_1Y_1)_{MX} - \dfrac{3R(T_2 - T_1)}{4}\ln\dfrac{M_M}{M_X}$
$T_1,\ M/MX_2/M,\ T_2$	$\dfrac{(T_2Y_2 - T_1Y_1)_M}{2} - \dfrac{(T_2Y_2 - T_1Y_1)_{MX_2}}{6} - \dfrac{R(T_2 - T_1)}{2}\ln\dfrac{M_M}{M_X}$
$T_1,\ X_2/MX/X_2,\ T_2$	$-\dfrac{(T_2Y_2 - T_1Y_1)_{X_2}}{2} + \dfrac{(T_2Y_2 - T_1Y_1)_{MX}}{2} - \dfrac{3R(T_2 - T_1)}{4}\ln\dfrac{M_M}{M_X}$
$T_1,\ X_2/MX_2/X_2,\ T_2$	$-\dfrac{(T_2Y_2 - T_1Y_1)_{X_2}}{2} + \dfrac{(T_2Y_2 - T_1Y_1)_{MX_2}}{3} - \dfrac{R(T_2 - T_1)}{2}\ln\dfrac{M_M}{M_X}$

Senderoff and Bretz (*45*) have verified Equations 11 and 14 experimentally for the silver-chlorine system and have calculated thermoelectric powers for the thermocells by the Pitzer method. The calculated and observed thermoelectric powers agree reasonably well in view of the theoretical uncertainties. There seems to be no adequate basis at present for attributing small disagreements between theory and experiment to "entropy of transport" effects. These govern the Soret equilibrium in cells for which concentration gradients can exist in the electrolyte. B. R. Sundheim and J. D. Kellner (*47*) have recently examined the Soret steady state in the mixed salt system $AgNO_3/NaNO_3$. In this system there seems to be no evidence for large ionic entropies of transport.

In some cases the choice of species thought to be present in an ionic salt can significantly affect the calculated thermoelectric powers. For purposes of illustration, the following two extreme mechanisms in a molten salt MX_2 may be considered:

$$2e^- + M^{++} = M \tag{A}$$

$$2e^- + MX^+ = M + X^- \tag{B}$$

If one neglects the entropy of transport and electronic terms in Equation 12, the thermoelectric powers are

$$2\mathfrak{F}\frac{d\epsilon}{dT} = S_M - \overline{S}_{M^{++}} \tag{A}$$

$$2\mathfrak{F}\frac{d\epsilon}{dT} = S_M + \overline{S}_{X^-} - S_{MX^+} \tag{B}$$

The internal entropy of a complex ion MX^+ can be estimated. In many cases the results of Calculations A and B will be quite different.

If one disregards entropy of transport and if complex species are not involved, using the Pitzer method for calculating individual ion entropies leads to an interesting result: the thermoelectric powers of thermocells with electrodes which are reversible to a particular ion should be nearly independent of the counter ions in the salt. The calculated chloride and iodide entropies in Table III illustrate this. The chloride ion entropies are all similar, so that $Cl_2:MX_\nu:Cl_2$ thermocells which utilize the chloride electrolytes shown in the table will have similar calculated thermoelectric powers. This would also be the case for the iodide salts shown. Of course the above assumptions of negligible effects from complex species or entropies of transport may not always be verified by experiment.

Energy Conversion Efficiency.   As shown by Equation 7, there is no irreversible entropy production arising from interaction of the current

Table III. Single Ion Entropies at 1000° K.

Ion	Salt	$\bar{S}_{X^-}$ (cal./mole °C.)
Cl⁻	KCl	20.7[a]
	AgCl	20.7
	CuCl	20.3
	TlCl	21.3
	FeCl₂	20.7
	MnCl₂	20.0
	ZnCl₂	20.5[b]
	PbCl₂	20.3
I⁻	LiI	24.5[b]
	NaI	24.9[b]
	KI	24.0[b]
	RbI	23.8[b]
	CsI	23.4[b]
	AgI	24.6[b]
	CdI₂	23.3[b]
	PbI₂	26.2

[a] Extrapolation of liquid data to 1000°K.
[b] Salt entropy estimates (5, 6).

with the temperature gradient. The analysis of the efficiency of a molten salt thermocell as a thermoelectric generator is straightforward if one neglects uncertainties associated with entropy of transport and unknown ionic species. One has only to compare the electrical energy produced to the sum of reversible electrode heat and irreversible conduction heat absorbed. Analyses of molten salt thermocell efficiencies are given by Wartanowicz (50) and Meissner et al. (28). The procedure can be illustrated by a specific example. To estimate the conversion efficiency for a simple AgCl thermocell with Cl_2 electrodes—e.g., the equivalent circuit shown below:

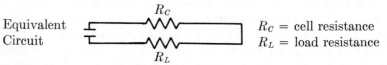

Equivalent
Circuit

R_C = cell resistance
R_L = load resistance

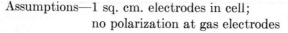

Assumptions—1 sq. cm. electrodes in cell;
                    no polarization at gas electrodes

The condition for maximum power through the load is

$$R_L = R_C$$

The Cl_2:$AgCl$:Cl_2 thermocell may be taken as an example of a system with several desirable properties. The liquid range of AgCl is long (455 to 1550°C.). The thermoelectric power $d\epsilon/dT$ is -665 $\mu v.°C.^{-1}$ for the above cell (45). If one assumes that a ΔT of 1000°C. is achievable, the open-circuit voltage will be 0.665 volts. The specific conductance of fused silver chloride is 4.44 ohm^{-1}-cm.$^{-1}$ at 600°C. (9). For numerical comparison with other systems, one may assume a spacing of 0.5 cm. between electrodes of 1 sq. cm. cross section.

$$R_C = \frac{0.5}{4.44} = 0.11 \; \Omega$$

Now the maximum load power may be calculated:

$$\text{Maximum power per sq. cm. of electrode} = \frac{\epsilon^2}{4R_C}; \; (R_L = R_C)$$

$$\text{Maximum power density} = \frac{(0.665)^2}{4(0.11)} \cong 1 \text{ watt/sq. cm.}$$

One may compare this electrical flux to the heat flux $dQ/dt = \dot{Q}$ through the cell.

$$\dot{Q} = \frac{KA}{L} \Delta T \qquad \begin{aligned} A &= 1 \text{ sq. cm.} \\ L &= 0.5 \text{ cm.} \\ \Delta T &= 1000°C. \end{aligned}$$

The thermal conductivity, K, is not known for molten AgCl but an average K for alkali metal salt melts is $K = 1.5$ Btu/hr. ft.-°F. (22), which is about 6.3×10^{-3} cal. cm.$^{-1}$ sec.$^{-1}°C.^{-1}$.

$$\dot{Q} = \frac{(6.3 \times 10^{-3})(1)(1000)}{(0.5)} = 12.6 \frac{cal.}{sec.} \text{ for 1 sq. cm. path}$$

$$\dot{Q} = (12.6)(4.2) = 53 \text{ watts}$$

The rate of absorption of the reversible electrode heat at the hot electrode is easily computed from the current and the entropy change, which amounts to about 11 cal./mole/°C. for the $Cl_2/AgCl$ half-cell at 1800°K. From the power density above, one computes a current of about 3 amp., or 3×10^{-5} equivalents of charge/sec. The reversible heat, $T\Delta S$, at 1800°K. is about 20 kcal./mole. Thus, the reversible heat flux associated with the electrode reaction is 0.6 cal./sec., or about 2.5 watts. The efficiency $\eta_{max.}$ is then

$$\eta_{max.} = \frac{\text{electrical power out}}{\text{rate of heat flux through cell}} \cong \frac{1}{55.5} \cong 0.02, \text{ or } 2\% \quad (20)$$

Since 1 watt/sq. cm. implies a current density of about 2 amp./sq. cm., it is totally unrealistic to ignore electrode polarization. It would be reasonable at this current density to reduce the 0.665 volt open-circuit value by at least one-half and, since this term appears as a squared term, it represents a drastic reduction in the energy efficiency. However, the data for KCl-LiCl of A. G. Turnbull (49) indicates that the value of 6.3×10^{-3} for K may be high by as much as a factor of 3 or 4. Solid AgCl has a K of about 2.6×10^{-3}, and the liquid should certainly be lower. The reduction in calculated efficiency resulting from polarization may thus be partially offset by introducing the lowered value for thermal conductivity.

Experimental Results. Several molten salt thermocell systems have been investigated at the Lockheed Palo Alto Research Laboratories. The work of Senderoff and Bretz (45) on AgCl was repeated in cells of varying geometries. In every case, the thermoelectric powers in AgCl were nearly identical with those found by Senderoff and Bretz. Graphite conducting electrodes were used with chlorine and iodine. Molten lead metal electrodes had quartz capillary tubes connected in such a way that a continuous column of lead formed the wire leading from the hot electrode to the potentiometer at room temperature. Most of the thermoelectric powers measured were relatively insensitive to absolute temperature. A summary of calculated and observed powers at 900°K. is given in Table IV. Calculations are based on the equations in Table I. Uncertainties of $\sim 1\%$ in thermochemical entropy data lead to the uncertainties shown for the calculated thermoelectric powers. The experimental uncertainties shown are the standard errors calculated from the spread among the individual $\Delta \epsilon / \Delta T$ values.

Table V compiles calculated and experimental Seebeck coefficients for molten salt thermocell systems studied elsewhere. Pitzer's method for calculation of single ion entropies was used. The residual terms in Column 5, expressed in entropy units, correspond to differences between the calculated thermoelectric powers and the experimental literature values.

Summary. The utility of the theory of irreversible thermodynamics in treating the near equilibrium steady state and its ability to treat non-

Table IV. Summary of Calculations and Results at 900°K.

Cell	Calculated Thermoelectric Power $d\epsilon/dT$ ($\mu V/°C.$)	Experimental Thermoelectric Power $d\epsilon/dT$ ($\mu V/°C.$)	Residual (cal./mole °C.)
$I_2/PbI_2/I_2$	-477 ± 19	-637 ± 17	-3.7 ± 0.6
$I_2/LiI/I_2$	-537 ± 19^a	-595 ± 71	-1.3 ± 1.7
$Cl_2/AgCl/Cl_2$	-494 ± 16	-675 ± 16	-4.1 ± 0.5
$Ag/AgCl/Ag$	-230 ± 13	-380 ± 12	-3.5 ± 0.5
$Cl_2/PbCl_2/Cl_2$	-521 ± 16	-579 ± 13	-1.3 ± 0.5
$Pb/PbCl_2/Pb$	$+9.1 \pm 15$	-7.9 ± 0.3	-0.4 ± 0.3
$Pb/PbI_2/Pb$	-34.2 ± 16	-48.2 ± 17	-0.3 ± 0.5

[a] Salt entropy estimated.

isothermal processes has been illustrated. Application has been made to molten salt thermocell systems through the Pitzer statistical mechanical method. The theory is used to calculate thermoelectric powers for thermocells studied in this laboratory and elsewhere. The calculated values are

Table V. Molten Salt Thermocells Studied Elsewhere

Cell	T (°K.)	Calculated Thermoelectric Power ($\mu v./°C.$)	Experimental Thermoelectric Power ($\mu v./°C.$)	Residual ($cal./mole\ °C.$)	Reference
$Cl_2/LiCl/Cl_2$	900	−530	−534	−0.1	20
$Cl_2/NaCl/Cl_2$	1100	−480	−450	+0.7	17
$Cl_2/NaCl/Cl_2$	1100	−480	−483	−0.1	20
$Cl_2/KCl/Cl_2$	1100	−475	−400	+1.7	17
$Cl_2/KCl/Cl_2$	1100	−475	−504	−0.7	20
$Cl_2/RbCl/Cl_2$	1000	−480	−544	−1.4	20
$Cl_2/CsCl/Cl_2$	1000	−475	−533	−1.3	20
$Cl_2/AgCl/Cl_2$	900	−495	−665	−3.9	20, 45
$Cl_2/PbCl_2/Cl_2$	900	−520	−587	−1.5	20
$Cu/CuCl/Cu$	900	−280	−430	−3.5	38
$Ag/AgCl/Ag$	900	−255	−375	−2.8	45
$Ag/AgCl/Ag$	800	−250	−440	−3.7	24, 34
$Ag/AgBr/Ag$	750	−250	−450	−4.6	34
$Ag/AgI/Ag$	850	−240	−500	−5.9	34
$Ag/AgNO_3/Ag$	580	−245	−320	−1.8	17, 47
$Pb/PbCl_2/Pb$	900	+9	−6	−0.3	17
$Pb/PbBr_2/Pb$	800	+18	−40	−1.3	17
$Sn/SnCl_2/Sn$	550	0^a	−28	−0.6	42

^{a} Entropy value estimated: $S_{SnCl_2} = 47.5$ entropy units at 550°K

compared with experimental values. It is suggested that, in light of other ambiguities such as self-complexing, specific electrode effects, etc., there is insufficient reason to assign differences between theory and experiment to "ionic entropy of transport," although one may choose so to define the term. Using the theory in its present form provides a method for estimating thermocell efficiencies, which are generally expected to be quite low, because of high fused salt thermal conductivity. The theory also provides a method for estimating absolute temperature dependencies of half cell emf's in molten salt electrolytes. The individual electrode temperature coefficients in fused salt galvanic cells should be almost equivalent to the thermoelectric powers of the corresponding thermocells, with the residual entropies discussed above as the remaining uncertain quantities.

Thermally Regenerative Galvanic Systems: Regeneration by High Temperature Electrolysis

General Considerations. The importance of a galvanic cell lies in the fact that chemical energy is directly converted into electrical energy.

The maximum useful work obtainable is equal to the change in the free energy of the reaction. The theoretical energy conversion efficiency limit in the cell itself represents 100% of the free energy change. The situation is quite different when one considers a galvanic cell together with an energy source for regeneration. If energy taken into the system is heat, the temperature of regeneration and the temperature at which the galvanic cell operates impose the Carnot efficiency limit on the total system. It appears desirable, therefore, to operate the galvanic cell at as low a temperature as possible and to perform the regeneration at the highest possible temperature. However, it is important to realize that if any system is constrained to absorb some heat at less than the upper temperature, T_2, it can never achieve the efficiency limit $(T_2 - T_1)/T_2$. For this reason, it is imperative that an analysis of thermally regenerative galvanic systems shed light on the seriousness of such a constraint, often a limitation for chemical systems, even under ideal conditions.

Furthermore, some attempt must be made to estimate the extent to which nonideal, or irreversible processes actually take place in a thermally regenerative galvanic cell. One of the major arguments put forth in favor of the regenerative galvanic heat engine, as compared with other thermal devices or conventional mechanical heat engines, is that electrochemical devices operate closer to thermodynamic reversibility, with relatively fewer irreversible heat losses than other systems and should, therefore, operate at relatively high thermal efficiencies. A realistic evaluation of operational efficiencies of proposed regenerative chemical systems often casts considerable doubt on the validity of such an argument.

In many well-known cyclic or regenerative energy conversion devices, a difference in electrical potential is established between hot and cold junctions. When current passes through the external load, heat is absorbed at the upper temperature. The electrical potential arises from the finite temperature coefficients of the chemical potentials of the circulated substances, or differences between these coefficients. A regenerative galvanic system, in which regeneration is accomplished by the high temperature electrolysis of the product of the low temperature galvanic cell reaction, is an example of such a cyclic energy conversion device. Any galvanic cell in which two simple elements react to form a compound can establish the basis for such a cyclic device if the requisite physical requirements are met. The standard free energy of formation of the simple compound will increase (become less negative) as temperature increases, so that less electrical energy is required to electrolyze the compound at elevated temperatures than that which is available from the galvanic cell. Therefore, a net potential remains for performing useful work. During electrolysis, heat is absorbed in the regenerator. An electrical path is provided for regeneration, but this does not alter the fact that it is thermal energy which is converted to electrical energy by the cycle.

In the previous section the value of applying the methods of irreversible thermodynamics to molten salt thermocells was shown to lie in elucidating the nature of fused salt electrode temperature coefficients. If galvanic cells in a cycle are operated as nonisothermal cells, the methods of the previous section may be used for system analysis by considering each half cell separately. In the analysis of thermally regenerative galvanic systems in this section, isothermal cell operation is assumed and the familiar reversible thermodynamics suffices to treat adequately the selected systems.

The thermodynamics of "coupled" galvanic systems has been discussed by Liebhafsky (*32*), deBethune (*13*), Matsen (*35*), Johnston (*27*), and Ludwig (*33*). In what follows, expressions are derived for appropriate operational parameters, based on thermodynamic considerations. These parameters are evaluated for regenerative systems in which iodine is combined with lead or lithium in the fuel cell. Relative merits and limitations of these systems are discussed, and the most important conclusions are summarized.

Theory. In principle, a simple cycle which utilizes an electrolysis cell and a galvanic cell can operate to convert thermal energy to electrical energy. To illustrate this, consider the electrolysis of a molten salt, MX_2, at temperature, T_2. Liquid metal, M, is to be formed at one electrode and gaseous X_2 at the other. These two substances are cooled and transferred to the galvanic cell, where they react at temperature T_1 to form MX_2. The MX_2 is heated to T_2 and returned to the electrolyzer, which completes the chemical cycle. The corresponding electrical circuit is completed when the electrolyzer is driven by the galvanic cell—i.e., when the two are connected to oppose each other electrically. If the difference in heat capacities of reactants and products ΔC_p is not zero, the efficiency of the reversible cycle is no longer given by the familiar Carnot efficiency expression, where heat input to the cycle occurs only at the higher temperature, T_2:

$$\eta_1 = \frac{\text{net work done}}{\text{heat absorbed at } T_2} = \frac{T_2 - T_1}{T_2} \qquad (21)$$

The efficiency can most easily be discussed, however, if it is assumed that ΔC_p is zero, in which case Equation 21 is correct (*13, 32*).

The above cycle is now equivalent to a heat engine, with electrical rather than mechanical work being produced. The details of such a cycle, or paths by which it operates, cannot alter the validity of Equation 21, as long as the operation is completely reversible and there is no net heat absorbed between T_2 and T_1.

The heat absorbed reversibly at T_2 is $T_2 \Delta S_2$, where ΔS_2 is the entropy change for the reaction $MX(l) = M(l) + X_2(g)$ at T_2. (In this, and in the following discussion, reactants and products are assumed to be in their standard states.) If the open-circuit potential for electrolysis is ε_2, the net potential for the system is $\mathcal{E}_1 + \mathcal{E}_2$, due regard being taken for sign. In practice, $\mathcal{E}_1$ is positive, $\mathcal{E}_2$ is negative, and the magnitude of $\mathcal{E}_1$ exceeds that of $\mathcal{E}_2$. Thus, a net positive potential for electrical work remains.

For reversible operation, one may write:

$$\eta_1 = \frac{T_2 - T_1}{T_2} = \frac{n\mathcal{F}(\mathcal{E}_1 + \mathcal{E}_2)}{T_2 \Delta S_2} \tag{22}$$

Equation 22 may be rewritten as follows:

$$\eta_1 = \frac{n\mathcal{F}(\mathcal{E}_1 + \mathcal{E}_2)}{T_2 \Delta S_2} = \frac{-(\Delta F_1 + \Delta F_2)}{\Delta H_2 - \Delta F_2} \quad (\Delta C_p = 0) \tag{23}$$

where ΔF and ΔH are molal free energy and enthalpy changes. Thus, it is seen that the heat absorbed reversibly is the difference between the enthalpy and free energy changes for the reversible electrolysis reaction, while the net reversible electrical potential obtained from the cycle arises from the temperature dependence of the free energy of formation of MX_2. One cycle, operating reversibly between temperatures T_2 and T_1, might absorb more heat and produce more work per equivalent of chemical reactant than some other reversible cycle which also operates between T_2 and T_1. However, the efficiency for each cycle, a ratio of work and heat, must be the same.

To examine in more detail the net work output for the reversible cycle and its conversion factors, the restriction $\Delta C_p = 0$ is removed in order to obtain suitable expressions for maximum efficiencies attainable with real chemical systems. The MX_2 cycle is as follows:

$$MX_2(l) = M(l) + X_2(g); \qquad T_2, Q_2, \mathcal{E}_2 \tag{24}$$

$$(M(l) + X_2(g))T_2 \rightarrow (M(l) + X_2(g))T_1 \qquad T_2 > T_1 \tag{25}$$

$$M(l) + X_2(g) = MX_2(l); \qquad T_1, Q_1, \mathcal{E}_1 \tag{26}$$

$$MX_2(l, T_1) \rightarrow MX_2(l, T_2) \tag{27}$$

The simple cycle, with return of MX_2 to the electrolyzer and of M and X_2 to the galvanic cell, is represented schematically in Figure 1. The system considered is a constant pressure system because the gas path is continuous. If the work done, W, consists solely of electrical and pressure-volume work, the first law of thermodynamics states that

$$dH = dQ - dW_{\text{elec.}} \tag{28}$$

where Q is heat absorbed, and H is enthalpy per mole of MX_2.

For the cycle, $\oint dH = 0$ and W cycle $= \oint dQ$; the total electrical work for the cycle equals the integral sum of all heat terms. If 1 mole of MX_2 is taken reversibly around the cycle, one writes

$$n\mathcal{F}(\mathcal{E}_2 + \mathcal{E}_1) = Q_2 + \int_{T_2}^{T_1} (C_{p_M} + C_{p_{X_2}}) \, dT + Q_1 + \int_{T_1}^{T_2} C_{p_{MX_2}} \, dT \tag{29}$$

where C_p is the molar heat capacity of the substance designated by subscript.

From the second law of thermodynamics, the sum of all entropy changes in a reversible cyclic process is zero:

$$\oint dS = 0 = \frac{Q_2}{T_2} + \int_{T_2}^{T_1} (C_{p_M} + C_{p_{X_2}})\,d\ln T + \frac{Q_1}{T_1} + \int_{T_1}^{T_2} C_{p_{MX_2}}\,d\ln T \quad (30)$$

When Equation 30 is solved explicitly for Q_1, then substituted into Equation 29, the result is as follows:

$$n\mathcal{F}(\mathcal{E}_1 + \mathcal{E}_2) = \frac{Q_2 \Delta T}{T_2} - \int_{T_1}^{T_2} \Delta C_p\,dT + T_1 \int_{T_1}^{T_2} \Delta C_p\,d\ln T \quad (31)$$

where $\Delta T = T_2 - T_1$ and $\Delta C_p = C_{p_M} + C_{p_{X_2}} - C_{p_{MX_2}}$.

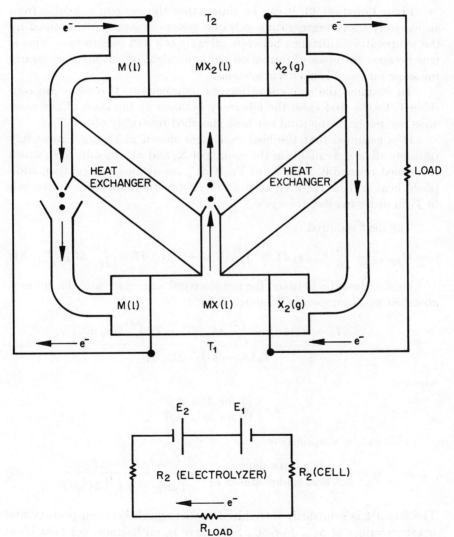

Figure 1. Thermally regenerative cycle and equivalent circuit

The two integral terms in Equation 31 are usually small in comparison with the first term, and they tend to cancel one another; hence, the first term usually serves as an accurate expression for estimating the net reversible work for one cycle. Because the electrolysis step is isothermal, one writes

$$Q_2 = T_2 \Delta S_2; \qquad \Delta S_2 = S_M + S_{X_2} - S_{MX_2} \qquad \text{at } T_2 \qquad (32)$$

Therefore

$$\mathcal{E}_1 + \mathcal{E}_2 \cong \frac{\Delta S_2 \Delta T}{n\mathcal{F}} \qquad (33)$$

From Equation 33, it can be shown that the net emf available from an electrolytically regenerative galvanic system is largely determined by the temperature difference between galvanic cell and electrolyzer. This is true because entropies of formation per equivalent of salt are very nearly the same for feasible chemical systems.

To examine the conversion factors (efficiencies), two cases are considered. In the first case, the efficiency is taken as the ratio of the work done reversibly to the total net heat absorbed reversibly above T_1.

It is assumed that the heat exchanger shown in Figure 1 reversibly transfers all heat available in the cooling of X_2 and M to a salt, MS_2, which is warmed reversibly from T_1 to T_2. If ΔC_p (as defined) is negative, additional heat will be required to heat reversibly the remainder of the salt to T_2 in order to close the cycle.

The heat required is

$$Q_{\text{heating}} = \int_{T_1}^{T_2} C_{pMX_2} \, dT + \int_{T_1}^{T_2} (C_{pM} + C_{pX_2}) \, dT = \int_{T_1}^{T_2} \Delta C_p \, dT \quad (34)$$

Hence, the ratio between the net electrical work done and the net heat absorbed at all temperatures above T_1 is

$$\eta_2 = \frac{(T_2 - T_1)\Delta S_2 - \int_{T_1}^{T_2} \Delta C_p \, dT + T_1 \int_{T_1}^{T_2} \Delta C_p \, d\ln T}{T_2 \Delta S_2 - \delta \int_{T_1}^{T_2} \Delta C_p \, dT} \qquad (35)$$

where

$$\delta = \begin{cases} 1 \text{ for } \Delta C_p < 0 \\ 0 \text{ for } \Delta C_p > 0 \end{cases}$$

This can be simplified to

$$\eta_2 = \frac{\text{net work done}}{\text{net heat added above } T_1} = \frac{-(\Delta F_1 + \Delta F_2)}{T_2 \Delta S_2 - \delta \int_{T_1}^{T_2} \Delta C_p \, dT} \qquad (36)$$

The factor δ is arbitrarily introduced to distinguish between positive and negative values of ΔC_p. For $\Delta C_p > 0$, there is, on balance, net heat liberated in the heating and cooling steps. This liberated heat cannot be fully used within the cycle. From Equation 35 it is evident in this case that $\eta_2 < \eta_1$, the Carnot efficiency. For $\Delta C_p < 0$, there is a net uptake of heat in the heating and cooling steps above T_i; from Equation 36 it is again evident that $\eta_2 < \eta_1$. For $\Delta C_p = 0$, $\eta_2 = \eta_1$, and Carnot efficiency is achieved.

As the second case, assume the heat exchanger is removed entirely so that none of the heat from the cooling step is reclaimed. Then the heat added reversibly in the warming step is

$$Q_{\text{heating}} = \int_{T_1}^{T_2} C_{p_{MX_2}} \, dT$$

The corresponding maximum conversion factor in this case is as follows:

$$\eta_3 = \frac{\text{net work done}}{\text{total heat added above } T_1} = \frac{-(\Delta F_1 + \Delta F_2)}{T_2 \Delta S_2 + \int_{T_1}^{T_2} C_{p_{MX_2}} \, dT} \tag{37}$$

Efficiency η_3 is the ratio of net work done to the total heat added above T_1. It does not reduce to the Carnot expression. Calculations for typical reactions show that the Carnot term $\Delta T / T_2$ is dominant for all three efficiency expressions.

The discussion above concerns one galvanic cell carried around a modified Carnot cycle. When two identical fuel cells are connected in one circuit, one at T_2 and the other at T_1, the situation differs in some respects from the case studied above. There is, at least, a temperature gradient down the connecting wires. In a regenerative system, some continuous transfer of products and reactant from one cell to the other might be included, and these connections might entail other temperature gradients and transfer processes. However, as a good first approximation, the maximum net voltage of the system is given by Equation 31 and the maximum thermal efficiency by Equation 36.

Further examination of Equation 31 shows that the right-hand side is simply the negative of the change of free energy for the reaction:

$$n\mathfrak{F}(\mathcal{E}_2 + \mathcal{E}_1) = -(\Delta F_2 + \Delta F_1) \tag{38}$$

Because $\mathcal{E}_1$ is positive, the counter potential $\mathcal{E}_2$ is negative, by convention.

The free-energy function Y, a product of the third law of thermodynamics, is

$$Y_T = -\frac{(F_T^0 - H_0^0)}{T} \tag{39}$$

These functions are extensively tabulated, and the net voltage is given by

$$\mathcal{E}_1 + \mathcal{E}_2 = \frac{\Delta(T_2 Y_2 + T_1 Y_1)}{n\mathfrak{F}} \tag{40}$$

Therefore, the maximum electrical work obtainable from systems utilizing high temperature electrolysis can be readily estimated from tables of thermodynamic data.

Irreversible Operation. Efficiencies η_2 and η_3 were derived for reversible operation of the fuel cell and the electrolyzer. Irreversibility is introduced at T_2 and T_1 when an appreciable current flows through the system. As before, the maximum efficiency is sought for the system under such conditions. For this reason, no attempt is made to take into account the consequent additional irreversibility introduced into the heating and cooling steps as the materials begin to circulate at finite rates to support appreciable current flows in the cycle. Coulombic efficiencies of 100% are assumed for the present discussion.

The actual voltage, V, at which a cell operates (irreversibly) differs from the reversible potential $\mathcal{E}$ by the product of the current I and the total cell resistance R, as measured when current I flows through the cell. The cycle to be considered is described by Equations 24 through 27. On completion of one cycle, there is no net change in any state function for the system. This is true regardless of path, whether the operation is performed reversibly or irreversibly. Thus, for the cycle, the following conclusions may be drawn from Equation 28.

$$\sum Q \text{ (reversible)} - \sum W \begin{array}{l} \text{reversible} \\ \text{electrical} \end{array}$$

$$= \sum Q \text{ (irreversible)} - \sum W \begin{array}{l} \text{irreversible} \\ \text{electrical} \end{array} \quad (41)$$

In Equation 41, $\sum Q$ (irreversible) is the total heat summation for the irreversible cycle, where all irreversibility has been introduced at T_2 and at T_1. From the definition of V (above), the net irreversible work done for one cycle is $n\mathcal{F}(V_1 + V_2)$. From the previous remarks, one writes

$$V_2 = \mathcal{E}_2 - IR_2; \qquad V_1 = \mathcal{E}_1 - IR_1 \quad (42)$$

The heat and work terms may now be summed around the cycle according to Equation 41.

$$T_2\Delta S_2 + T_1\Delta S_1 + \int_{T_2}^{T_1} \Delta C_p \, dT - n\mathcal{F}(\mathcal{E}_1 + \mathcal{E}_2)$$

$$= \sum Q \text{ (irreversible)} - n\mathcal{F}(V_1 + V_2) \sum Q \text{ (irreversible)}$$

$$= T_2\Delta S_2 + T_1\Delta S_1 + \int_{T_2}^{T_1} \Delta C_p \, dT - n\mathcal{F}I(R_1 + R_2) \quad (44)$$

The net work for the cycle is

$$W_{\text{cycle}} = n\mathcal{F}(V_1 + V_2) = n\mathcal{F}[\mathcal{E}_1 - IR_1 + \mathcal{E}_2 - IR_2] \quad (45)$$

$$W_{\text{cycle}} = -(\Delta F_1 + \Delta F_2) - n\mathcal{F}I(R_1 + R_2) \quad (46)$$

(R_1 and R_2 are the resistances of the galvanic cell at T_1 and electrolyzer at T_2, respectively, as measured when current I flows in the circuit shown in Figure 1.)

Heat produced at T_1 is rejected from the system and cannot be counted as useful heat; only those terms in Equation 44 which correspond to heat absorbed or produced at temperatures above T_1 are potentially useful in the cycle. After eliminating the terms $T_1 \Delta S_1$ and $n\mathfrak{F} I R_1$ from Equation 44, one has the net heat absorbed by the cycle:

$$Q \text{ (absorbed)} = T_2 \Delta S_2 + \int_{T_2}^{T_1} \Delta C_p \, dT - n\mathfrak{F} I R_2 \qquad (47)$$

Although the last quantity in Equation 47 represents irreversible heat produced in the electrolyzer, in the most favorable limiting case this heat can be utilized in the cycle, thereby diminishing the heat absorbed isothermally from the surroundings at T_2. The maximum efficiency which the system can have in actual (irreversible) operation is given by the ratio of Equations 46 and 47. This is maximum operational efficiency with maximum power to load (reversible heat exchange).

$$\eta_4 = \frac{W \text{ (cycle)}}{Q \text{ (absorbed)}} = \frac{-(\Delta F_1 + \Delta F_2) - n\mathfrak{F} I (R_1 + R_2)}{T_2 \Delta S_2 - \delta \int_{T_1}^{T_2} \Delta C_p \, dT - n\mathfrak{F} I R_2} \qquad \delta = \begin{cases} 1 \text{ for } C_p < 0 \\ 0 \text{ for } C_p > 0 \end{cases}$$
$$(48)$$

Without the reversible heat exchanger shown in Figure 1, the maximum operational efficiency with maximum power to load becomes

$$\eta_5 = \frac{-(\Delta F_1 + \Delta F_2) - n\mathfrak{F} I (R_1 + R_2)}{T_2 \Delta S_2 + \int_{T_1}^{T_2} C_{p_{MX2}} \, dT - n\mathfrak{F} I R_2} \qquad (49)$$

These efficiency expressions are evaluated below for the lithium-iodine and lead-iodine systems. It should be mentioned that the expressions for η_2 through η_5 are easily generalized for any chemical reaction and any number of cells and electrolyzers in series. Regardless of the number of series units, however, the efficiencies calculated for a given T_1, T_2, and chemical system are maximum reversible and operational efficiencies for that system. These values can only be approached in practice.

In order to make calculations for operational efficiencies of specific systems, an arbitrary condition is imposed on the current and on the nature of the cell and electrolyzer. The load resistor in Figure 1 is so selected that maximum power is obtained. In order to find the condition for maximum power in the equivalent circuit shown in Figure 1, something must be known about the nature of the cell and electrolyzer resistances. Let us assume that they are purely ohmic resistances. Then the circuit can always be reduced to one with a single voltage source of internal ohmic resistance R_I and a single load resistor R_L. The power through the load is then given by:

$$P_L = \frac{\mathcal{E}^2 R_L}{(R_L + R_I)^2} \qquad (50)$$

where $\mathcal{E} = I(R_L + R_I)$ is the open-circuit potential of the source.

It is easily shown that the condition for the optimum load resistor (maximum power) is

$$R_L = R_I \tag{51}$$

Condition 52 is perfectly general for maximum total load power when M cells (electrolytic or fuel cells) with ohmic internal resistances are arranged in series with n loads.

$$\sum_m R_I = \sum_n R_L \tag{52}$$

Equation 50 can then be written

$$P_{L_{max.}} = \frac{\sum\limits_m \mathcal{E}^2}{4 \sum\limits_m R_I} \tag{53}$$

The smallest electrode in the series will have the highest, or maximum, power density. If this electrode is always taken for reference, then Equation 53 (divided by the area of the electrode) is the condition for maximum power density. It is this condition which is imposed in the present analysis of chemical systems. For simplicity, the circuit shown in Figure 1 is assumed, and the area of the smallest of the electrodes is taken as unity. The maximum power density will therefore be given by the following:

$$P_0 = \frac{(\mathcal{E}_1 + \mathcal{E}_2)^2}{4(R_1 + R_2)}; \qquad (R_1 + R_2 = R_L) \tag{54}$$

The load voltage is always the same for a given chemical system at one pressure of X_2 with fixed values of T_1 and T_2, if the above "optimum" power is being drawn. Because, by Equation 52 the load resistance equals the sum of all internal resistances, the optimum load voltage is just half of the net open circuit potential:

$$V_0 = \tfrac{1}{2} \sum_m \mathcal{E} = \tfrac{1}{2}(\mathcal{E}_1 + \mathcal{E}_2) \tag{55}$$

Application to Lithium-Iodine and Lead-Iodine Systems. Available data for systems based on lead iodide and lithium iodide have been collected to calculate and compare the relative contributions of various terms (such as ΔC_p and $T\Delta S$) with performance parameters (efficiencies and power densities). These systems were initially selected because Coulombic efficiencies are virtually 100% for the electrolysis of lead iodide (2), and because lithium iodide has a long liquid range and a reasonably low melting point. The requisite data are presented in Table VI. The function ΔY is the standard free energy function $(\Delta F - \Delta H_{298})/T$ for forming the salt from iodine gas and the metal. The standard state of iodine has been taken as the perfect gas at 1 atm. at each temperature. Other standard states are conventional. Estimated quantities have been indicated. Specific resistances for the fused salts at their melting points have been estimated by extrapolating electrical conductivity data for temperatures above the melting point.

Table VI. Data for Calculation of Performance Parameters for PbI₂ and LiI Systems

Property	System Component					Reference
	PbI_2	Pb	LiI	Li	I_2	
Melting Point (°K.)	$T_1 = 685$	600	$T_1 = 713$	454		*6, 46*
Boiling Point (°K.)	$T_2 = 1145$	2024	$T_2 = 1444$	1604		*6, 46*
ΔH (fusion) (cal./mole)	6010	1225	1420	723		*6, 46*
$-\Delta H$ (formation at 298°K.)	56,500	0	72,500	0		*46*
ΔY at $T°K$. (cal./°C. mole):						
298°K.	35.6		16.9			*46*
500°K.	35.1		16.4			*46*
1000°K.	30.6		16.1			*46*
1500°K.			14.2			*46*
C_p (solid); (cal./°C. mole)	$18 + 4.7 \times 10^{-3}T$	$5.82 + 1.9 \times 10^{-3}T$	$12.5 + 2 \times 10^{-3}T$	$3.15 + 8.4 \times 10^{-3}T$		*6, 29, 31*
C_p (liquid); (cal./°C. mole)	32.4	6.8	16ᵃ	$7.2 - 4 \times 10^{-4}T$		*6, 29, 31*
C_p (gas); (cal./°C. mole)					8.89	*29*
Specific Resistance at T_1 (ohm-cm.)	2.14ᵃ		0.294ᵃ			*3, 9*

ᵃ Estimated.

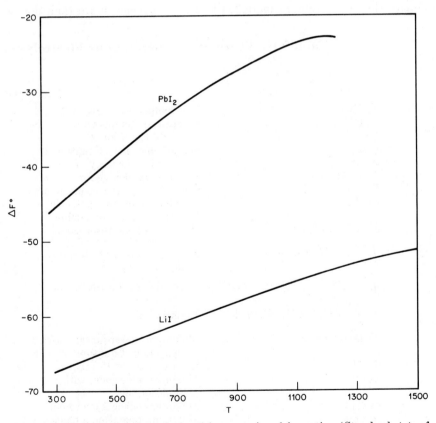

Figure 2. Temperature dependence of free energies of formation (Standard state of iodine is perfect gas at 1 atm. for all T.)

The standard free energies of forming lithium iodide and lead iodide are plotted as a function of temperature in Figure 2.

The following conditions have been assumed for calculating the quantities which appear in Table VII. Iodine in the cycle is maintained at a pressure of 1 atm. The temperatures T_1 and T_2 have been taken as the normal melting and boiling points of the salts, respectively. The cell resistance at T_1 has been taken as that for a cell with electrodes of 1 sq. cm. area, separated by 0.5 cm., with the fused salt as electrolyte. The total resistance of the electrolyzer unit has been set equal to the cell resistance. The standard entropy changes at T_2 have been calculated by the usual methods, with the aid of the heat capacity data and values of ΔH_{298} given in Table VI.

Discussion. We first examine the criteria for selection of systems suitable for thermal-electrolytic regeneration. An examination of Equation 33 shows that a long liquid range for both metal and salt is essential for good performance. Equation 22 indicates why a lowering of the melting point of the electrolyte T_1 increases thermal efficiency more than does a

Table VII. Thermal Regeneration by Electrolysis:

Parameter or Term	Definition and
T_1 (°K.)	Cell temperature, Figure 1,
T_2 (°K.)	Electrolysis temperature,
ΔT	$T_1 - T_2$, Equation 21
η_1 (%)	Carnot efficiency, Equation 22
ΔF_1 (cal./mole)	Standard free energy of
ΔF_2 (cal./mole)	Free energy change for
$\mathcal{E}_1$ (V)	Open-circuit potential of galvanic cell,
$\mathcal{E}_2$ (V)	Standard reversible potential
$\mathcal{E}_1 + \mathcal{E}_2$ (V)	Net potential for reversible
$T_2 \Delta S_2$ (cal./mole)	Reversible heat absorbed at
$\int_{T_2}^{T_1} \Delta C_p \, dT$ (cal./mole)	Net reversible heat absorbed 35, 36, and 37
$\int_{T_1}^{T_2} C_p MX_{2(1)} \, dT$ (cal./mole)	Reversible heat absorbed in
$T_1 \int_{T_1}^{T_2} \Delta C_p d \ln T$ (cal./mole)	Equation 31
P_0 (mw./sq. cm.)	Maximum power density with separation, Equation 54
V_0 (V)	Load voltage at P_0 (above),
η_2 (%)	Maximum efficiency, with Equation 36
η_3 (%)	Maximum efficiency without
η_4 (%)	Maximum operational efficiency separation, maximum
η_5 (%)	Maximum operational efficiency

corresponding increase in the boiling point T_2. Therefore, materials which have low melting points are to be sought. Equation 33 also indicates the importance of a large entropy change accompanying the reversible electrolysis. Above the boiling point of the salt and below that of the metal, this entropy change often becomes very small, as has been shown previously (*2*). Thus, an increase in T_2 above the boiling point of the salt is of no advantage; the standard free energy of formation ceases to change appreciably with temperature, and an additional separation problem is introduced. For these reasons, the melting and boiling points of the salts and metals are of utmost importance in the selection of systems regenerable by either electrolysis or thermal dissociation.

Another important consideration is that of Coulombic efficiency. Two related effects often act to reduce greatly Coulombic efficiency below 100% in metal-fused salt systems. Electronic conduction in the melt allows power to be dissipated internally. The presence of dissolved metal allows direct combination of reactants to take place in the cells without electrical work being produced. In general, more electrolyzer units than galvanic cells

Performance Parameters for the PbI$_2$ and LiI Systems

Place Referred to in Text	System and Value	
	PbI$_2$	LiI
Equation 21	685	713
Figure 1, Equation 21	1145	1444
	460	731
	40.1	50.6
formation at T_1, Equation 23	−32,700	−61,000
electrolysis at T_2, Equation 23; (standard)	21,200	51,600
Figure 1, Equation 22; (standard)	0.71	2.65
for electrolysis at T_2, Equation 22	−0.50	−2.24
cycle	0.21	0.41
T_2, Equation 22	19,610	15,670
in heating and cooling steps, Equations	7,680	3,562
heating steps, Equations 36 and 37	14,900	11,700
	−5,850	−2,175
optimum load and 0.5-cm. electrode	5.2	142
Equation 55	0.105	0.205
reversible heat exchange, Figure 1,	35.5	48.4
heat exchanger, Equation 37	28.1	34.0
with heat exchange (0.5-cm. electrode load power), Figure 1, Equation 48	19.6	27.2
without heat exchanger, Equation 49	15.2	18.4

must be included in the circuit because low current efficiencies allow fewer equivalents of reactants to be regenerated from one electrolyzer than are consumed per faraday of electricity in the fuel cell. With individual electrolyzer cells arranged in series, all current in the circuit must pass through each unit, thereby regenerating reactants at each pair of electrodes. The units cannot function in the above manner if they are not isolated—i.e., if they have a common electrolyte, unless the electrolyte bridges between units have small cross sections. It is obvious that the net effect of low current efficiency is complex; however, it is clearly a detrimental effect not to be overcome by the beneficial effects of electronic conductivity which are occasionally obtained in systems utilizing solid electrolytes.

The storage capability of the system may give rise to its use as a simple fuel cell for transient power demands—i.e., with the electrolyzer circuit open. For this mode of operation a large value of $\mathcal{E}_1$ is desirable. Salts which have relatively low melting points and large free energies of formation are therefore indicated.

As is seen from Equation 54, the maximum power density is inversely proportional to the sum of the internal resistances. The desirability of a salt with high electrical (ionic) conductivity when fused is obvious. Equation 54 also indicates the dependence of power on the square of the net potential; an examination of Table VII shows the importance of this term (and of low cell resistance) in making the lithium-iodide system so much better theoretically than the lead-iodide system. It should be stressed, however, that the large value of $\mathcal{E}_1 + \mathcal{E}_2$ for the lithium system arises as a direct consequence of the larger value of ΔT for that system. It is important to realize that the values of $\Delta S/n$—i.e., the standard entropy of formation of the salt divided by n, the number of electrons transferred for the electrochemical formation of one molecule of salt are very nearly the same for feasible chemical systems. As examples, we may take the values of $\Delta S_{298}/n$ for various systems. Some of these are given in Table VIII. The values are based on a gaseous standard state for iodine at 298°K.

From Figure 2 it is apparent that the change of free energy of formation with temperature is very nearly linear within the operating temperature ranges of the two systems. Thus one can see that, among feasible systems, it is the magnitude of the obtainable ΔT which limits the system—i.e., which largely determines the values of $(\mathcal{E}_1 + \mathcal{E}_2)$. Hence, one should seek

Table VIII. Entropies of Formation per Equivalent of Salt for Feasible Regenerative Systems

Salt	LiH	PbI_2	SnI_2	LiBr	LiI	$BiCl_3$
n	1	2	2	1	1	3
$\dfrac{\Delta S_{298}}{n}$	16.4	17.8	17.0	17.0	16.9	16.0

those systems which allow large operational values of ΔT, whether thermal dissociation or thermal electrolysis is to be used for regeneration, because it is ΔT that most greatly affects the voltage obtainable from the cycle.

Finally, as can be seen from Table VII, the magnitudes of the integral terms which contain ΔC_p are so small in comparison with other important terms [*cf.* Equations 26, 31, 43, 47, and 48] that these integrals do not represent important criteria for system selection.

Thermal regeneration by electrolysis has several advantages and limitations in comparison with other energy conversion schemes. One obvious advantage is that of product separation upon regeneration by electrolysis. The metal and gas are liberated at different surfaces and cannot readily recombine. This is ordinarily a serious limitation to practical thermal regenerative methods. Energy storage is an advantage of the electrolytic method which is not inherent to ordinary thermoelectric devices. The lithium-iodine (thermal-electrolytic) system, for example, when operated temporarily as a galvanic cell, has a standard open-circuit potential of 2.65 volts.

Another advantage of the electrolytic cycle over thermoelectric converters, such as the thermocouple or simple thermocell, is that the galvanic cell and electrolyzer units are nearly isolable thermally—i.e., the thermal and electrical paths can be separated. Efficiency losses which arise through simple thermal conduction between T_2 and T_1 (as *via* the gas path) are neglected; this is done because these effects can be minimized in the thermal-electrolytic cycle. Thermal conduction losses cannot be ignored in a simple thermocell, however, where the thermal and electrical conduction paths are intimately related and inseparable. In this latter case, the heat conducted through the system is very large in comparison with the corresponding electrical work produced, and overall efficiencies are low.

Fused salt electrode reactions are highly reversible so that efficiencies are relatively high for cycles utilizing thermal electrolysis. This advantage (reversibility) may be seen more graphically if one compares the reversible efficiency for the electrolytic cycle η_3, Table VII, for lead and lithium iodides with the efficiency which would result if regeneration could somehow be carried out by an irreversible thermal dissociation process. In this case, the heat absorbed irreversibly at T_2 would simply be $\Delta H_{(T_2)}$ calories per mole of dissociated salt. The efficiencies for the lead- and lithium-iodine systems would then be 19 and 13%, respectively, instead of 35 and 48% for the reversible electrolytic regeneration at T_2.

Plugging of critical regions in the fuel cell often presents a serious problem. This difficulty may be encountered in any system in which the boiling point of the salt (or metal) is approached in the regenerator. For example, in the system shown in Figure 1, the presence of $MX_2(g)$ in the $X_2(g)$ line means that as the gas mixture approaches the galvanic cell at T_1, $MX_2(l)$ will condense from the gas stream. The gas electrode will

eventually become plugged, or flooded, as a result. The practical consideration here is that one cannot actually raise T_2 to the boiling point (1 atm.)
of the salt, and ΔT (and therefore the net potential) is diminished below
the theoretical maximum.

A commonly encountered problem, at least from a practical, developmental point of view, is polarization at gas electrodes. In the theoretical
treatment of power and operational efficiencies at maximum power, the
tacit assumption was made that cell resistances follow Ohm's law. This
assumption represents the limiting, most favorable situation, in which gas
pressure and electrode porosity have been so adjusted that no gas polarization develops in operation. As gas is consumed at the salt-electrode interfaces within a porous electrode, the local pressure (or concentration) of
the gas is reduced. Unless gas is able to diffuse into the low pressure
regions as rapidly as it is consumed, the total cell resistance will rise. Such
effects are minimized by maintaining a high pressure of gas within the
system. Another effect which must be considered is the effect of gas
pressure on the net potential $(\mathcal{E}_1 + \mathcal{E}_2)$.

It is easily shown that, because of the elevated electrolyzer temperature, an increase in the pressure of $X_2(g)$ in the system decreases the net
potential $(\mathcal{E}_1 + \mathcal{E}_2)$ in opposition to the beneficial lowering of polarization
which is brought about by an increase in gas pressure. The logarithmic
dependence on pressure makes the above effect quite small.

There are many considerations involved in selecting suitable materials
and conditions for energy conversion cycles which employ thermal regeneration by electrolysis. Here, the underlying principles for such systems
have been outlined so that meaningful evaluation and comparison may be
made with other types of energy conversion devices.

Conclusions. The following conclusions may be drawn from the
thermodynamic analysis given in this section:

· The magnitude of the net voltage output for the cycle is directly
proportional to the temperature difference between the electrolyzer and
the galvanic cell.

· The net potential decreases slightly as the pressure of the gas X_2 is
increased.

· Although the cycle is not a simple Carnot cycle, in general, the
efficiencies expected for reversible operation are only slightly lower than
efficiencies for the corresponding Carnot cycles. (Comparison of η_2 and
η_1)

· The importance of including an efficient heat exchanger in the cycle
has been established. (Comparison of η_3 and η_2)

· Theoretical operational efficiencies at maximum power are much
lower than efficiencies for reversible operation. (Comparison of η_4 and
η_2)

The method of thermal regeneration by electrolysis has the following merits:

· Product separation during regeneration is inherent to the system.

· The system may be operated temporarily as a galvanic cell alone, in addition to its normal function as an energy converter.

· Theoretical operational efficiencies are higher, in general, than corresponding efficiencies for conventional thermoelectric devices, where thermal and electrical conduction paths cannot be separated.

Thermal regeneration by electrolysis has the following limitations:

· The system is not physically simple; materials must be transferred between galvanic cells and electrolyzers.

· The problems encountered for any regenerative system utilizing gas electrodes are also inherent to the type of system discussed here (plugging and flooding of electrodes).

· Current efficiencies are always less than 100%; thus, even the simplest complete system would require two electrolysis cells coupled with one galvanic cell.

Thermally Regenerative Galvanic Systems: Regeneration by Low Pressure Electrolysis

It has been shown that Carnot efficiencies are theoretically approached in cycles utilizing thermal regeneration by electrolysis at elevated temperatures. However, these efficiencies cannot generally be realized because of the finite heat capacity changes which occur in simple electrochemical reactions and the thermal losses which accrue when these are integrated over an appreciable temperature range. An alternate approach is to examine nearby isothermal, regenerative, galvanic systems which exploit the change in free energy of formation with pressure and to compare the ideal efficiency deduced for this system with the Carnot efficiency. In such systems, the electrolyzer operates at or near the operational temperature of the galvanic cell.

In this scheme, identical galvanic cells are run back-to-back (wired with polarities opposing); each cell is at the same temperature, but with the activity of a chemical element in one cell differing from the activity of that element in the other cell. If this elemental species is a gas, its activity is controlled by its pressure. In this case, the net driving force for a reversible electrochemical reaction is controlled by the gas pressure ratio in the two cells (raised to a power commensurate with stoichiometry). Because the effect of total pressure on the free energy of condensed phases is negligible under the conditions considered, the net driving force of the cycle is independent of any property of the electrolyte. The maximum theoretical efficiency for the cycle then depends only on the temperatures and the thermal properties of the gas, in particular, its heat of condensation.

Figure 3 depicts a schematic representation of the type of system considered in this section. Both cells are at the same temperature, and

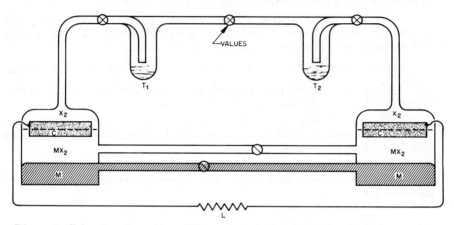

Figure 3. Galvanic cell system utilizing electrolytic regeneration at low pressure

either cell can function as a galvanic cell, utilizing the reaction between a liquid metal M and a halogen X_2, with molten salt MX_2 as electrolyte. The porous carbon cathodes, C, are in series with load L. The electronic circuit is completed through the pipe connecting liquid metal anodes. If condensed X_2 is present in each trap at temperatures T_1 (trap at left in Figure 3) and T_2 (trap on right, Figure 3), with $T_2 > T_1$, the electrons flow from left to right through the load—i.e., the right-hand cell is a galvanic cell, and electrolysis of MX_2 takes place in the left-hand cell. Trap temperatures and valves may also be adjusted so that MX_2 can be transferred from the right to the left cell by gravity flow, with both cells at the same total pressure. In the same way, M can be transferred from left to right. The transfer of X_2 from left to right is accomplished by vaporizing condensed X_2 from the left-hand trap and condensing X_2 in the right-hand $(T_1 > T_2)$.

When a difference in gas pressure exists, the high pressure cell will generate current and electrolysis will take place in the low pressure cell. The halogen trap of the galvanic cell may be heated to supply gaseous fuel for the cathode. Alternately, or simultaneously, the trap of the electrolysis cell may be cooled to lower the pressure of the halogen at this cathode. The operation can be repeated in the opposite direction by reversing trap temperatures, or material may be transferred between cells through the valves. The electrolysis cell may also be maintained at a higher temperature than the galvanic cell. For this theoretical analysis, it is assumed that both cells are at the same temperature. The chemical cycle, which starts and ends with MX_2 at cell temperature T_c, may be written as follows:

$$MX_2(l, T_c) \rightarrow M(l, T_c) + X_2(g, P_1, T_c)$$
$$X_2(g, P_1, T_c) \rightarrow X_2(s, T_1)$$
$$X_2(S, T_1) \rightarrow X_2(g, P_2, T_2)$$
$$X_2(g, P_2, T_2) \rightarrow X_2(g, P_2, T_c)$$
$$X_2(g, P_2, T_c) + M(l, T_c) \rightarrow MX_2(l, T_c)$$

Solid, liquid, and gaseous states are designated by s, l, and g.

For analysis, it is appropriate to specify a particular chemical system and compute the heat and work terms for transfer of 1 mole X_2 around the cycle. This has been done for the lead-iodine system.

Analysis of the System: Lead-Iodine. The fuel cell reaction is:

$$Pb(l) + I_2(g, P_2) = PbI_2(l)$$

while the regeneration reaction, at the same temperature, is

$$PbI_2(l) = Pb(l) + I_2(g, P_1)$$

A net positive reversible potential for electrical work will exist for a complete chemical cycle in such a "coupled" system if the pressure P_2 of $I_2(g)$ in the galvanic cell is greater than the pressure P_1 in the electrolysis cell.

Standard conditions in the galvanic cell are selected for convenience in applying available data. A cell temperature well above the melting point of the salt is desirable to ensure good electrolyte conductivity. The temperature T_1 of a cold trap connected to the electrolyzer determines the equilibrium pressure of iodine in the electrolysis cell. A typical set of conditions chosen for analysis is presented in Table IX.

For the lead-iodine system, the reversible electrolysis of PbI_2 at low pressure is selected as the first step of the cycle shown in Table X.

Open-Circuit Potential. The net maximum electrical work is given by Steps 1 and 9 of the above cycle:

$$n\mathcal{F}(\mathcal{E}_1 + \mathcal{E}_9) = -(\Delta F_1 + \Delta F_9)$$

Table IX.   Values of Parameters Chosen for Analysis of Iodine PbI_2 Cycle

Symbol	Definition	Value
T_c	Cell and Electrolyzer Temperature	750°K.
P_1	I_2 Pressure in Electrolyzer	4×10^{-4} atm.
T_1	Cold-Trap Temperature	273°K.
T_M	Melting Temperature of Iodine	387°K.
T_2	Temperature of Traps Connected to Galvanic Cells	456°K.
P_2	I_2 Pressure in Galvanic Cell	1 atm.

Table X. Analysis of Thermal Cycle for Low

Step	Change	Thermal Function
1	$PbI_2(l, T_c) \rightarrow Pb(l, T_c) + I_2(g, P_1, T_1)$	$Q_1 = T_c \Delta S$
2	$I_2(g, P_1, T_c) \rightarrow I_2(g, P_1, T_1)$	$Q_2 = \int_{T_c}^{T_1} C_p \, dT$
3	$I_2(g, P_1, T_1) \rightarrow I_2(s, T_1)$	$Q_3 = \Delta H_s$
4	$I_2(s, T_1) \rightarrow I_2(s, T_m)$	$Q_4 = \int_{T_1}^{T_m} C_p \, dT$
5	$I_2(s, T_m) \rightarrow I_2(l, T_m)$	$Q_5 = \Delta H_s$
6	$I_2(l, T_m) \rightarrow I_2(l, T_2)$	$Q_6 = C_p(T_2 - T_m)$
7	$I_2(l, T_2) \rightarrow I_2(g, P_2, T_2)$	$Q_7 = \Delta H_v$
8	$I_2(g, P_2, T_2) \rightarrow I_2(g, P_2, T_c)$	$Q_8 = \int_{T}^{T_c} C_p \, dT$
9	$I_2(g, P_2, T_c) + Pb(l, T_c) \rightarrow PbI_2(l, T_c)$	$Q_9 = T_c \Delta S = -T_c \Delta S^0$

The thermodynamic symbols have their usual significance, and open-circuit potentials $\mathcal{E}_1$ and $\mathcal{E}_9$ correspond to the electrolyzer and galvanic cell reactions, respectively.

$$\Delta F_1 = \Delta F_1^0 + RT_c \ln P_1$$
$$\Delta F_1^0 = -\Delta F_9^0$$

Superscript zeros denote standard values. Because 1 atm. pressure of iodine was chosen (Table IX) for the galvanic cell, one has

$$\Delta F_9 = \Delta F_9^0$$

and

$$n\mathcal{F}(\mathcal{E}_1 + \mathcal{E}_9) = -RT_c \ln P_1$$

With substitution of the values from Table X, the net potential $\mathcal{E} = \mathcal{E}_1 + \mathcal{E}_9$ becomes 0.26 volts for a cold-trap temperature of 0°C.

If the cold-trap temperature T_1 is lowered from 0 to $-78°C.$, the temperature of a dry-ice slush-bath, the equilibrium vapor pressure of iodine in the electrolysis cell drops from 4×10^{-4} atm. to approximately 10^{-10} atm. Vapor pressures for solid iodine were computed from the following formula (23).

$$\log P = 18.685 - \frac{3700}{T} - 2.75 \log T$$

Thus, with a dry ice trap, the net emf would be 0.7 volts.

Theoretical and Operational Efficiencies. The maximum theoretical conversion efficiency for the cycle may be defined as the ratio of the net maximum electrical work produced to the net heat absorbed—i.e.,

Pressure Reversible Electrolysis of PbI$_2$

Heat Change (kcal. mole^{-1})	Comments
$T_c \Delta S^0 + 11.7$	$\Delta S = \Delta S^0 - R \ln P$, is entropy change for low pressure electrolysis
$\int_{T_c}^{T_2} C_p\, dT - 1.64$	C_p for I$_2$ = 8.94 cal. °C. mole^{-1} is nearly constant with temperature between T_2 and T_1 (29)
-15.0	Heat of sublimation at T_1 (40) is heat rejected in cycle (irrecoverable)
1.1	C_p for I$_2$(S) = 9.59 cal. °C. mole^{-1} (29)
3.77	Heat of fusion (29)
1.33	C_p for I$_2$(l) = 19.2 cal. °C. mole^{-1} (29)
9.97	Heat of vaporization (29)
2.63	Cancels first term in Step 2
—	Cancels first term in Step 1

one considers a system with perfect heat recovery for the warming and cooling steps. The only rejected heat is the heat lost isothermally at the lowest temperature. The limiting Carnot efficiency η_1 for the cycle, under the conditions specified in Table IX, is as follows:

$$\eta_1 = \frac{T_c - T_1}{T_c} = \frac{750 - 273}{750} \cong 0.64$$

The maximum efficiency η_2 defined by Equation 36 in the previous section is:

$$\eta_2 = \frac{\text{net work done}}{\text{total heat absorbed}} = \frac{n\mathcal{F}\mathcal{E}}{\Sigma Q}$$

The heat terms Q, corresponding to each step of the cycle given above, will now be examined. These terms were evaluated using parameters given in Table IX. Results are shown in Table X.

If the only heat rejected from the system is Q_3, the net heat absorbed is

$$\Sigma Q = 26{,}230 \text{ cal.}$$

Hence, the maximum efficiency for the cycle is

$$\eta_2 = \frac{-RT_c \ln P_1}{26{,}230} = \frac{11{,}700}{26{,}230} \cong 0.45$$

As a consequence of the fact that net heat is absorbed below T_c, Carnot efficiency $\eta_1 = 0.64$ cannot be achieved.

Without a heat exchanger, the maximum theoretical efficiency is given by:

$$\eta_3 = \frac{-RT \ln P_1}{Q_1 + \Sigma_4^8 Q}$$

To compute η_3, $T_c \Delta S^0$ must be evaluated.

The slope of the free energy of formation of lead iodide *vs.* temperature curve at 750°K. is approximately 26.6 entropy units (Figure 2), which is the standard entropy change for the electrolysis reaction.

Therefore

$$\eta_3 = \frac{11,700}{51,500} \cong 0.23$$

Operational efficiencies are much lower, of course. For the same cell parameters as given in the preceding section for calculating operational efficiencies, the present system is only about 15% efficient when used without a heat exchanger.

Discussion. As computed above, the net emf of a regenerative galvanic system based on PbI_2 with regeneration by electrolysis at reduced pressure (10^{-10} atm. I_2; dry-ice bath) is 0.7 volts.

Because the standard open circuit potential for a lead-iodine fuel cell at 750°K. is 0.7 volts, a dry-ice bath theoretically fixes the iodine pressure in the electrolysis cell at about the same partial pressure of iodine which is reached by the equilibrium thermal dissociation of lead iodide at 750°K.— i.e., $\Delta F \cong 0$ for electrolysis under these conditions. For still lower pressures of iodine, thermal decomposition of the electrolyte would occur spontaneously. In any case, such low pressures could never be achieved in this system because the vapor pressure of lead iodide is approximately 10^{-3} atm. at 750°K. (*29*), which is much higher than the calculated partial pressure of iodine.

Working pressures below that which corresponds to a trap temperature 0°C. should be considered unfeasible for the lead-iodine system. One can expect a maximum net potential of about 0.26 volt for the coupled system. Clearly, intermittent operation of the fuel cell alone, at an open-circuit potential of 0.7 volt, followed by regeneration (with several electrolyzers in series), is the preferable alternative here. Although the net maximum potential for the coupled system does not depend on the iodide salt chosen as electrolyte, other factors may influence this choice. For example, the vapor pressure of molten lithium iodide at 750°K. is only 10^{-6} atm. (*6*), and the standard open-circuit potential of a single lithium-iodine fuel cell is 2.6 volts at 750°K. (Table VII). However, the extremely corrosive action of lithium salts in contact with lithium metal is well-known; no insulating (ceramic) material has been found which will suitably contain molten lithium salt systems (*18*).

Several features of the systems, as disclosed by this analysis are summarized below:

· Efficiency—The step of the cycle in which the greatest amount of heat is absorbed is the isothermal electrolysis at reduced iodine pressure. For reversible electrolysis, the heat term associated with this step is energetically equivalent to the net maximum electrical work produced during one cycle. However, heat is also absorbed in phase transitions which occur between the cell temperature and the temperature of the cold trap, so that the ideal efficiency is considerably below the corresponding Carnot efficiency. For example, a system with a Carnot efficiency of 64% is found to have an ideal efficiency of only 45%. Without an efficient heat exchanger, the maximum possible efficiency for the same system is only 23%. Optimum operational efficiencies for the latter case are estimated to be in the neighborhood of 15%.

· Net voltage—For standard conditions in the fuel cell, a feasible "coupled" regenerative system is expected to yield rather low reversible potentials, of the order of 0.3 volt, even though the standard potential for the fuel cell alone may be as high as 2.6 volts (for the lithium-iodine system).

General limitations for the systems discussed in the previous section (systems utilizing high-temperature electrolysis) also apply to the present systems.

Thermally Regenerative Galvanic Systems: Regeneration by High Temperature Thermal Dissociation

One of the simplest chemical systems on which to base a thermally regenerative galvanic cell is a compound, AB, and its elements, A and B. The regenerative galvanic cell operates by means of a heat cycle in which the molal heat of dissociation of AB, absorbed at an elevated temperature T_2, acts to dissociate a mole of AB into its elements. The elements A and B are separated, cooled to a lower temperature T_1, and are then allowed to recombine electrochemically in the operation of a galvanic cell. In the operation of this cell, Q calories of heat are evolved. The electromotive force, $\mathcal{E}$, obtained from such a cell is $-\Delta F_f/n$, where ΔF_f is the molal free energy of formation of the compound AB at T_1, n is the number of faradays of electricity obtained per mole of AB formed in the cell reaction, and $\mathfrak{F}$ is the value of the faraday.

The efficiency of this cycle is given by Equation 36 for the case where all heat absorbed about T_1 is included:

$$\eta_2 = \frac{\text{net work done}}{\text{net heat added above } T_1} = \frac{-(\Delta F_1 + \Delta F_2)}{T_2 \Delta S_2 - \delta \int_{T_1}^{T_2} \Delta C_p \, dT} \tag{56}$$

In the derivation of Equation 56 all substances in the cycle are assumed to be in their standard states and all operations are carried out reversibly.

At first sight, it would appear for regeneration by thermal dissociation, where no electrical energy is required for compound dissociation at T_2, that all of ΔF_1 would be available for electrical work in the cell, and hence, a higher net emf would be available than when regeneration is done by electrolysis. The point overlooked is that, for the dissociation process to be reversible at T_2, it must be carried out at the vapor pressure P_e of the compound AB (Figure 4) in equilibrium with its gaseous dissociation products. If the reactant gas produced at equilibrium partial pressure P_e is fed to the galvanic cell at T_1 the resulting emf would be identical to the net emf from an electrolytically regenerative system which evolves gas at 1 atm. to feed to the cell at T_1. If the gas evolved at P_e were first compressed to 1 atm. at T_2 and then fed to the cell at T_1 an emf equivalent to ΔF_1 would be generated. But to do this, an additional amount of energy would have to enter the cycle to effect the compression; the efficiency would remain the same—i.e., η_2. For regeneration by thermal electrolysis, a more stable compound, such as CD (Figure 4), can be used which cannot be thermally dissociated at workable temperatures; the higher voltage given by the galvanic cell at T_1 is advantageous, even though the net emf is about

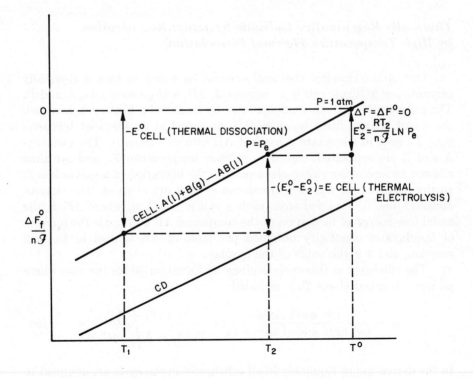

Figure 4. Regeneration by thermal dissociation vs. thermal electrolysis

the same as that for AB because the slopes of the lines, given by ΔS_f^0, are approximately equal. (This point is discussed later in the section.)

In the choice of a compound AB for use in such a system, several factors become of utmost importance. Many of these factors, such as electrolyte conductivity and operational temperature, are strongly influenced by the specific requirements for the overall system. However, there is one requirement which must be met regardless of other considerations—the dissociation products must be separable from each other. Whereas a conventional galvanic cell operates as an open system with continuous input of fresh reactants and output of the product of the cell reaction, a regenerative galvanic cell operates as a closed system in which the quantity of reactants is maintained constant by regeneration from the reaction product. The problem of separating chemically reactive species in a closed system at elevated temperatures is one of the most restrictive limitations to the selection of systems in which regeneration occurs by thermal dissociation.

The possibility of utilizing a thermal dissociation reaction of the type discussed above has been widely considered:

$$AB(l) \rightarrow A(l) + B(g)$$

The suffixes (l) and (g) denote liquid and gas. Probably the best known chemical systems of this type, which form bases for regenerative galvanic cells, are the Groups I and II metal hydrides. For example, the lithium-hydrogen system (7) has been extensively studied. Molten lithium and hydrogen gas react, respectively, at the anode and cathode of a galvanic cell, with a molten salt electrolyte containing lithium hydride. The lithium hydride can then be heated, below its boiling point, and dissociated into liquid lithium and hydrogen gas. Because only one gas is present in the regenerator, the problem of separating the elements for re-use in the galvanic cell is greatly simplified.

The desirability of having only one gaseous species liberated in the dissociation process leads to considering halides of the low-melting, high-boiling metals for possible use in a thermally regenerating galvanic (TRG) system. Many of the electrochemical characteristics of galvanic cells based on these salts are excellent. For example, iodine electrodes in molten iodides support high current densities with low polarization.

Furthermore, the exchange current density at the boundary between a liquid metal and a fused salt of this metal is large; consequently, these two phases are always in thermodynamic equilibrium (16). Hence, the primary consideration for TRG devices based on salts of the above type is the feasibility of regeneration by thermal dissociation.

A guiding principle, of great assistance in understanding the changes in compositions of phases that are produced by changes in temperature, is the so-called "principle of successive entropy states" (44). According to this principle, the stable products produced by increased temperature must always be phases whose total energy content and total entropy content are increased over those for the system at lower temperature.

This principle is important in considering a thermally regenerative galvanic system in which thermal dissociation is the mechanism of regeneration. In particular, it is desired to calculate the increase in extent of dissociation of a chemical system as the temperature is raised. Then one may know, if the desired amount of thermal dissociation can be achieved, whether experimental means to obtain it are available or not.

The galvanic cells discussed here utilize the reaction between gases and liquid metal elements to form a compound. Such a reaction is exothermic at feasible fuel cell temperatures. The reverse reaction, or the regeneration reaction, is endothermic. Dissociation is accompanied by absorption of Q calories of heat:

$$Q + AB \leftrightarrows A + B$$

Raising the temperature of the system tends to shift the position of the equilibrium to the right, provided, of course, that the reaction remains endothermic. This does not necessarily mean that the standard free energy of the reaction must change as the temperature is raised. From the relationship $(\partial \Delta F^0 / \partial T)_p = -\Delta S^0$, K for the above reaction must increase as the temperature is raised, but the product $T \log K$ will remain invariant if the standard entropy change is zero. This very situation is encountered above the boiling temperatures of several dihalide salts of the high boiling metals, as exemplified by stannous iodide. A thermochemical summary for this system is shown in Figure 5. For the calculations, it was assumed that the total pressure on the system is maintained at 1 atm. with an inert gas, so that the salt boils at its normal boiling temperature. No account has been taken of the species SnI in the equilibrium calculation. Liquid tin and gaseous iodine are the desired products of the thermal dissociation. The dissociation to tin and iodine is thermodynamically unfavorable, as is seen in Figure 5, and the situation becomes even less favorable for a more realistic appraisal, which takes into account the step-wise dissociation reactions. In all calculations, the standard state of iodine was taken as ideal gas at 1 atm. pressure for all temperatures.

The general behavior shown in Figure 5 for stannous iodide is also exhibited by lead iodide. Above the boiling point of the salt, the standard free energy for the reaction remains nearly constant as the temperature is raised. As a result, the shift in the equilibrium with temperature is very small, and there is little point in raising the temperature further. As has been pointed out, the equilibrium constant slowly continues to increase with increasing temperature, even though the standard free energy of reaction remains constant.

It is important to understand the far-reaching consequences of the restriction that only one gas may be produced in the reaction. As is well-

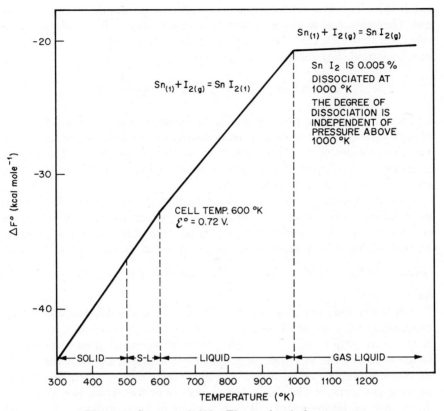

Figure 5. Stannous iodide: Thermochemical summary

known, the negative of the temperature coefficient of free energy of reaction is the entropy of reaction ΔS.

In the following table (44) average entropy changes are presented for a number of classes of reactions that involve changes in the number of gas molecules in the system:

Reaction Type	Number of Examples Averaged	Average ΔS (cal./°C.)
$1/nM(s) + F_2/2(g) = 1/nMF_n(s)$	10	-21.5 ± 1.6
$1/nM(s) + X_2/2(g) = 1/nMX_n(s)$	30	-19.8 ± 1.8
(X is Cl, Br, I)		
$2/nM(s) + O_2/2(g) = 1/nM_2O_n(s)$	19	-23.2 ± 1.5
$2/nM(s) + S_2/2(g) = 1/nM_2S_n(g)$	15	-20.8 ± 3.2
$3/nM(s) + N_2/2(g) = 1/nM_2N_n(s)$	7	-22.4 ± 2.3

It is immediately apparent from an examination of this table that, as an approximation, an entropy increase of 20 cal./°C. occurs whenever 0.5 mole of a diatomic gas is produced in a reaction that takes place under standard conditions. This is a consequence of the large translational entropy of the gas. Therefore, one might expect the entropy change to be small for simple reactions in which the number of gas molecules consumed and produced exactly cancel. For reactions of the type,

$$MX_\nu(g) = M_{(s, l)} + \frac{\nu}{2} X_2(g) \qquad (\nu = 1, 2)$$

i.e., above the boiling point of MX_2, ΔS becomes small, and ΔF ceases to change rapidly with increasing temperature, unless ΔS changes with temperature. Values of $\Delta C_p/T$ for reactions of the type considered above are generally so small that ΔS does not increase greatly again until the boiling point of the liquid metal is exceeded.

In this discussion it has been assumed that the metal from the thermal dissociation is present as a condensed phase, which means that the vapor pressure of the metal at the temperature of interest is less than or equal to the partial pressure of gaseous M, as calculated for the overall dissociation reaction $MX_\nu = M(g) + \frac{\nu}{2} X_2(g)$. This condition is satisfied for the tin-iodine system.

If the boiling point of the salt is not to be exceeded, the upper temperature limit is specified for a given system. Most important is the fact that the reversible emf of the galvanic cell operated near the melting temperature of the salt then places a practical upper limit on the degree of dissociation of the salt in the regenerator, for standard conditions, because the slope of the curve of free energy of formation per MX bond in the salt vs. temperature will have a value of approximately 20 entropy units.

$$M(l) + \frac{\nu}{2} X_2 = MX$$

$$\frac{\partial \Delta F^0/\nu}{\partial T} \sim -20 \text{ cal./mole } °C.$$

where p is constant.

For the metal halides, the galvanic cell anode reaction is:

$$M(l) = M^\nu + \nu e^-$$

There are ν electrons transferred for each mole of metal consumed electrochemically in the galvanic cell. But $\Delta F^0 = -\nu \mathfrak{F} \mathcal{E}^0$. Therefore,

$$-\left(\frac{\partial \mathcal{E}}{\partial T}\right)_p^0 = \frac{20}{23,060} \simeq 8.7 \times 10^{-4} \text{ volts/}°C.$$

This value generally decreases with increasing temperature. In any case, the negative temperature coefficients of galvanic cells of the above type will not exceed 1 mv./°C. A cell giving an open-circuit potential of 0.5 volt at the melting point of the salt would require a liquid range of more than 500°K. if an equilibrium constant of unity were to be reached at the dissociation temperature under standard conditions. The normal melting and boiling points of bromides and iodides for low melting, high boiling metals are given in Table XI, together with the standard reversible galvanic cell potentials at 500°K. The values of $\mathcal{E}^0$ were calculated from thermodynamic data (*33*).

In light of these considerations and the data in Table XI, it is easily seen that none of these systems is very attractive for regenerative galvanic cells utilizing thermal dissociation. The higher voltage systems cannot be regenerated by thermal dissociation. For the trihalides, there is some merit in exceeding the boiling point of the salt because there is still a net increase of 0.5 mole of diatomic gas for the reaction:

$$MX_3(g) = M(l) + \tfrac{3}{2}X_2(g)$$

The entropy change for the above reaction will still be roughly one-third of the entropy value at temperatures below the boiling point of the salt— i.e., for the following reaction:

$$MX_3(l) = M(l) + \tfrac{3}{2}X_2(g)$$

Therefore, ΔF^0 will continue to change as the temperature is raised, and the equilibrium constant for dissociation will increase more rapidly with temperature than it would if ΔF^0 remained constant ($\Delta S^0 = 0$).

Complex Ion Formation in Thermally Regenerative Galvanic Systems. Some of the primary drawbacks for utilizing regenerative galvanic systems arise from the rather high regenerator temperatures which must be reached in order to regenerate reactants for cells with appreciable voltages (~ 1 volts). This situation is a natural consequence of the fact that, for liberation of 0.5 mole of a diatomic gas from a simple salt of the gaseous element, the standard entropy change is ~ 20 entropy units.

Table XI. Melting and Boiling Points of Some Metals and Their Bromides and Iodides, and Their Galvanic Cell Potentials at 500°K.

	Metal		Bromide			Iodide		
Element	M. P. (°C.)	B. P. (°C.)	M. P. (°C.)	B. P. (°C.)	$\mathcal{E}^0$ (volts)	M. P. (°C.)	B. P. (°C.)	$\mathcal{E}^0$ (volts)
Bi^{3+}	271	1450	218	453	0.69	439	500	0.29
Ga^{3+}	30	1700	122	279	1.17	212	345	0.71
In^{3+}	155	1450	436	subl.	1.22	210	500	0.84
Li^{1+}	186	1340	547	1265	3.42	446	1190	2.80
Pb^{2+}	327	1620	373	918	1.22	402	954	0.84
Sn^{2+}	232	2260	216	620	1.15	320	720	0.80
Tl^{1+}	303	1650	460	815	1.59	440	824	1.24

Therefore, the rate of change with temperature of the standard free energy of formation of a simple salt, MX_ν, is roughly 20 entropy units times the number of M-X bonds which are broken, when X_2 is the only gas formed. This limit for the temperature coefficient of emf of about -0.87 mv./°C. applies to metal-halogen galvanic cells in which the electrolyte is the pure salt. It does not apply as a limit for salt-solvent electrolytes in which appreciable complex ion formation can take place. In principle, a complexing agent which acts to increase the open-circuit potential of a cell above the standard potential—i.e., the potential calculated for the same cell with pure salt electrolyte, can also increase the magnitude of the temperature coefficient. Under such circumstances, high cell voltage and regeneration by thermal dissociation become more compatible with each other than has been indicated thus far.

In the $M + X_2$ galvanic cell, each X-ion formed by the galvanic reaction is accompanied by the transfer of one electron from anode to cathode *via* the external circuit. Each M-X ionic bond formed in the galvanic cell reaction must later be broken by thermal energy in the dissociator, if the standard open-circuit voltage for formation of MX_ν is to be achieved by the regenerative system. One consequence of this energy balance is that, in order to reduce ΔF to a value near zero for regeneration of a 1-volt system (23 kcal./M-X bond), the dissociator temperature must be roughly 1000°C. above the temperature of the galvanic cell. This is desirable from the viewpoint of high ideal efficiency for the cycle. However, in view of the definite relationship between temperature and maximum electrical work, W, reversible heat absorbed, Q, and the ratio of work and heat (the efficiency), the range of choice among possible systems becomes extremely narrow. One seeks an additional independent variable so that, for given chemical elements M and X_2, and a given ratio of W to Q—i.e., for a given efficiency, the voltage and the absorbed heat can both be increased by a similar factor. This could be done if the electrochemical step, involving electron transfer, could be partially uncoupled from the heat step—i.e., from bond formation.

There is a way in which this might conceivably happen. If complex ion formation can occur, heat may be associated with formation of a number of relatively weak bonds to the electroactive ion which bonds are not involved in the electron transfer step. These bonds may be broken easily by thermal energy at higher temperatures, but to do so requires a large heat input per ion because there are many bonds involved. Thus, the complex ion regenerative galvanic system absorbs more heat per coulomb and produces a higher voltage than a simple galvanic system which operates between the same two temperatures and at the same ideal efficiency (neglecting the differences in ΔC_p between the simple galvanic reaction and the more complex reaction).

To illustrate further the above arguments, one may begin with the overall galvanic cell reaction:

$$M + X_2 = MX_2$$

Suppose the M^{2+} ion forms a complex ion with the element X when X_2 is dissolved in the electrolyte. The anode reaction then becomes

$$M + \left(\frac{\nu}{2}\right) X_2 = MX_\nu^{2+} + 2e^-$$

Although the standard free energy of formation of MX_2 may be close to zero, the open-circuit voltage of the cell can be appreciable because of the lowering of the M^{2+} ion activity through forming the MX_ν^{2+} complex. If ν is large and the solution (apart from the complexing) is an ideal solution, the entropy for dissociation of MX_ν^{2+} can be very large, perhaps as great as 20ν entropy units. If all the M-X bonds are relatively weak bonds, thermal dissociation can be accomplished at moderate elevations in temperature above the cell temperature, in order to regenerate X_2 and M. The ideal efficiency for the complete cycle will be low because of the relatively small temperature difference between galvanic cell and regenerator, but the open-circuit potential can still be appreciably high. As far as the qualitative argument is concerned, the complexing agent might be any species in the electrolyte. A large ratio of ν to n (n is the number of electrons transferred per mole of metal consumed) is desirable—i.e., the complex ion MX_ν^{n+} should have many ligands.

This same general argument should also apply for redox-type regenerative galvanic cells—i.e., for electrode reactions involving dissolved ions of polyvalent elements.

Suppose the following electrode reactions are considered:

Anode	$M^{2+} = M^{4+} + 2e^-$
Cathode	$M^{3+} + 2e^- = M^+$

Suppose that only the M^{4+} ion can form a complex ion when a complexing agent is present in the electrolyte. The effect of this complexing in an otherwise ideal solution is to increase the reversible cell potential and the magnitude of the entropy change for reaction. It is then conceivable that conditions might be found for which high cell voltages and thermal regeneration at only moderately elevated temperatures would become compatible conditions.

Product Separation. It has been stated that an inherent difficulty arises in devising a regenerative galvanic system whenever thermal dissociation and product separation are required. Before illustrating this, let us first review some of the previous remarks.

Suppose substances A and B are to react in a galvanic cell:

$$A + B \rightarrow C$$

For the cell to operate satisfactorily and with adequate current densities, the chemical reaction must be rapid at the low operating temperature. Generally, reaction rates increase with temperature. If the cell reaction is fast at low temperatures, then the back reaction of the thermal regeneration process must be very fast.

A few representative examples emphasize the arguments given here. Suppose the cell reaction is carried out at 500°K., and the thermal regeneration process is conducted at 1500°K. Assume that the products of the regeneration process have at 1500°K. equilibrium partial pressures of 0.1 atm. each. The half-time for the back reaction is

$$t_{1/2} = \frac{\ln 2}{k(A)_{eq.}} = \frac{\ln 2}{k(B)_{eq.}}$$

where k is the rate constant. The order of magnitude of the rate constant can be estimated from reaction rate theory and expressed as follows:

$$k = 10^8 \exp.\left(-\frac{E_A}{RT}\right) atm.^{-1} sec.^{-1}$$

The activation energy is E_A, and R is the gas constant. Thus, for A and B, the products of the thermal decomposition each at approximately 0.1 atm., the half-life of the back reaction is as follows:

$$t_{1/2} = 10^{-7} \exp.\left(\frac{E_A}{RT}\right) sec.$$

If the back reaction has zero activation energy, the half-life for recombination is about 10^{-7} sec. If the activation energy for the back reaction is 7 kcal./mole, the half-life is 10^{-6} sec. If the activation energy for the back reaction is 14 kcal., the half-life is 10^{-5} sec., etc. For the back reaction to be as slow as 0.01 sec. at 1500°K., the activation energy would have to be 35 kcal./mole. In this case, the half-life of the reaction at 500°K. would be ~ 1 yr.

These principles of system analysis will now be applied to the cadmium-iodine system.

Kinetic Evaluation of the Cadmium–Iodine System. For divalent metal halides MX_2, the following gaseous dissociation equilibria are commonly established at elevated temperatures:

(1) $MX_2 \leftrightarrows M + X_2$
(2) $MX_2 \leftrightarrows MX + \frac{1}{2}X_2$
(3) $X_2 \leftrightarrows 2X$

Thus, one would expect to find five gaseous species present in varying amounts when MX_2 is heated above its boiling point. For cadmium iodide, these species would be $CdI_2(g)$, $CdI(g)$, $I(g)$, and $I_2(g)$. Polynuclear species formation might also be possible, $Cd_xI_y(g)$. However, cadmium iodide vapor has not been examined for the existing polymeric species; they will be ignored here. In some cases, the MX radical may not be present in significant quantities in the equilibrium mixtures at high temperatures. Thus, Reaction 2 is apparently unimportant in the thermal dissociation of the mercury halides (*4*). In the case of cadmium iodide, however, radical formation is appreciable upon thermal dissociation. Weiland and Herczog (*51*) have calculated the theoretical partial pressures for each species in the equilibrium mixture of gases at elevated temperatures. The partial pressures of each of the five main species present in equilibrium with cadmium iodide at several temperatures and pressures are presented in Table XII.

An examination of the values in Table XII shows that the main equilibrium which is established between cadmium iodide and its dissociation fragments at 1400°K. at a total pressure of about 1 atm. is the following:

$$CdI_2 \leftrightharpoons CdI + I$$

From the free energy data (*51*), the pressure equilibrium constant may be calculated for the above reaction at 1400°K.:

$$\Delta F^0 = 13.8 \text{ kcal./mole}, \quad \text{and} \quad K_p = 7.25 \times 10^{-3} \text{ atm.}$$

It is convenient to convert K_p to K_c, the concentration equilibrium constant.

$$K_c = \frac{K_p}{RT} = 8.25 \times 10^{-5} \text{ moles/liter}$$

The following mechanism is assumed for the thermal dissociation of cadmium iodide:

Table XII. Partial Pressures at Equilibrium

Temperature (°K.)	Pressure (mm. of Hg)					
	CdI_2	CdI	I	Cd	I_2	Total
1200	6.15	0.57	1.94	0.75	0.07	9.48
	191.00	5.00	6.90	1.80	0.90	205.60
	581.10	10.00	10.50	2.40	2.10	606.10
1300	4.95	1.15	4.83	2.00	0.14	13.07
	197.10	11.80	18.60	5.40	2.00	234.90
	611.80	23.90	28.60	7.10	4.80	676.20
1400	2.95	1.65	9.53	4.12	0.19	18.44
	193.40	24.10	42.90	13.30	3.90	277.60
	624.60	50.00	68.60	17.70	9.40	768.50
1500	1.13	1.63	14.42	6.57	0.18	23.93
	176.50	42.30	86.50	28.50	6.50	340.30
	610.70	92.00	137.50	39.00	16.30	895.50

$$CdI_2 = CdI + I$$
$$I + CdI = Cd + I_2$$
$$I_2 = 2I$$

Treating unimolecular decomposition leads to the following expression for the forward rate constant:

$$k_1 = \frac{KT}{h} \exp. \left(-\frac{E_A}{RT}\right)$$

In this mechanism, the activation energy E_A may be taken as 50 kcal. mole^{-1} (10), the dissociation energy of Cd-I bond. Substituting appropriate constants and substituting 1400°K. for T yield the following:

$$k_1 = 5.24 \times 10^5 \text{ sec.}^{-1}$$

The specific rate constant for the recombination reaction may now be obtained:

$$CdI + I \xrightarrow{k_2} CdI_2$$

$$k_2 = \frac{k_1}{k_c} = \frac{5.24 \times 10^5 \text{ sec.}^{-1}}{8.25 \times 10^{-5} \text{ moles liter}^{-1}}$$

$$k_2 = 6.35 \times 10^9 \text{ liter mole}^{-1} \text{ sec.}^{-1} \cong 10^{10} \text{ liter mole}^{-1} \text{ sec.}^{-1}$$

Because a normal frequency factor for bimolecular reactions is about 10^{11} liter mole^{-1} sec.$^{-1}$ (21), the above value for k_2 indicates a very low energy barrier for recombining CdI and I. This result is as expected for radical reactions. A half-life of only 3×10^{-7} sec. is calculated for the above bimolecular association, as reckoned from the equilibrium concentrations of CdI(g) and I(g). (Each partial pressure is taken as about $\frac{1}{15}$ atm. at 1400°K., at a total pressure of 1 atm.)

Attempts to separate cadmium or iodine from the vapors in equilibrium with the thermally dissociated salt have been unsuccessful (2), as might be anticipated from the preceding analysis.

Photochemically Regenerative Galvanic Systems

Photochemically regenerative electrochemical systems may be analyzed on grounds which are conceptually similar to those for thermally regenerative cycles. In absence of illumination, the half-cell reaction proceeds in the usual way, as characterized by the thermodynamic and kinetic properties of the electrode-electrolyte system. However, light energy incident on the system may raise the potential of the electrode or electrolyte by raising the average energy of the charge carriers or reacting molecules. This process might be brought about thermally, except that the distribution of thermal energies at ordinary temperatures is such that only a very small fraction of the particles contain kinetic energies sufficiently great to collisionally excite a process in the energy range corresponding to the visible portion of the spectrum. There is not much point in discussing the Carnot-limiting efficiencies for photochemical cycles; the source temperatures entering such an analysis are so high that the energy distributions no longer resemble those found at ordinary temperatures. Solar photons emanate from a blackbody whose surface temperature is about 6000°K. The limiting Carnot efficiency for such a high source temperature is obviously very high.

The light energy absorbed is converted to potential energy in the absorber; this energy manifests itself as electrical energy through the mechanism of the electrode reactions, which may be used to reverse the normal or "dark" cell reaction, thereby storing energy for later use by regenerating the electrode reactant materials.

Before proceeding to a detailed discussion of particular systems, it is worthwhile to consider some of the criteria for photochemical reactions suitable for solar energy utilization (11):

· The photochemical reaction must be endothermic for energy storage to be possible.

· The quantum efficiency (i.e., ratio of the number of molecules of product formed to the number of photons absorbed) must be large.

· The reaction must be reversible, with the forward reaction being significantly faster than the reverse reaction.

· The reactants (or photosensitizer) should absorb a large fraction of the incident solar flux.

· The energy stored in the photoproducts should be large.

The conceptual basis for a photochemically regenerative galvanic system is a photo-induced reaction which results in products capable of being stored for use in a galvanic cell. Although many techniques have been suggested for incorporation into such a system, they can be generally classified into three basic approaches: direct or sensitized photolyses; photogalvanic effects; and photovoltaic processes. A detailed discussion of these processes is beyond the scope of this work, but is presented elsewhere (53).

From a kinetic standpoint, the direct photolysis and photogalvanic approaches are limited by the general rapidity of the back reactions characteristic of endothermic dissociation reactions. However, a photovoltaic process involving an electronic excitation followed by an interfacial electron-transfer reaction need not be subject to these limitations. Such a system would serve as an electrochemical analog of a p-n junction solar cell, while retaining an inherent electrochemical energy storage capacity.

Model Photochemically Regenerative Galvanic System. Consider the system composed of a photosensitive electrode immersed in an electrolyte containing an oxidation-reduction couple and separated from the counter electrode by a semi-permeable membrane (Figure 6).

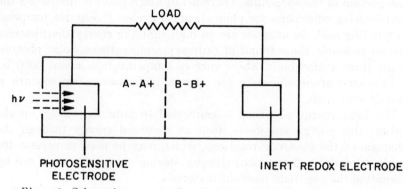

Figure 6. Schematic representation of a photochemically regenerative galvanic cell

At open circuit in the dark, the photosensitive electrode assumes a potential E_d^0, while the counter electrode assumes a potential E_B^0. With light incident upon it, the photosensitive electrode assumes a photo-induced potential E_*^0, characteristic of the light intensity, I_0. The photopotential E_ϕ^0 is the difference between the photo-induced potential and the dark potential ($E_\phi^0 = E_*^0 - E_d^0$). Thus, the open-circuit potential for the cell V^0 in the dark is equal to $E_B^0 - E_d^0$ while in the light it is $V^0 = E_B^0 - E_*^0$. By a judicious choice of the couple B^-B^+ and an appropriate light intensity I_0, it is possible to achieve the situation whereby $E_B^0 = E_*^0$, so that the cell potential, $V^0 = 0$. If the light intensity is now changed by an infinitesimal amount, V^0 will be infinitesimally different from zero. Completing the circuit through a load now allows this cell to run in a reversible fashion.

The regenerative aspects of such a system can be envisioned by considering the electrode reactions. For convenience, it is assumed that upon illumination the photosensitive electrode assumes an open-circuit potential more negative than that in the dark ($E_\phi^0 = E_*^0 - E_d^0 < 0$). The reaction then proceeding at this electrode would correspond to an oxidation of component A

$$A \rightarrow A^+ + e^-$$

At the counter electrode, component B^+ would be reduced

$$B^+ + e^- \rightarrow B$$

The overall cell reaction corresponds to

$$h\nu + A + B^+ \rightarrow A^+ + B$$

If illuminating the photosensitive electrode is terminated, the electrode reassumes its dark potential, E_d^0, and the cell potential now becomes $V^0 = E_B^0 - E_d^0$. Since E_d^0 is more positive than E_ϕ^0, the cell will tend to operate in the reverse direction, thereby returning to the original cell condition. This alternate light and dark cycle fulfills the conditions for regenerative operation of a galvanic cell.

The experimental details and a consideration of the mechanism and efficiency of a typical photovoltaic regenerative system are discussed in the following section. It should be emphasized that this discussion of photochemically regenerative cells is not intended to be a comprehensive treatment of all such conceivable systems, but rather to serve as an illustration of the concepts involved in such an approach.

Experimental Results.   Photogalvanic systems consisting of inert electrodes immersed in photochemically active solutions have received considerable attention in relation to regenerative galvanic cells. The conceptual feasibility of systems such as thionine-iron (*43*) and proflavine-ascorbic acid (*19*) has been demonstrated. However, such systems are limited by the fact that the photochemically generated species are created in the liquid phase and must diffuse to electrode surfaces to liberate energy. This diffusion process allows for considerable back-reaction of photochemical products and thus low operational efficiencies. These drawbacks can be overcome by restricting the photochemically active component to the electrode surface. The result of this type of modification is manifested in the occurrence of a photovoltaic rather than photogalvanic effect in the sense that the primary absorption act now occurs at the electrode surface rather than in the electrolyte.

A detailed study of such a system has been conducted, utilizing the diphenylnapthylmethane derivative dye Victoria Blue B (VBB) (*26*), deposited on platinum electrodes. Absorption spectra of VBB dissolved in methanol and of VBB deposited on glass, as well as reflection spectra of dye deposited on platinum, were measured. The absorption occurs in a broad band between 500 and 700 mμ, corresponding to the absorption of approximately 25% of the energy in the solar spectrum. The threshold wavelength is about 700 mμ. The energy content of 1 mole of quanta, which is an einstein, is given by the relation

$$Nh\nu = \frac{2.86 \times 10^4}{\lambda} \text{ kcal.}$$

where N is Avogadro's number, ν is the frequency of light, and h is Planck's constant (6.624×10^{-27} erg sec.). Thus, at 700 mμ, 1 einstein is equivalent to

$$\frac{2.86 \times 10^4}{700} = 40.8 \text{ kcal.}$$

The voltage equivalent of this energy is given by

$$\mathcal{E} = \frac{40.8 \text{ kcal}}{n\mathcal{F}}$$

where n is the electron exchange per molecule and $\mathcal{F}$ is the faraday (-23.060

kcal./volt equivalent). Assuming a 1-electron change and a thermodynamically reversible reaction, the maximum photopotential (i.e., the change of potential due to absorption of light quanta) to be expected is approximately 1.8 volts. Measured photopotentials are about 0.450 volts or about 10.4 kcal. Part of this loss is represented by the difference in electrochemical potential between the excited state of the dye and the electrolyte. The efficiency of energy absorption is $(10.4/40.8) \times 100$ or $\sim 25\%$.

EFFECT OF ELECTROLYTE COMPOSITION. Dye-coated electrodes, unlike soluble dyes, exhibit large photopotentials in the absence of reactive species in the electrolyte. Thus, a VBB-coated platinum electrode will develop a photopotential of ~ 0.4 volts at pH 7.0 in a deaerated solution (dark potential = 0.240 volt and photo-induced potential = -0.192 volt vs. Ag/AgCl electrode). However, only negligible currents can be obtained under these conditions.

Adding various inorganic redox couples influenced the direction and magnitude of the photopotential of VBB-coated electrodes, as shown in Table XIII. Both the dark and photo-induced potentials varied in the same fashion as the standard oxidation potential of the electrolyte.

For the systems described in Table XIII, only Sn^{2+} resulted in appreciable photocurrents. However, on repeated cycling of this system, the photocurrent and the photopotential decreased. Indeed, when equimolar solutions of Sn^{2+} and Sn^{4+} were used, the result was a rapid irreversible photobleaching of the dye. This suggests that the build-up of Sn^{4+} upon repeated cycling causes an irreversible bleaching of the dye.

The failure of inorganic couples led to an investigation of ascorbic acid. At pH 1.0, ascorbic acid did not produce any appreciable current because the dissociated acid is required for the electrode reaction. However, when the pH was increased to above 4, this reagent proved to be very effective. Because dehydroascorbic acid, the assumed product of the photochemical reaction, is known to undergo an irreversible hydrolysis above pH 5 (8), further investigation of this system was restricted to pH 4.0.

Table XIII. Photopotential of Victoria Blue B-Coated Electrodes with Various Inorganic Reagents

Reagent[a]	Standard Potential, E^0 (V)	Dark Potential,[b] E_0^0 (V)	Photo-induced Potential,[c] E_*^0 (V)	Photopotential,[c] E_ϕ^0 (V)
$Cr_2O_7^2$	-1.10	0.705	0.765	0.060
Fe^{2+}	-0.77	0.360	0.330	-0.030
Cu^{1+}	-0.15	0.130	-0.047	-0.177
Sn^{2+}	-0.07	0.041	-0.385	-0.426

[a] The concentration in all cases was 1×10^{-2} mole/liter of species indicated. The pH was 1.0.

[b] Potential vs. Ag, AgCl.

[c] $E_\phi^0 = E_*^0 - E_\phi^0$.

CONCENTRATION OF ASCORBIC ACID.   Increasing the concentration of ascorbic acid increased both the photopotential and the photocurrent. As shown in Figure 7, both the dark potential and the photo-induced potential increase logarithmically with the concentration of the ascorbic acid. However, the absolute slope of the photo-induced potential, -50 mv./log $[H_2A]$, where $[H_2A]$ is the concentration of the ascorbic acid, is larger than that of the dark potential -25 mv./log $[H_2A]$. The net result is an increase in the photopotential. The slopes also indicate that the potential–determining step in the light is a 1-electron change involving ascorbic acid, whereas that in the dark is a 2-electron change. This is based on assuming that the potential dependence on the ascorbic acid concentration is represented by a relationship similar in form to the Nernst equation—e.g.,

$$E = K \frac{RT}{n\mathfrak{F}} \ln Q$$

or that the following expression for its derivative at 25°C. holds:

$$\frac{\partial E}{\partial \ln Q} = \frac{59 \text{ mv.}}{n}$$

where E is the measured potential; K is a constant related to the standard

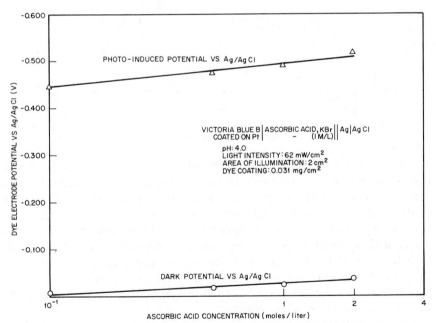

Figure 7. Dark potential and photo-induced potential of Victoria Blue B-coated electrodes as a function of ascorbic acid concentration

potential; Q is a function of the concentration of ascorbic acid; and n, R, $\mathfrak{F}$, and T have their usual meanings.

In Figure 8 current-potential curves for the VBB-coated electrodes as a function of ascorbic acid concentration are shown. The differences in the curves observed at low current density merely reflect the variation of the zero current potentials of the electrode with concentration. At the limiting current, there is little difference between the curves except at a 0.1 mole/liter concentration where the limiting current is appreciably smaller. These current-potential curves indicate that concentration polarization of some kind is limiting the current output.

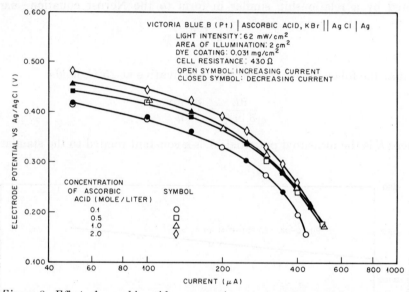

Figure 8. Effect of ascorbic acid concentration on current-potential curves for the Victoria Blue B-coated electrode

WAVELENGTH DEPENDENCE.   The photo-induced potential (and thus the photopotential) was found to be independent of wavelength. This confirms the threshold theory, which states that the incident quanta must contain sufficient energy to excite the electron and that any energy above this value is wasted. However, the current (and therefore the energy output) is a direct function of the rate at which quanta are absorbed and should be a function of the rate at which incident energy is absorbed. As shown in Figure 9, the relative energy conversion yield closely follows the absorption spectrum, verifying that protons absorbed by the dye only are responsible for the observed photo effects.

LIGHT INTENSITY DEPENDENCE.   Light intensity is expected to have two effects. The limiting current is expected to have a linear dependence

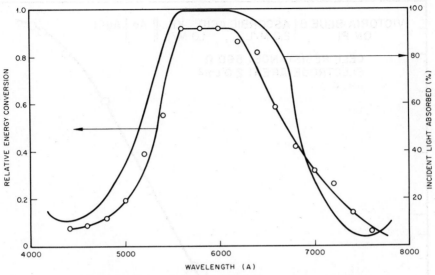
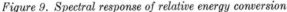

Figure 9. Spectral response of relative energy conversion

on intensity, and the open-circuit, steady-state concentration of the electrode active material is expected to increase with intensity, resulting in a logarithmic change in the zero current potential.

Figure 10 shows the variation of the logarithm of the current as a function of the logarithm of the light intensity. The current is shown to increase linearly up to a light intensity of 100 mw./sq. cm., followed by a current saturation region.

The variation of the photopotential as a function of the logarithm of the light intensity is shown in Figure 11. It can be seen that the photopotential is a monotonic function of the light intensity. The linear portion between 1 and 100 mw./sq. cm. has a slope of 0.055 volt/log I_φ. This could be explained by a Nernst-type relationship of the form

$$E = E_0 - \frac{RT}{n} \log I_\phi$$

where I_ϕ is the light intensity and the other symbols have their usual meanings. In this case, the slope of the straight-line plot is $0.059/n$. The actual slope of 0.055 strongly suggests a reaction mechanism involving a 1-electron change as the rate-determining step.

EFFECT OF THE THICKNESS OF THE DYE COATING. It was expected that, as the thickness of the dye coating increased, a larger percentage of the incident light would be absorbed, as was found to be the case. However, the quantum yield of electrons defined as

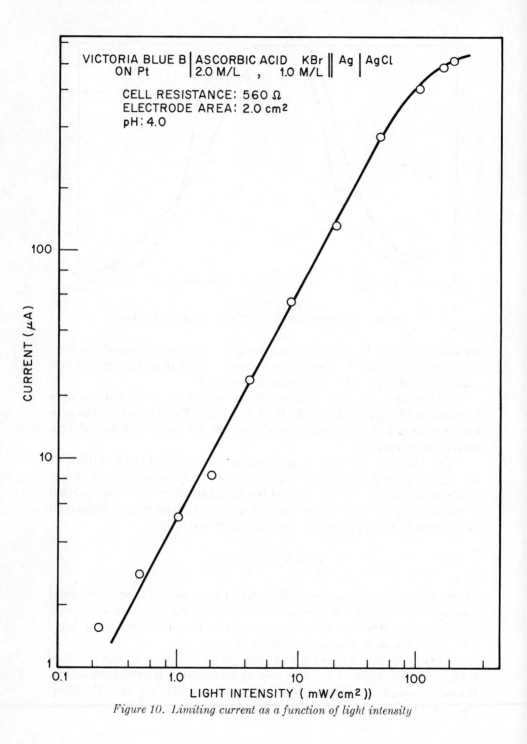

Figure 10. *Limiting current as a function of light intensity*

$$\phi_\lambda = \frac{\text{electrons produced}}{\text{photons absorbed}}$$

at a fixed load and at a wavelength λ of 598 mμ decreased (Figure 12).

Figure 13 shows the effect of the dye thickness on the energy-conversion ratio energy (energy output/energy absorbed). It can be seen that the energy conversion efficiency decreased rapidly as the thickness of the dye film increased. The optimum value occurred with 5×10^{-6} gram of dye/sq. cm. electrode surface, corresponding to a surface coverage of approximately 10 monolayers of dye.

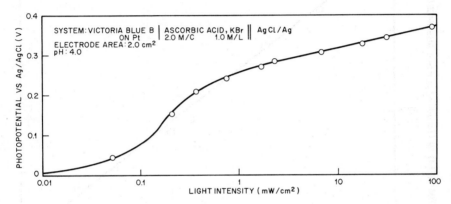

Figure 11. Photopotential as a function of light intensity

MECHANISM OF DYE-COATED ELECTRODE ENERGY CONVERSION. It is generally accepted that photogalvanic effects are associated primarily with volume properties of material, whereas photovoltaic effects are associated with surface properties and the interfaces between phases. The interface may be between two solids such as a metal semiconductor, two semiconductors, a solid and a gas, or a solid and a liquid. The interface presents an energy barrier to the diffusion of electrons. Upon illumination, electrons are excited to higher energy levels and are transferred across the interface, causing a potential difference across the barrier.

In the case of dye-coated electrodes, two such interfaces exist: one between the dye and the metal and the other between the dye and the solution. When the dye is illuminated, electrons are raised to the conduction band of the dye. These electrons may recombine with the vacated holes, in which case they would not contribute to the photopotential; they may be transferred to the platinum electrode, in which case a negative photopotential would be observed; or they may migrate to the solution interface and generate a positive photopotential. The sign and magnitude of the photopotential are thus determined by the potential of the electrolyte

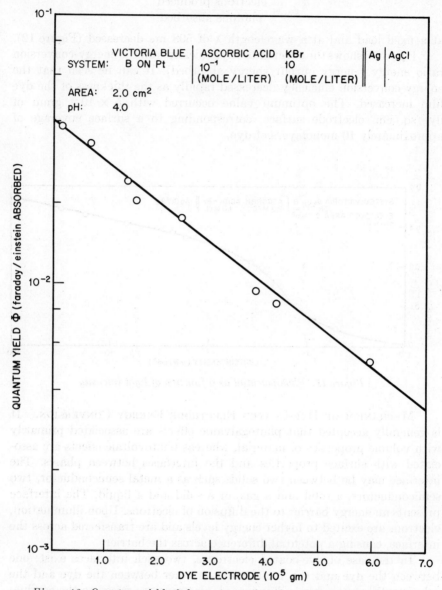

Figure 12. Quantum yield of electrons as a function of dye coating thickness

in contact with the dye. Strong reducing agents will repel electrons so that the electrons will tend to flow toward the metal interface, thereby creating a negative photopotential.

On the other hand, in the presence of weaker reducing agents or stronger oxidizing agents, the direction of electron migration will tend to be reversed, causing more positive photopotentials. The dye thus acts as an electron pump between an electron reservoir and an electron sink.

On this basis, an explanation of the effect of dye thickness on the quantum efficiency can be given. Increasing the film thickness of the dye, which is a poor conductor, presents increased resistance to the flow of electrons. In addition, for current to flow, the carriers generated by light

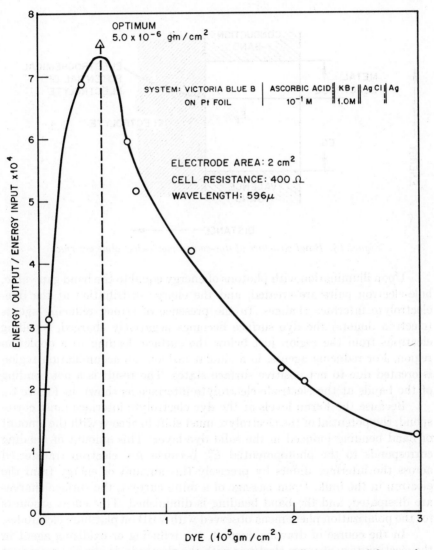

Figure 13. Energy conversion efficiency as a function of the amount of dye on the electrode

must migrate to one of the interfaces. The probability of a charge carrier diffusing to the interface falls off rapidly as the thickness of the dye layer increases.

This model is most easily described in terms of band theory of solids. As shown in Figure 14, the valence band is separated from the conduction band by a forbidden energy gap, the electrochemical potential of electrons (Fermi level E_F) residing in this gap. At equilibrium, the electrochemical potential of the solid dye coincides with that of the contacting solution.

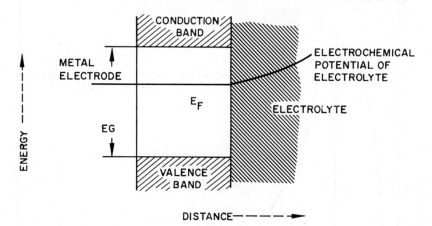

Figure 14. Band structure of dye-coated metal-electrolyte interface

Upon illumination with photons of energy equal to the band gap value, hole-electron pairs are created, and the charge distribution at the dye-electrolyte interface changes. In the presence of strong reducing agents (electron donors) the dye surface becomes negatively charged, repelling electrons from the region just below the surface, leading to a depletion region. For reducing agents, in a similar fashion, an accumulation region is created due to net positive surface states. The result is a net bending of the bands at the electrode-electrolyte interface as shown in Figure 15.

Because the Fermi levels at the dye-electrolyte interface must correspond, the potential of the electrolyte must shift in accord with the amount of band bending induced in the solid dye layer. This amount of bending corresponds to the photopotential E_ϕ^0, because any electron transferred across the interface differs by precisely this amount of energy from the electron in the bulk. Upon passage of a finite current, the surface charges are dissipated, and the band bending is diminished. This effect accounts for the polarization phenomena observed with VBB on platinum electrodes.

In the course of drawing current, the reducing or oxidizing agent in the electrolyte exchanges electrons with the electrode, leading to a product in the solution of a distinctly different oxidation state from the original

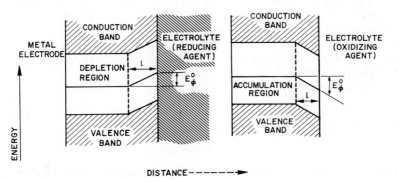

Figure 15. Changes in band structure of dye-coated electrode-electrolyte when illuminated in presence of reducing and oxidizing solutions

reactant. In the case of ascorbic acid as the reducing agent, the product is dehydroascorbic acid. This stable species accumulates and can be used as fuel in a parallel cell or used to run the original cell in reverse of the photochemical mode.

ENERGY CONVERSION EFFICIENCY OF THE VICTORIA BLUE B-ASCORBIC ACID SYSTEM.   The maximum power density box cell, using 2 moles/liter of ascorbic acid and an Ag/AgCl working electrode, was 135 μw./sq. cm. at a power input of 62 mw./sq. cm. Thus, the overall power conversion efficiency was 0.22%.

During the course of operating this system, the number of faradays of electricity generated at the dye-electrolyte interface was greater than 1000 times the number of moles of dye on the electrode. This conclusively demonstrates that the Victoria Blue B electrode is not consumed during the reduction of ascorbic acid, but functions as an inert electrode which exchanges electrons with the oxidation-reduction couple in contact with it under the influence of photons of appropriate energy.

The properties of a dye-coated electrode dipping into an electrolyte may be likened to a *p-n* junction type of solar cell. The dye is considered to be a *p*-type semiconductor and the electrolyte with an *n*-type reducing agent. The losses of efficiency can now be compared to those of solar cells. Kleinman (*30*) and Wolfe (*52*) attributed losses of efficiency in solar cells to the following:

    · Reflection loss. This is a surface effect and with dye systems is probably low.

    · Absorption of only part of the solar spectrum.

    · Utilizing only part of the energy of the incident photon in the excitation step. Only those photons whose energy is equivalent to the threshold energy can be completely utilized. Energy in excess of that needed to excite the electron is dissipated as heat.

· Incomplete collection of the current-carrying particle. Applied to the dye system, this is caused by radiative decay or collision with foreign particles before reaction with the reducing agent can take place.

· Junction loss. This is the difference between the theoretical energy gap and the observed open-circuit voltage and is due to diffusion of charges across the p-n junction.

· Resistive loss.

For solar cells, the efficiency defined as the quotient of power output to incident solar power may be written as

$$\eta = t_s v m \mu$$

where μ is the ultimate efficiency based on energy gap considerations, v is the ratio of the open-circuit voltage to the gap voltage, t_s is the probability that an incident photon creates an electron hole pair, and m is an impedance matching factor defined as the ratio of the power obtainable in a matched load to the product of open-circuit voltage and short-circuit current (52).

The dye-coated electrode system differs somewhat from ordinary solar cells, so that two more factors must be introduced into the expression for the efficiency: f is the fraction of incident light absorbed in the visible region and must be included because the dye does not absorb all wavelengths greater than threshold, and η_e is the electrochemical efficiency at the dye-solution interface. Thus, the expression for overall efficiency is given by

$$\eta_{\text{overall}} = t_s v m \mu f \eta_e$$

In this work it has been found that

$$\mu = 0.42$$
$$v = 0.26$$
$$m = 0.46$$
$$f = 0.40$$

No estimates of η_e have been possible, so that maximum values of unity have been assigned to these quantities. Using these values, an estimate of the maximum efficiency can be made. Based on quantum yield measurements, mobility estimates, and lifetime of hole-electron pair calculations, a value of 0.1 for t_s appears reasonable.

Using the tabulated values, it is apparent that

$$\eta \cong 0.2\%$$

under idealized conditions.

The maximum power-conversion efficiency found under static conditions was of the order of 0.2%, corresponding well to the maximum calculated efficiency.

Conclusions.   This study clearly indicates the conceptual feasibility of a model photochemically regenerative emf cell but also strikingly demonstrates the practical efficiency limitations of such systems. The system described is by no means an optimum one, and efficiency improvements of at least an order of magnitude may be readily anticipated. However, it is unlikely that such systems could even approach such conventional power sources as solar cells and storage batteries in terms of simplicity, efficiency, and reliability.

Nomenclature. Because some confusion exists in the literature, the definitions and symbols used in this section are summarized below:

· The dark potential E_d^0 is the potential relative to a standard reference cell, which the photosensitive electrode assumes in the absence of light under open-circuit conditions.

· The photo-induced potential E_*^0 is the potential which the photosensitive electrode assumes upon illumination at open-circuit relative to a standard cell.

· The photopotential E_ϕ^0 is the change in the photosensitive electrode potential resulting from illumination. Thus, $E_\phi^0 = E_*^0 - E_d^0$.

Conclusions

The desirability of any power source is, in general, determined by two major considerations: efficiency and reliability. For regenerative systems, designed to operate continuously for long periods of time without maintenance, these factors assume even greater importance. Efficiency considerations demand that practical thermal or photoregenerative electrochemical systems have efficiencies comparable with those of conventional devices, such as silicon solar cells or thermoelectric systems. High degrees of reliability and compatibility with environment demand simplicity of design and operation, a minimum number of moving parts, and, for space applications, operational characteristics independent of gravitational effects.

Photochemically regenerative electrochemical devices must compete with solar cell-storage battery systems. Therefore, efficiencies must be comparable or storage capacity must compensate for lower efficiencies. The photochemical system described here, however, proved to have operational efficiencies two orders of magnitude lower than desired. In this case, the energy storage capacity does not compensate for the low efficiency. Many of the factors which set an upper limit on the efficiency of solar cells, however, cannot be applied to photoregenerative chemical systems. Therefore, efficiencies of the order of 20% are theoretically possible. The possibility is not to be precluded that future developments in photochemistry may result in new systems that can be incorporated into photoregenerative electrochemical systems capable of achieving more efficient conversion of light into electrical energy.

Thermally regenerative chemical systems pose many basic problems. Although high power density galvanic cells can be operated, continuous regeneration of the reactant materials is not easily achieved. Thermal dissociation of the cell reaction product is thermodynamically possible in many cases. However, efficient separation of dissociation products is complicated in most instances by rapid back reactions.

Evaluation of alternative methods of regeneration has indicated that electrolytic regenerative methods conceivably could be incorporated into high efficiency systems. Any of these systems, while theoretically feasible, appear to be operationally limited owing to the inherent complexity of the complete assemblies.

Thermocell devices are feasible, but efficiencies are low, and no energy storage capacity exists. It is in the studies of thermocells, however, that the key to understanding individual electrode temperature response is to be found. Such understanding is basic for analyzing nonisothermal electrochemical systems.

At present, developing reliable and efficient thermally regenerative electrochemical systems is severely hampered by materials problems. Lack of suitable construction materials resistant to high temperature corrosion by fused salts and reactive gases remains a major obstacle to future progress. It is evident that at the present state-of-the-art, neither photochemically nor thermally regenerative electrochemical systems can compete with conventional power sources. Advances in this area will depend upon well-conceived basic research efforts in photochemistry, high-temperature electrochemistry, and material sciences.

Acknowledgments

We wish to acknowledge the valuable contributions of Dr. Herbert P. Silverman who formulated and directed the work on photochemically regenerative electrochemical systems.

We also wish to thank Prof. Harold S. Johnston, Department of Chemistry, University of California, Berkeley, for his help in the theoretical analysis of the thermally regenerative systems discussed.

Most of this work was supported by the Advanced Research Projects Agency through the United States Army Electronics Command (Contract DA 36-039 SC-85245 ARPA Order Nos. 80-59 and 80-61).

The major portion of the work on thermocells was done on the Lockheed Missiles & Space Co. Independent Research Program.

Literature Cited

(1) Agar, J. N., Breck, W. G., *Trans. Faraday Soc.* **53,** 167 (1957).
(2) Anderson, L. B., Ballou, E. V., Greenberg, S. A., Final Report, Contract DA-36-039 SC-85245, Lockheed Missiles & Space Co., Sept. 1962.

(3) Bockris, J. O'M. *et al.*, *Proc. Roy. Soc.* **A255,** 558 (1960).
(4) Braune, H., Knoke, S., *Z. Physik. Chem.* **152,** 409 (1931).
(5) Brewer, L., Somayajulu, G. R., Brackett, E., *Chem. Rev.* **63,** 111 (1963).
(6) Brewer, L. *et al.*, "The Chemistry and Metallurgy of Miscellaneous Materials —Thermodynamics," L. L. Quill, ed., p. 76, McGraw-Hill, New York, 1950.
(7) Ciarlariello, T. A., McDonough, J. B., Shearer, R. E., "Study of Energy Conversion Devices," Report No. 7 (Final), prepared for USRDL by MSA Research Corp., MSAR 61-99, Callery, Pa., 1961.
(8) Clark, W. M., "Oxidation—Reduction Potentials of Organic Systems," Williams and Wilkins Co., Baltimore, 1960.
(9) Conway, B. E., "Electrochemical Data," Elsevier Publishing Co., New York, 1952.
(10) Cottrell, T. L., "The Strength of Chemical Bonds," London, Butterworths Scientific Publications, 1954.
(11) Daniels, F., Heidt, L. J., Livingston, R. S., Rabinowitch, E., "Photochemistry in the Liquid and Solid States," pp. 1–8, John Wiley & Sons, New York, 1960.
(12) deBethune, A. J., Licht, T. S., Swendeman, N., *J. Electrochem. Soc.* **106,** 616 (1959).
(13) deBethune, A. J., *J. Electrochem. Soc.* **107,** 937 (1960).
(14) deGroot, S. R., *J. Phys. Radium* **8,** 188, 193 (1947).
(15) deGroot, S. R., "Thermodynamics of Irreversible Processes," p. 225, Interscience, Inc., New York, 1952.
(16) Delimarksi, I. V. K., Markov, B. B., "Electrochemistry of Fused Salts," chap. 7, Sigma Press, Washington, D. C., 1961.
(17) Detig, R. H., Archer, D. H., *J. Chem. Phys.* **38,** 661 (1963).
(18) Dworkin, A. S., Bronstein, H. R., Bredig., A. M., *J. Phys. Chem.* **66,** 572 (1962).
(19) Eisenberg, M., Silverman, H. P., *Electrochem. Acta* **5,** 1 (1961).
(20) Fischer, W., *Z. Naturforsch.* **21a,** 281 (1966).
(21) Frost, A. A., Pearson, R. G., "Kinetics and Mechanisms," John Wiley & Sons, New York, 1953.
(22) Gambill, W. R., *Chem. Eng.* **129,** 10 August 1959.
(23) Haber, F., Kerschbaum, F., *Z. Electrochem.* **20,** 303 (1914).
(24) Holtan, H., Jr., Thesis, Utrecht, 1953: *Proc. Akad. Wetenshop.* **56B,** 498 (1953): **57B,** 1109 (1953).
(25) Holtan, H., Jr., Mazur, P., deGroot, S. R., *Physica.* **19,** 1109 (1953).
(26) I. G. Farbenindustrie, FIAT 1313, Vol. II, p. 321 (PB 85172).
(27) Johnston, H. S., private communication.
(28) Meissner, H. P. *et al.*, *Adv. Energy Conversion* **5,** 205 (1965).
(29) Kelley, K. K., "Contributions to the Data on Theoretical Metallurgy: XIII, High Temperature Heat-Content, Heat-Capacity, and Entropy Data for Inorganic Compounds," U. S. Bureau of Mines Bull. **584** (1960).
(30) Kleinman, D. A., *Bell Systems Tech. J.* **40,** 85 (1961).
(31) Latimer, W. M., "Oxidation Potentials," Prentice-Hall, Inc., Englewood Cliffs, N. J., 1952.
(32) Liebhafsky, H. A., *J. Electrochem. Soc.* **106,** 1068 (1959).
(33) Ludwig, F. A., ASTIA Report AD 255463, November 1960.
(34) Markov, B. F., *Doklad. Akad. Nauk, SSR* **108,** 115 (1956).
(35) Matsen, J. M., *J. Electrochem. Soc.* **108,** 608 (1961).
(36) Mazur, P., *J. Phys. Chem.* **58,** 700 (1954).
(37) Miller, D. G., *Chem. Rev.* **60,** 15 (1960).
(38) Nichols, A. R., Jr., Langford, C. T., *J. Electrochem. Soc.* **107,** 842 (1960).
(39) Onsager, L., *Phys. Rev.* **37,** 405 (1931); **38,** 2265 (1931).
(40) Oredale, T., Wallace, W. N. W., *Phil. Mag.* **88,** 1097 (1929).
(41) Pitzer, K. S., *J. Phys. Chem.* **65,** 147 (1961).
(42) Poincare, L., *Ann. Chim. Phys.* (6) **21,** 289 (1890).
(43) Rabinowitch, E., *J. Chem. Phys.* **8,** 551 (1940).
(44) Searcy, A. W., "Progress in Inorganic Chemistry," F. A. Cotton, ed., Interscience, New York, 1962.

(45) Senderoff, S., Bretz, R. I., *J. Electrochem. Soc.* **109**, 56 (1962).
(46) Stull, D. R., Sinke, G. S., "Thermodynamic Properties of the Elements,"
    J. Am. Chem. Soc., Washington, D. C. (1956).
(47) Sundheim, B. R., Kellner, J. D., *J. Phys. Chem.* **59**, 1204 (1965).
(48) Temkin, M. I., Khoroshin, A. V., *Zh. Fiz. Khim.* **26**, 500 (1952).
(49) Turnbull, A. G., *Australian J. Appl. Sci.* **12**, 324 (1961).
(50) Wartanowicz, T., *Advan. Energy Conversion* **4**, 149 (1964).
(51) Wieland, K., Herczog, A., *Helv. Chim. Acta* **29**, 1702 (1946).
(52) Wolfe, M., *Proc. I. R. E.* **48**, 1246 (1960).
(53) Zarem, A. M., ed., "Introduction to the Utilization of Solar Energy,"
    McGraw-Hill, New York, 1963.

RECEIVED May 25, 1966.

16

Chemically Regenerative, Fuel Cell Systems

JOHN M. MATSEN

Esso Research & Engineering Co., Linden, N. J.

Chemically regenerative, fuel cell systems have long been studied in the hope of circumventing the problems of direct electrochemical reaction of fuels and air. These cells employ reaction intermediates which readily react at the electrodes and which are then regenerated with fuel and/or air. Such schemes received considerable attention at the turn of the century, and some studies have been made recently with difficult fuels such as coal. The present trend, however, is to highly reactive fuels which readily undergo direct electrode reaction and to military or space applications where the additional weight and complexity of chemically regenerative systems is highly undesirable.

The possibility of obtaining electrical energy from an electrochemical reaction between air and common fuels has been recognized for over 160 years, almost as long as knowledge of any type of galvanic cell has existed. Progress toward this end has been slow, primarily for two reasons: (1) common fuels and air are typically unreactive in processes less violent than combustion; (2) difficulties exist in bringing even the more reactive fuels, such as hydrogen, properly to an electrode surface to cause the desired reaction, accompanied by the release of electrons. Chemically regenerated, fuel cell systems try to circumvent these problems. Such cells use reactive (but expensive) intermediate substances which readily participate in the electron-exchanging reactions of oxidation at the anode or reduction at the cathode. Having reacted within the cell to produce an electric current, the intermediate reaction products are then removed from the electrodes and regenerated by chemical reaction with fuel or air. The regeneration is facilitated because no electrodes take part and because it can be carried out under optimum conditions for regeneration with little regard for conditions within the fuel cell.

Chemically regenerative systems are generally inefficient because intermediate reactions are introduced that can never be totally efficient. There are no inherent limitations, however, such as exist for thermally regenerative, fuel cell systems which are subject to Carnot cycle efficiency.

For research purposes, a regenerative, fuel cell system can be broken down into four reactions—anode reaction, intermediate fuel regeneration, cathode reaction, and intermediate oxidant regeneration, all of which may be investigated separately. These individual reactions are either already known or easy to postulate with pencil and paper. It is possible, too, to combine one regenerative electrode with another direct electrode or, for experimental work, with a driver electrode. Much of the effort on chemically regenerative cells has not resulted in complete integrated systems but has rather studied only one of the reactions or, occasionally, has postulated the entire scheme.

Chemically regenerative cells may be classified according to the type of the reactant fed to the electrode. Many studies have been made with metallic and gaseous intermediates, although these are now mostly of historical interest. Redox fuel cells, using dissolved reactants, have historical aspects but have also been subject to extensive research in the past decade.

Cells with Metallic Intermediates

Perhaps the first chemically regenerative, fuel cell system to be proposed was that of Faure (12) in 1891. His system used a consumable iron anode in an aqueous sodium chloride electrolyte. After the iron had been oxidized to ferrous ion, it was separated by precipitation as iron carbonate. The carbonate was then reduced to iron by reaction with fuel.

Rawson (34) proposed a high temperature cell in which a fused salt oxidized a metal such as lead in the anodic reaction. The metal oxide was then reduced by carbon or other reducing agent, and the salt was regenerated by oxygen. No performance figures were quoted, but temperatures of 1850°F. were necessary for best operation with lead. Such temperatures present formidable problems even today.

Tourneur (45) patented a system in which K_2S was anodically oxidized to K_2SO_4. This was separated by crystallization and reduced to the sulfide in a furnace. The cathode consisted of air bubbled over a carbon electrode which was immersed in an electrolyte of nitric acid. A semipermeable membrane separated the anode and cathode compartments so that direct reaction could not occur.

One of the few American workers in fuel cells at the turn of the century was Jone (19), who patented a rather roundabout system. When a consumable tin anode was immersed in an electrolyte of potassium hydroxide, potassium stannite formed. Barium hydroxide was added periodically to precipitate barium stannite. The precipitate was removed from the cell and heated with carbon or carbon monoxide to yield tin and barium oxide. At the cathode, mercuric oxide was reduced to mercurous oxide, which was removed and dissolved in nitric acid. The resulting mercurous nitrate was heated to regenerate the mercuric oxide and yield nitrogen oxides, which were reconverted to nitric acid by air oxidation. Jone claimed a 20% energy recovery was possible for this scheme.

Rideal and Evans (*37*) in 1921 suggested several types of regenerative cells. One used tin anodes in an electrolyte of molten sodium carbonate. The reaction product was sodium stannate dissolved in the electrolyte and, when this was treated with fuel, tin globules precipitated for reuse at the anode. A second cell used tin anodes in an aqueous HCl electrolyte. Tin chloride precipitated and could then be filtered and reduced to tin. A third type was essentially a chemical regeneration scheme superimposed on the Edison cell. An iron anode was oxidized to iron hydroxides while nickel hydroxides were reduced cathodically. The electrolytes were periodically regenerated by heat and a reducing or oxidizing agent.

There has recently been a report (*29*) of a metal anode, regenerative cell which is being developed in the Department of Fuel Technology at Sheffield University. At room temperature, the cell oxidized a metal and, at a high temperature, this was then reduced with coal. In 1961 the scheme had been developed at the prototype stage.

Most recently, Roulin and Lehmann (*38*) operated a high-temperature tin, regenerative cell with an electrolyte of alumina or calcium oxide in molten cryolite. A layer of tin on the base of the cell served as anode. Being insoluble, the tin oxide product floated to the electrolyte surface. Carbon monoxide sparged through the electrolyte and reduced the oxide so that tin precipitated back to the anode. The cathode was molten silver, through which air was bubbled. At 980°C., the cell gave 0.8 volt at open circuit. All polarization losses seemed to be resistive, and at short circuit the cell produced 1.3 amp. from a cathode area of 3.8 sq. cm.

Cells with Gaseous Intermediates

The second type of cell with chemical regeneration uses a gaseous intermediate as the cell fuel or oxidant. The first one of this type was perhaps the Reed's (*35*) cell, which consumed CS_2 at the anode and SO_2 at the cathode to give the overall cell reaction of $2H_2S + SO_2 \rightarrow 2H_2O + 3S$. The regeneration reactions were:

$$S + O_2 \rightarrow SO_2$$

and

$$C + S_2 \rightarrow CS_2$$

$$CS_2 + 2H_2O \rightarrow 2H_2S + CO_2.$$

Heat was exchanged between several steps in the process, and an overall efficiency of 61% was thermodynamically possible. From a working cell, Reed obtained 0.36 volt, compared with the figure of 0.63 volt that was theoretically attainable.

Jungner (*20*) used SO_2 as the anode fuel, oxidizing it to H_2SO_4 by bubbling it through an anode compartment filled with carbon chunks. A porous diaphragm isolated the cathode which used air with a catholyte of nitrosyl sulfuric acid. The cell gave 0.5 volt at 70°C. and open circuit.

Taitlebaum (*43*), working with the same anode system, substituted redox couples at the cathode. The V^{+4}/V^{+5} couple worked best, giving up to 0.6 volt without load, but it polarized rapidly.

Taking advantage of the relatively high, cathodic activity of chlorine, Nernst (*26*) devised a hydrogen-chlorine cell. Hydrochloric acid was both the reaction product and the electrolyte. Chlorine was recovered from this by the Deacon process,

$$2 \, HCl + \tfrac{1}{2} O_2 \rightleftarrows Cl_2 + H_2O.$$

Unfortunately, the Deacon process has an unfavorable equilibrium at high temperatures and a low reaction rate at thermodynamically reasonable temperatures.

The patents of Gorin (*13, 14, 15*) in the early 1950's disclosed an integrated coal gasification-carbon monoxide cell which might be classed as partially regenerative. The cell consumed CO and oxygen: $2 \, CO + O_2 \rightarrow 2 \, CO_2$. Half of the CO_2 was then recycled to the regenerator, $CO_2 + C \rightarrow 2 \, CO$, so that the overall reaction would be $C + O_2 \rightarrow CO_2$. Heat must be transferred from the exothermic cell reaction to the endothermic regeneration reaction. This process circumvents the inefficiency inherent in consuming CO obtained from a direct reaction between carbon and oxygen. Gorin and Recht (*16*) at Consolidation Coal Co. did extensive work on a high-temperature cell suitable for such applications. The integrated system combining cell and gasifier has never been operated, however.

Additional cells using SO_2 obtained from reduction of H_2SO_4 have been studied by Posner (*32*) and Randolph (*33*) and are mentioned with the redox cell work in the next section.

Redox Fuel Cells

The redox cell has probably received more attention than any other type of regenerative fuel cell. In this scheme, the electrolytes in the anode and/or cathode compartments contain ions of metals which can exist in more than one valence state. At the anode such a redox couple is oxidized, while another couple is reduced at the cathode. These couples are then regenerated by reaction with fuel or air. A typical redox cell is shown in Figure 1. Here Fe^{+2} is oxidized to Fe^{+3} at the anode and then circulated to an external reaction chamber for regeneration with the fuel. Bromine is reduced to Br^- at the cathode and externally reoxidized with air. A semipermeable membrane separates the anode and cathode compartments to prevent mixing and direct reaction of the anolyte and catholyte ions.

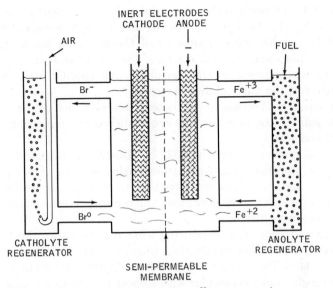

Figure 1. Schematic redox cell arrangement

Perhaps the first to attempt a redox cell was Borchers (*8*) in 1894. A single redox couple, Cu^{+2}/Cu^+, was used, with CO as the fuel and with air as the oxidant. The postulated reactions were as follows:

Anode: $\qquad\qquad\qquad$ $2\ Cl^- \rightarrow Cl_2 + 2\ e^-$

Anode regeneration: $\qquad$ $Cl_2 + CO$ (as CuCl complex) $+ H_2O$
$\qquad\qquad\qquad\qquad\qquad \rightarrow CO_2 + 2\ H^+ + 2\ Cl^-$

Cathode: $\qquad\qquad\qquad$ $2\ Cu^{+2} + 2\ e^- \rightarrow 2\ Cu^+$

Cathode regeneration: $\frac{1}{2} O_2 + 2\ Cu^+ + 2\ H^+$
$\qquad\qquad\qquad\qquad\qquad \rightarrow 2\ Cu^{+2} + H_2O.$

Copper anodes were used, and no weight loss was noted. An open-circuit voltage of 0.4 volt was measured. Tatlow (*44*) did additional work on such a cell, finding an initial voltage of 0.2, and 0.36 as soon as the coal gas fuel was admitted to the anolyte regenerator. There seems to have been considerable doubt as to the validity of this work, however. Barnes and Veesenmayer (*4*) reported that the cell voltage did not depend on the presence of CO, that no CO_2 was found in the anode gases, and that the cell was almost inactive when the copper anode was replaced by one of carbon. Later reviews (*1, 37*) tended to discredit Borchers' results.

Several other early workers used salts of variable valent metals. Welsbach (*46*) and Baur (*5*) applied the cerous-ceric couple. Keyzer (*21*) used the ferrous-ferric system, and Nernst (*27, 28*) reported that the addition of titanium, thallium, or cerium salts increased the current in a cell.

Eggert (11) measured the adsorption velocity of hydrogen and oxygen by salts of V, Mo, Co, Sn, Fe, Mn, U, and Ti. A heterogeneous reaction occurred here, with the employment of the platinum black stirrer. The rate was proportional to surface area of the stirrer and was highest when the stirrer was exposed to the gas phase. No specific fuel cell use was mentioned, but the applicability is clear.

Siemens-Schuckertwerke (39) patented a cell which oxidized hydrogen iodide to iodine. Regeneration was accomplished by contacting the iodine with fuel and water.

A novel system reported in 1921 by Rideal and Evans (37) consisted of a molten phosphate glass containing redox couples of Mn, U, V, Ce, Cr, Ni, Cu, and Fe. These were reduced by coal gas or oxidized by air. Transport properties were poor, and much more current could be drawn when the cell was stirred.

Lamb and Elder (22) conducted what was probably the first careful kinetic study of a redox regeneration process—the air oxidation of ferrous to ferric sulfate. They found the rate unimolecular with respect to oxygen partial pressure and bimolecular with respect to ferrous ion concentration. It was independent of acid concentration above $0.23M$ but increased rapidly below that. Catalysts noted were $CuSO_4$, charcoal, and platinum black, which also catalyze hydrogen peroxide decomposition; the possibility of a relationship was mentioned. This main series of measurements was made by following the change in redox potential with time. Later, a working cathode was run in the redox electrolyte with air regeneration taking place. A current of 21.5 ma./sq. cm. could be drawn at 0.606 volt vs. hydrogen.

Carson (9), at Ohio State, constructed a complete redox, fuel cell system using air on the cathode side and carbon monoxide as the fuel. The catholyte, redox couple was ferric-ferrous, and the anolyte couple was the iodine-iodide system. The flow pattern of this cell was unusual in that the same electrolyte was circulated through all the reaction zones of the system—from fuel reaction zone to anode to air oxidation zone to cathode. The result of this pattern, however, was a concentration cell which was poised at two potentials rather than at one potential as is common in concentration cells, so that a finite E_o existed, and concentration polarization was less critical. A salt bridge provided electrolytic connection between anode and cathode. Palladium was required as a catalyst for the reaction between carbon monoxide and iodine. For the air oxidation of ferrous ion, copper served as catalyst; unfortunately, solid cuprous iodide formed in the complete cell system and caused serious mechanical problems. Finally the copper was omitted, and oxygen with ozone was used as oxidant. The total cell was run for over three hours, giving open-circuit voltages of 0.26 0.33 volt and producing 0.86 ma./sq. cm. at short circuit.

Sir Eric Rideal directed work on redox cell systems at Kings College, London, from 1950 to 1955. Posner (*32*) described their attempts at anolyte regeneration by reaction with the fuel—in this case coal. Preliminary studies showed a reaction between coal and acid solution of Fe^{+3}, Cu^{+2}, and Hg_2^{+2} but not with Cr^{+3} or Sn^{+4}. Low rank coal was more reactive. A more intensive study was made on Cu^{+2}, although meaningful rate data were not obtained. Reduction of Cu^{+2} was about four times that needed to produce the amount of CO_2 evolved. Because no CO, H_2, or soluble carbon compounds were found, the formation of large quantities of solid reaction products was indicated. About 15% of the carbon present was apparently affected "without any exceptionally rapid decrease in activity." The final report of the Kings College group (*6*) included data on the reduction rate of H_2SO_4 to SO_2. Rates were greatest in acid concentrations above 80% and were independent of particle size. The activation energy was 33 kcal./mole. First- or second-order reaction kinetics could not be fitted to the data, and no analytic expression of rate compared with time or compared with extent of reaction was made. The initial rate was high (as much as 15% of the coal was consumed in the first half hour) but decreased rapidly, so that the total time of 844 hrs. was needed to oxidize 51% of the coal.

For catholyte regeneration, Posner (*30, 31*) first studied oxidation of Fe^{+2} to Fe^{+3} by air. Results were similar to those already mentioned for Lamb and Elder (*22*). The rate equation could be written as:

$$d[Fe^{+3}]/dt = k[O_2][Fe^{+2}]([H^+] - 5.5).$$

When catalyzed by charcoal of surface area $[S]$, the rate became:

$$d[Fe^{+3}]/dt = k[O_2][Fe^{+2}][H^+][S]/([Fe^{+2}] + [Fe^{+3}]).$$

The system is undesirable because the standard potential of the Fe^{+2}/Fe^{+3} couple is not close to the O_2 standard potential. As Strocchi and Foraboschi (*41*) emphasized, this couple could reach oxygen potential; however, it would be unpoised, so that a very small extent of reaction would cause a large change in redox potential. Merton-Bingham and Posner (*25*) reported work on the Br^0/Br^- couple which has a much more favorable standard potential. Finding the reaction to be catalyzed by NO, they proposed a six-step reaction scheme.

The latter group of investigators also reported work on an actual cell, using some of the redox couples which have been found to be regenerable. Their cell was 9 cm. in diameter with porous carbon electrodes placed 1 mm. apart and separated by a semipermeable membrane. Most studies were performed with Sn^{+2}/Sn^{+4} in the anolyte and Br^-/Br^0 in the catholyte. No attempt was made to regenerate the tin couple with fuel in these runs, but regeneration of the bromine was successfully carried out in a 30 × 6 cm.-packed column. In runs of up to 8 hrs., no loss of activity of the NO catalyst in the bromine regeneration unit was apparent. At

50 ma./sq. cm., the cell produced 0.28 volt with an anode polarization of 0.20 volt, a cathode polarization of 0.04 volt, and ohmic losses of 0.3 volt, as compared with open circuit. Theoretical voltage of the cell is about 0.9 volt. This is very good performance except for the ohmic loss, and present technology should be able to reduce this to about 0.04 volt at this current density.

Randolph (33), at Massachusetts Institute of Technology, worked on several redox regeneration schemes. At temperatures up to 100°C., no reaction was found between coal and Sn^{+4}. Following this, hydrogen was tried and found to reduce Sn^{+4} very slowly at 30°C. A substantial reaction was found between coal and 96% H_2SO_4 at 100°C., with initial rates as high as 0.94 mmole/min. noted for 10 grams of coal. Different types of coal exhibited strikingly different rates.

In 1959 Carson and Feldman (10) reported on redox cell work at the General Electric Co. with hydrogen used as fuel. Most of the mechanical problems of direct gas electrodes had already been solved, and advanced porous hydrogen electrodes were well-known. A hydrogen redox system still had the possible advantage, however, of being able to consume impure hydrogen (from a reformer), containing not only CO, CO_2, CH_4, etc., but also such catalyst poisons as SO_2 and H_2S. Using palladium black, Carson and Feldman were able to catalyze this fuel to react with the Ti^{+4}/Ti^{+3} couple. Their cathode couple was Br^0/Br^- catalyzed by NO. A seven-cell, 100-watt battery was built and operated continuously for 16 days with satisfactory regeneration of the anolyte and catholyte couples.

Bond and Singman (7), of the Diamond Ordnance Fuze Laboratories, studied electrode kinetics of several redox couples on electrodes of platinum, carbon, titanium, and tantalum. On porous carbon electrodes, the Ti^{+3}/TiO^{+2} and Br^-/Br_2 couples were found suitable at anode and cathode. The couples react fairly reversibly, and at 200 ma./sq. cm., polarizations of 0.18 and 0.09 volt, respectively, were found.

The Br^-/Br^0 couple for air regeneration was also investigated by Reneke (36) at the University of Florida. He followed the work on Merton-Bingham and Posner (37) but had serious problems with their analytical techniques and concluded their results were in error. Using their data, he nevertheless calculated the size of packed tower needed for the regeneration reaction. A 10 kw. unit required a tower 130 ft. high and 1.5 ft. in diameter, clearly a prohibitive size.

Austin (2) at Pennsylvania State University studied the possibility of regenerating tin and titanium couples for use at redox anodes. The Ti^{+4} ion could not be reduced by formic acid, formaldehyde, or methanol. Irreversible hydrolysis to TiO_2 occurred, too, except under conditions of high acid concentration and low temperature. With Sn^{+4} there were no hydrolysis problems, but no significant reactions with fuels occurred. Austin et al. (3) also developed equations for porous electrodes operating on redox couples, and they checked their solutions experimentally, using the Sn^{+4}/Sn^{+2} couple.

The Rome Air Development Center, Griffiss Air Force Base, N. Y., is reported (*18*) to be working on a redox cell using the Sn^{+2}/Sn^{+4} and Br_2/Br^- couples in acid solution. Commercial carbon electrodes catalyzed with platinum have been used, with NO also used as a cathode catalyst.

One of the most successful electrodes has been developed at Esso Research and Engineering Co. in the form of their nitric acid redox cathode. Nitric acid, typically at concentrations of 1% or 2% in 30% sulfuric acid, was reduced cathodically to nitric oxide and then externally regenerated to the acid by contact with air. Shropshire and Tarmy (*40*) elucidated the mechanism of the electrode reaction as follows:

$$H^+ + NO_3^- \rightleftarrows HNO_3 \text{ (undissociated)} \tag{1}$$
$$HNO_3 + 2\,NO + H_2O \rightarrow 3\,HNO_2 \text{ (slow, rate-limiting)} \tag{2}$$
$$3(HNO_2 + H^+ + e^- \rightarrow H_2O + NO) \text{ (electron transfer)} \tag{3}$$
$$\text{or} \quad 4\,H^+ + NO_3^- + 3\,e^- \rightarrow 2\,H_2O + NO \text{ (overall)} \tag{4}$$

Thus, it is seen to be a rather complex autocatalytic reaction. A polarization curve for this system on a platinum-black electrode is shown in Figure 2. The performance is much better than that obtainable from direct air electrodes with such electrolytes and temperatures, presumably because the redox electrode does not operate through a peroxide intermediate which causes considerable polarization at a direct electrode.

Regeneration of the nitric oxide proceeds by the well-known scheme:

$$2\,NO + O_2 \rightarrow 2\,NO_2$$
$$3\,NO_2 + H_2O \rightleftarrows 2\,HNO_3 + NO$$

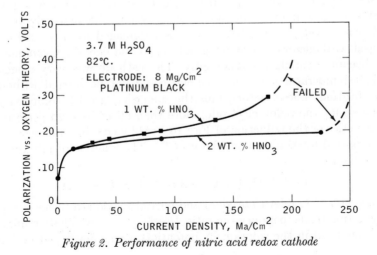

Figure 2. Performance of nitric acid redox cathode

This fairly rapid reaction could be carried out quite well in the apparatus shown in Figure 3 and was reported by Tarmy et al. (42). Air was sparged into the electrolyte where it mixed with the NO produced at the cathode. A surfactant was added so that a foam would be produced. The foam gave a large liquid-gas interface so that almost complete conversion could be effected in the small regenerator shown. Some losses of NO in the exhaust gas are inevitable. These were reduced to one mole lost for every 32 moles regenerated and could doubtless be reduced further. Total cell performance for this unit with a methanol anode is shown in Figure 4.

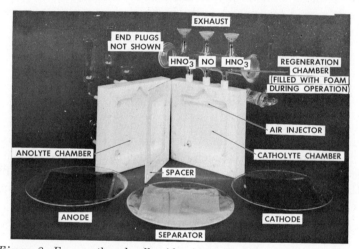

Figure 3. Esso methanol cell with air regenerated nitric acid cathode

Despite its excellent performance, the system is no longer under investigation. Like so many other regenerative schemes, it was a victim of advancing technology in more direct systems. A new, highly active anode was developed which was seriously damaged by nitric acid. New, direct-air cathodes were also being developed and one, the Cyanamid type AA1, became available commercially. The cathode was very sluggish at ambient temperatures so that the cell could not be started without external heating. These factors, plus the somewhat greater complexity and NO losses for the redox electrode, more than offset its high performance.

Kinetics of the reduction of Fe^{+3} to Fe^{+2} by coal in an aqueous slurry were reported by Matsen and Linford (24). The reaction of interest might be represented as:

$$2\ Fe^{+3} + H_2O + C \rightarrow 2\ Fe^{+2} + 2\ H^+ + C:O$$

where C and C:O refer to original and partially oxidized forms of the fuel. The reaction tends to reduce the ratio, $[Fe^{+3}]:[Fe^{+2}]$, which determines the redox potential in the solution. A potentiostat was developed (23) which

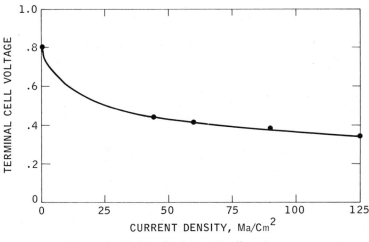

Figure 4. Methanol-nitric acid cell performance

anodically reoxidized the ferrous ion at just such a rate as to keep the redox potential of the bulk solution constant. The current supplied by the potentiostat was then directly proportional to the rate of reduction of Fe^{+3} by coal. Such a technique avoids problems of sampling and analytical procedures and is adapted to long-term unattended operation. Because the fuel reactivity changed considerably as the reaction proceeded and because the rate was potential-dependent, the potentiostat technique greatly facilitated the gathering of meaningful data on this system.

The rate (expressed as current from 1 gram of coal) *vs.* time relationship is seen in Figure 5 to consist of three, straight-line segments on a log-log plot. The initial portion of this curve had a slope of -0.4 for all conditions studied and seemed to correspond to a fairly definite amount of reaction. The second portion had a slope of -1.16; the slope of the third portion varied from run to run between -0.58 and -0.78. The rate-time relationship does not represent any simple order of reaction, but it does permit mathematical manipulation for calculating amount reacted and comparing reaction rates at equal extent of reaction.

Correlation could be made only on the first portion of the rate curve. Here R, the specific rate (i.e., at equal extent of reaction), could be calculated from the rate at one hour, k, and was equal to $(k)^{1.67}$. The value of R was found proportional to $([Fe^{+3}]/[Fe^{+2}][H^+])^{1/2}$, while k was proportional to the surface area, S. This is shown in Figure 6. The concentration dependence of R does not follow usual kinetic models. If, however, one thinks of these concentrations as determining the potential η of the solution relative to the solid fuel, then the rate may be expressed as the Tafel relationship:

$$\eta = \frac{RT}{\alpha F} \ln \frac{R}{R_o} = \frac{RT}{\alpha F} \ln \frac{I}{I_0}$$

with α, the transfer coefficient, being $\frac{1}{2}$, as it usually is for electrode reaction. This would indicate the novel phenomenon of a rate-limiting step of

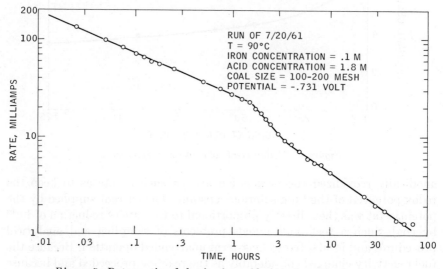

Figure 5. Rate vs. time behavior for oxidation of coal by ferric ion

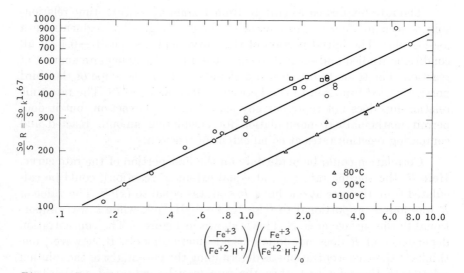

Figure 6. Dependence of coal oxidation rate at constant extent of reaction (specific rate) on reaction conditions (Subscript "o" refers to standard reaction conditions)

electron transfer, not at an electrode surface, but rather at the surface of a particle in suspension.

These results were not encouraging from the standpoint of fuel cell use. Rates were low so that only 1% of the coal could ever be oxidized in the first hour. Rates fell off rapidly with time with only 5% reaction taking place in 72 hrs., which means that utilization would be low for realistic reaction times. No reaction occurred below about 0.4 volt relative to reversible carbon electrode, and this would cause large voltage efficiency losses. It should be noted, however, that Posner (*32*) obtained much higher rates for coal redox reactions, and that he apparently used much more porous, reactive coals. The limits of temperature, particle size, and other reaction variables likewise can be extended beyond the ones of these experiments so that higher rates may be expected on that count also. Although such a fuel cell system has not proved attractive, there yet remain avenues of approach that may make it so.

Status and Outlook

When research in fuel cells surged to popularity in the generation from 1890 to 1920, systems using chemical regeneration constituted a substantial portion of the work. They were probably about as successful as direct fuel cells in trying to achieve the goal of consuming air and primary fuels such as coal and natural or manufactured gas. Lately, however, chemically regenerative cells have accounted for only a small portion of the effort. A shift in the intended uses of fuel cells is partly responsible. Large scale, power generation no longer seems close at hand for fuel cells because, thus far, fuel cells have not shown attractive efficiencies with cheap fuels, and because great strides have been made in increasing the efficiency of thermal power plants and in harnessing nuclear energy. Instead, recent emphasis has been on using fuel cells for specialized military or space applications, where cost of fuel is not of prime importance and where more expensive, highly reactive, direct fuels can logically be chosen. The new emphasis also places a premium on compactness and simplicity, putting regenerative cells at some disadvantage.

A second factor has been the many advances in direct chemical cells which have eliminated what were once strong points of regenerative operation. Problems of getting reaction at the three phase interface of gas, electrolyte, and electrode have been solved with the recent introduction of more sophisticated gas electrodes which can sustain high reaction rates. Advances in catalysis have made possible the direct use of such fuels as alcohols and hydrocarbons at reasonable polarizations. Direct fuel cell batteries have been built in compact, self-contained units which produce useful power for operating demonstration equipment. This not only attests to their advanced technology but also acts as a magnet for further support.

Finally, performance of chemically regenerative cells has hardly been spectacular. Often the intermediate reactants chosen have inherently limited the thermodynamic efficiency of the process. Howard (17) has noted, for instance, that in a regenerative iron-air cell, 77 grams of coal are needed to regenerate iron from 1 gram-mole of ferric oxide, and this can produce 0.1 kwh. of power in a cell operating at 100% efficiency. The same amount of coal would produce 0.12 kwh. in a steam-generating plant. Most intermediates react fairly well at electrodes, but regeneration rates are usually slow. When such rates are high, as with air redox couples using bromine or nitric acid, substantial amounts of the intermediate may be lost.

Thus, although chemical regeneration for fuel cell cycles has attractive features on paper, there has been no translation to practical advantages over direct fuel cells. A small effort in the area will justifiably continue, and perhaps a desirable combination of application plus system will be found. At present, however, the regenerative systems are not competitive and offer no great promise of becoming so.

Literature Cited

(1) Allmand, A. J., Ellingham, H. J. T., "The Principles of Applied Electrochemistry," Edward Arnold, London, 1931.
(2) Austin, L. G., "Redox Fuel Cells," Quarterly Progress Reports, Contract No. DA 49-186-502-ORD-917, 1960-1963.
(3) Austin, L. G., Palasi, P., Klimpel, R. R., ADVAN. CHEM. SER. 47, 35 (1965).
(4) Barnes, Veesenmayer, Z. Angew. Chem. 8, 101 (1895).
(5) Baur, E., Glaessner, A., Z. Elektrochem. 9, 534 (1903).
(6) Benjamin, A. L., Merton-Bingham, B. E., Posner, A. M., Final Report to Central Electricity Authority, United Kingdom (Nov. 25, 1955).
(7) Bond, A. P., Singman, D., D.O.F.L. Rept TR 835 (April 15, 1960).
(8) Borchers, W., Electrician 34, 139 (1894).
(9) Carson, W. N., Dissertation, Ohio State University, 1948.
(10) Carson, W. N., Feldman, M. L., Proceedings, Thirteenth Annual Power Sources Conference, p. 111, 1959.
(11) Eggert, J., Z. Elektrochem. 20, 370 (1914).
(12) Faure, C. A., German Patent 57, 315 (1891).
(13) Gorin, E., U. S. Patent 2,570,543 (1951).
(14) Ibid. 2,581,650 (1952).
(15) Ibid. 2,581,651 (1952).
(16) Gorin, E., Recht, H. L., "Fuel Cells," G. J. Young, ed., Reinhold, New York, 1960.
(17) Howard, H. C., "Chemistry of Coal Utilization," (H. H. Lowry, ed.) 2, pp. 1568–1585, John Wiley and Sons, Inc., New York, 1945.
(18) Hunger, H. H., Franke, F. R., Murphy, J. J., "Third Status Report on Fuel Cells," ASTIA No. AD 286,686, 1962.
(19) Jone, H., U. S. Patent 764,595 (1904).
(20) Jungner, E. W., British Patent 15,727 (1906).
(21) Keyzer, H. J., British Patent 3,913 (1904).
(22) Lamb, A. B., Elder, R. W., J. Am. Chem. Soc. 53, 137 (1931).

(23) Matsen, J. M., Linford, H. B., *Anal. Chem.* **34,** 142 (1962).
(24) Matsen, J. M., Linford, H. B., Paper No. L-40, ACS Meeting, Detroit, April 1965.
(25) Merton-Bingham, B. E., Posner, A. M., *J. Am. Chem. Soc.* **77,** 2634 (1955).
(26) Nernst, W., German Patent **259,241** (1911).
(27) Nernst, W., German Patent **264,025** (1913).
(28) *Ibid.* **265,424** (1913).
(29) *New Scientist* **11,** 589 (1964).
(30) Posner, A. M., *Trans. Faraday Soc.* **49,** 382 (1953).
(31) *Ibid.*, 389 (1953).
(32) Posner, A. M., *Fuel* **24,** 330 (1955).
(33) Randolph, K. B., Thesis, Mass. Inst. Tech., 1957.
(34) Rawson, W. S., British Patent **24,570** (Nov. 22, 1898).
(35) Reed, C. J., *Elect. World* **28,** 134 (1896).
(36) Reneke, W. E., Thesis, Univ. of Florida, 1961.
(37) Rideal, E. K., Evans, U. R., *Trans. Faraday Soc.* **17,** 466 (1921).
(38) Roulin, M., Lehmann, G., *C. R. Acad. Sci. Paris* **258,** 3851 (1964).
(39) Siemens-Schuckertwerke, British Patent **112** (1915).
(40) Shropshire, J. A., Tarmy, B. L., ADVAN. CHEM. SER. **47,** 153 (1965).
(41) Strocchi, P. M., Foraboschi, F. P., *Rend. Ist. Lombardo Sci. Lettere, A* **92,** 43 (1957).
(42) Tarmy, B. L., *et al.*, "Soluble Carbonaceous Fuel-Air Fuel Cell," Report No. 2, Contract DA 36-039 SC-89156, Dec. 1962: Report No. 3, Contract DA 36-039 AMC-00134(E), June 1963.
(43) Taitelbaum, I., *Z. Elektrochem.* **16,** 286 (1910).
(44) Tatlow, W., *Electrician* **34,** 344 (1895).
(45) Tourneur, H., French Patent **332,982** (1903).
(46) Welsbach, A. von, *Chem. Z.* **1,** 690 (1902).

RECEIVED November 10, 1965.

17

Electrolytically Regenerative
Hydrogen/Oxygen Fuel Cell Battery

E. FINDL and M. KLEIN

Electro-Optical Systems, Inc., Pasadena, Calif.

The regenerative H_2/O_2 cell is basically a combination of a H_2/O_2 primary fuel cell and a water electrolysis cell in one compact package. Various size experimental units have been built from single cells (6-in. diameter electrodes) to a 34-cell series unit with nominal ratings of 28 volts, 500 watts, and 21 amp.-hrs. capacity. Electrical testing has been conducted over a range of variables. Cycle life performance of 350 cycles on a test regime of 35 min. discharge and 65 min. charge has been achieved.

Electrolytically regenerative fuel cells, unlike the continuously regenerated thermal or photolytic types, are energy storage devices rather than primary energy converters. As such, they operate in a pulsed or cyclical mode in the manner of a secondary battery. In principle, any regenerative fuel-cell system can be electrolytically regenerated (recharged). However, the H_2/O_2 system appears to be the most suitable for this application, although a number of other systems have been investigated.

Electro-Optical Systems, Inc. (EOS) entered the H_2/O_2 regenerative fuel-cell field in 1960. Since that time, a great deal of progress has been made in developing the concept from a laboratory curiosity to the engineering prototype stage (*1, 2, 3*). Details of the concept and current state of the art are presented along with performance data and projections.

Technical Description

The EOS cell is basically a combination of a hydrogen/oxygen primary fuel cell and a water electrolysis cell in one compact package. During the charge mode of operation, water contained within an asbestos matrix separating the electrodes is electrolyzed to produce hydrogen at the anode and oxygen at the cathode. As gas is evolved, it is fed by appropriate manifolds to integral tankage. During discharge, the stored gases are recombined to form water, which returns to and is absorbed by the asbestos matrix. The same electrodes serve as the reacting surface for both the charge and discharge mode of operation.

Concentrated aqueous potassium hydroxide, contained in the asbestos matrix, serves as the electrolyte and the source of water for electrolysis. The quantity of electrolyte employed is such that the solution is totally absorbed by the asbestos matrix, and no free liquid exists within the system. Typically, fuel cell-grade asbestos (Johns Manville, Inc.) is utilized having a dry thickness of 0.060 in. Our standard asbestos matrix is a disc, 6 in. in diameter, weighing 27 grams (dry), and containing 32 grams of 40 weight% KOH. The asbestos mat is placed between the electrodes and is compressed during cell assembly to 0.040 in. This compression severely decreases cross leakage of H_2 and O_2 through the mat and causes a partial penetration of the electrolyte into each of the electrodes.

During charge—i.e., the electrolysis mode of operation, water is decomposed from the mat at the rate of 0.336 gram/amp. hr. of charge. Figure 1 shows residual KOH concentration as a function of amp. hrs. of charge for a standard 6-in. diameter cell.

Limitations exist as to the extent of charging, aside from the obvious one of increased resistance due to loss of ionic conductivity. Using the 32/27 ratio of electrolyte to asbestos weight, beyond $\approx$ 25 amp. hrs., cross leakage of H_2 and O_2 through the asbestos matrix becomes appreciable. This cross leakage results in water formation at the electrodes. At the limit, the water formation rate due to cross leakage equals that due to electrolysis, resulting simply in the formation of heat.

As discharge proceeds, water is formed that is absorbed by the asbestos matrix. Here too, limitations exist because too rapid formation of water results in the reaction zones being flooded and a decrease in performance. The effects and limitations of the system in regard to drying out toward the end of charge and flooding toward the end of discharge are mass transport, rate-dependent processes. Slower rates of charge and discharge allow the use of higher capacities without encountering performance fall-offs.

Because the electrodes serve both in the charge (electrolysis) and discharge (fuel cell) mode, their design criteria are somewhat different from that of an electrode used exclusively for either of the above operations. From a purely electrolysis standpoint, it is desirable to have a nearly flooded system, whereas for the primary fuel cell mode, a somewhat dryer reacting surface, maximizing the triphase reaction area, is desirable. These two criteria are in conflict. Therefore, a design compromise must be made for use in a regenerative mode, as to electrolyte quantity within the asbestos matrix, concentration of electrolyte, matrix compression, and

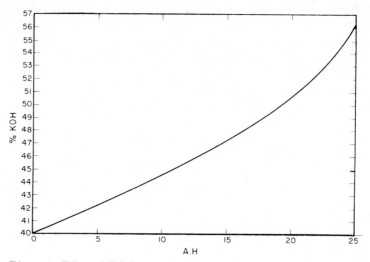

Figure 1. Effect of KOH concentration as a function of A. H. charge

electrode structure. A number of electrodes have been developed for this application. A normal type consists of a porous plaque that is fabricated by sintering carbonyl nickel powder evenly spread over a nickel screen. (The plaques employed are nominally 0.020 in. thick.) These plaques are then uniformly catalyzed with platinum black to loadings of 20 mg. Pt/sq. cm.

As opposed to primary fuel cells, the reaction zone within the regenerative cell electrodes shift in and out as the water content in the asbestos changes during the charge and discharge cycle. Therefore, fixed zone-type electrodes are not desirable. By utilizing an electrode catalyzed in depth, continual peak performance can be obtained over a longer time period of charge and discharge.

Construction principles of the EOS cell are shown schematically in Figure 2. The design employs a bipolar plate which contains integral manifold channels upon which hydrogen and oxygen electrodes are attached. The asbestos mat is placed between the bipolar plates, and a ring spacer is employed to obtain the desired compression on the asbestos. Integral manifolding allows the hydrogen and oxygen gas to flow out the backside of the electrode through the manifold and into respective gas storage compartments. In the integral gas storage tank concept, the fuel-cell stack is placed within the gas storage tanks and used to separate the hydrogen and oxygen compartments.

Figure 3 shows the bipolar plate, spacer, asbestos mat, fuel cell electrode, gas distribution screen, and the two halves of the gas tank of a prototype 75-watt, six-cell unit. Figure 4 shows the assembled 75-watt unit, which consists of six series-connected cells with valves and pressure instrumentation on the ends of the tank.

Figure 5 shows a 34-series, cell-assembled stack that is nominally rated at 500 watts. Also shown are the gas storage tanks for the unit that have an internal volume sufficient to store 21 amp. hrs. of compressed gas at 500 psig. On one end of the stack, a free floating bellows is attached.

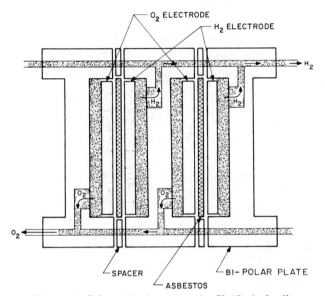

Figure 2. Schematic of regenerative H_2/O_2 fuel cell

Figure 3. Component of 75-watt, six-cell unit

Figure 4. 75-Watt fuel-cell assembly

Figure 5. 500-Watt regenerative, hydrogen-oxygen,
fuel-cell assembly

Hydrogen gas from the H_2 storage compartment is contained internally. (Externally it is positioned in the O_2 tank.) This bellows compensates for differential pressures that may arise between the two stored gases. The gases are generated in a 2:1 volume ratio, and the gas compartments are likewise designed in that ratio to maintain equal pressurization in both compartments. Slight imperfections in the volume balance are taken up by the floating bellows as cycling occurs. Typical differential pressures that are obtained with the 500-watt unit range between $\frac{1}{2}$ and 1 psi. However, differential pressures as high as 10 psi have not noticeably affected performance.

Performance Data

During the course of development, a large number of electrical tests have been conducted in order to establish performance parameters and improve the operating characteristics. The great majority of our data has been taken using a high rate charge/discharge cycle. This consists of charging for a 65-min. period and discharging for a 35-min. period, for a total of 100 min./cycle (m.p.c.). The cycle represents the battery load characteristics of a 300 nautical mile, orbiting satellite. This test cycle has been selected for use in the cycling of the regenerative fuel cell because it enables the rapid accumulation of cycle life information under a very rigorous load profile.

The normal operating temperature for the units is 70–90°C. Figure 6 shows typical individual electrode performance on a charge/discharge

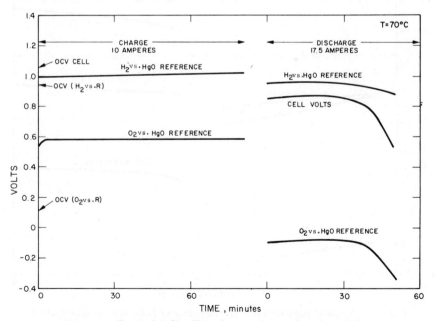

Figure 6. Typical half-cell performance as a function of time

cycle. The data were obtained by implanting a mercuric oxide reference electrode centrally located in the asbestos matrix between the hydrogen and oxygen electrodes. Therefore, individual electrode performance includes approximately one-half the IR drop of the cell. (Typical cell impedance for a 6-in. diameter cell at 70°C. is 0.005 ohm.) For the discharge portion of the tests, the discharge was continued beyond the normal period, and a condition of flooding and rapid fall-off in performance was induced. As can be seen, the oxygen electrode was the electrode that contributed to the major portion of the performance fall-off. Also, throughout the entire cycle, it is the oxygen electrode that represents the major polarization loss.

Figure 7 shows current *vs.* voltage data for a similar cell set-up employing a reference electrode as described previously. Here again, it can be seen that the oxygen electrode represents the major source of inefficiency and polarization loss.

Figure 8 shows the voltage performance of a cell subjected to a test cycle to obtain maximum capacity. During the high rate discharge, the cell was capable of delivering 21 amp. hrs. but showed a rapid drop-off in voltage, indicating flooding. Elevated temperature (125°C.) data are shown in Figure 9. It can be seen that peak power is achieved at approximately 100 amp., which represents 555 ma./sq. cm.

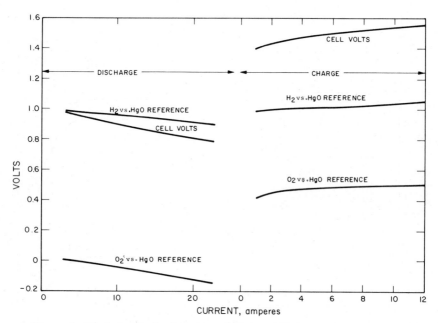

Figure 7. Typical polarization characteristics of H_2O_2 regenerative fuel cell (Cell No. 85) (T = 70°C.)

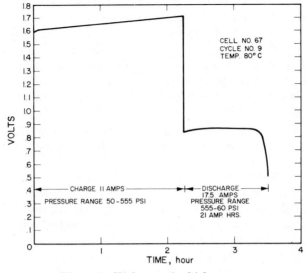

Figure 8. High capacity high rate test

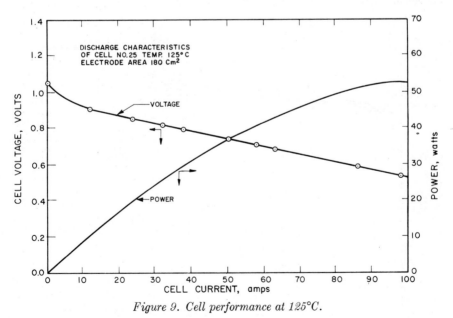

Figure 9. Cell performance at 125°C.

To demonstrate multicell performance capabilities, a six-cell unit, nominally rated at 75 watts, was assembled and subjected to cycle life testing. Figure 10 shows the effect of a long-term cycling of the unit. As can be seen, cycling increased the charge voltage and decreased discharge voltage. The degradation in performance observed is attributed to the gradual deterioration in performance of the oxygen electrode. This occurred as a result of the oxidation of the porous nickel substrate in these electrodes. Removal or masking of this nickel substrate offers the promise of obtaining increased cycle life. However, long-term cycling of cells employing masked types of electrodes has not yet been conducted.

A 34-series cell, nominal 500-watt unit, has also been subjected to electrical tests to demonstrate feasibility of a 28-volt system. (The unit tested was constructed as shown in Figure 5 and is described in the previous section.)

Figure 11 shows a typical charge/discharge cycle on 100 min. orbit test regime. The linear pressure rise and decline as a function of capability shown is one of the attractive features of the regenerative H_2/O_2 battery concept. Capacity or state of charge is determinable quite simply by measuring tank pressure. Figure 12 shows voltage and power *vs.* current data on the same unit. Due to test equipment limitations, the maximum current density obtained to date on the 500-watt unit has been limited to 1300 watts. However, it is felt that power levels to 2000 watts can be achieved with the 500-watt unit. Figure 13 shows a slow rate charge and discharge of the unit, delivering in excess of 600-watt hrs. under the test condi-

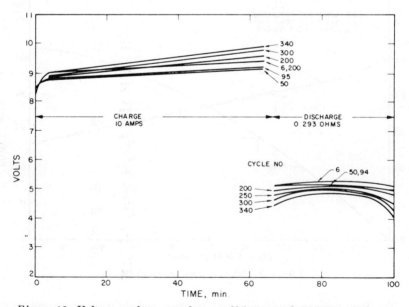

Figure 10. Voltage performance data at different cycles of 75-watt battery
(S/N107)

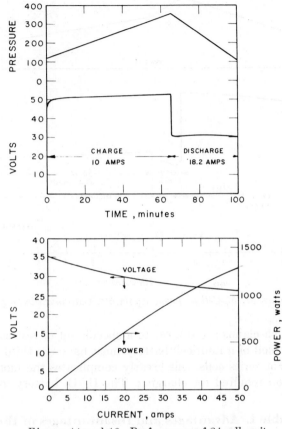

Figures 11 and 12. Performance of 34-cell unit

tions shown. This cycle is being considered for use on the Voyager Lander (Mars probe) program. (It was made after 72 hrs. of cycling the 500-watt unit on the 100 min. cycle.) Although not shown, 21 amp. hrs. of capacity were obtained from the battery under this test regime.

Features of the H₂/O₂ Secondary Battery

As with any other device, there are both good and poor features of the H_2/O_2 regenerative fuel cell. These are shown as advantages and disadvantages in Table I. The advantages are quite remarkable when compared with conventional batteries.

State of charge indication is quite a dilemma in conventional batteries because charge and discharge efficiencies are quite variable. Three electrode batteries have been built that supposedly can monitor state of

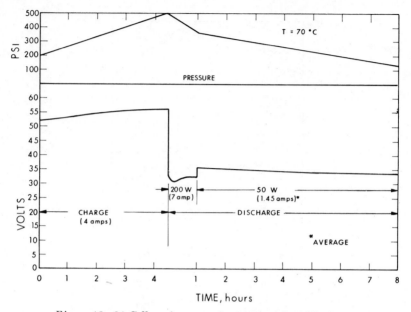

Figure 13. 34-Cell performance for 600 watt-hour discharge

charge, but such claims are subject to a specific set of test conditions. In addition, each cell of a multicell battery must have the third electrode or it is useless. For series cells, this greatly complicates the monitoring and instrumentation required for charging. The H_2/O_2 battery, on the other

Table I. Advantages and Disadvantages of the H_2/O_2 Regenerative Fuel Cell

Advantages	*Disadvantages*
1. Battery has a simple state of charge indicator—i.e., pressure	1. Low watt hr./cu. ft. ratio
2. Long potential cycle life at full depth of discharge	2. Poor ambient temperature operation capability
3. Very high charge/discharge rate capability	3. Low charge retention
4. High watt hr./lb. ratio	4. High pressure operation
5. Good voltage regulation	
6. High overload capability	
7. High shock stability potential	
8. High temperature operation potential	
9. No problem of series cell balance	

hand, requires only a simple pressure switch to control the charging process. Further, by monitoring, pressure state of charge can be determined directly at any stage of the charge or discharge process.

In conventional batteries, cycle life is limited by changes in the physical or chemical states of the electrode reactants, such as dendritic growths, flaking off of reactive components, and irreversible side reactions. As charge and discharge proceeds, the density changes in the active material causing flaking, crumbling, and loss of active material. Full utilization cannot be made of all the active material because some is covered over and buried in the depths of the electrodes.

These conditions necessitate the use of shallow depth of discharges in conventional batteries to obtain long cycle life. Because the reactive components of the EOS cell are in the gas phase, such limitations will not apply and less than full depth of discharge has no significance in relation to cycle life.

Unlike conventional batteries, charge rates of the H_2/O_2 cell can be as rapid as desired, limited in practice only by the heat rejection capability of the system and charge-power, equipment limitations. Where conventional battery charge rates must be kept below the point at which the water electrolyte decomposes, the H_2/O_2 cell operates by water decomposition. During discharge, the H_2/O_2 fuel-cell mode of operation is capable of sustaining 2–3 times the current density of standard batteries with little change in performance.

A critical requirement of all batteries is the energy density they are capable of producing. The literature contains numbers ranging from 0.5 to 100 watt hrs./lb. for conventional batteries. For practical space applications as secondary batteries, the useful watt hr./lb. values are 1–2 for Ni-Cd cells, 5–8 for Ag-Cd cells, and 8–12 for Ag-Zn cells. The present state of the art indicates a 10–12 watt hr./lb. figure with a factor of two improvement probable within two years.

Voltage regulation of the EOS cell is excellent. There is an essentially linear, low rate decline of voltage as a function of current density over a wide range. Silver batteries, on the other hand, suffer from a step function voltage owing to the conversion of silver peroxide to silver in steps.

Because of the excellent voltage-current relationships inherent with a well-designed H_2/O_2 cell, high overloads can be readily handled. Our data indicate an overload capability of $\approx 3{:}1$ over nominal can be achieved without unduly taxing the battery.

Because the EOS cell does not have any pressed powder reactants to handle or store, mechanical vibration or shock cannot cause flaking off of reactants. Further, the bipolar plate design used in the EOS cell eliminates the miltiplicity of wire connections used in conventional cells which are subject to vibration damage.

A major difference between the H_2/O_2 battery and conventional batteries is the operating temperature range. Whereas most batteries have optimum performance at or slightly above ambient temperature, the H_2/O_2 cell shows performance improvement with increasing temperature. The EOS cell is presently limited to 300°F. operation because of rubber seal deterioration. However, operation to 400°F. should be attainable with different high temperature seals.

Because of variations in cell capacity during fabrication and differences in charge/discharge efficiency during operation, standard batteries are subject to cell capacity variations. This variation prevents utilization of the total capacity of such cells and, in the extreme, can cause cell reversal in a series stack. The EOS cell, owing to the common manifolding and tankage design, is not subject to this form of failure.

The negative features of the H_2/O_2 battery are primarily the result of the gas phase mode of operation. On a comparative basis, the EOS cell occupies three times the volume of a conventional cell owing to the volume of the reactant gases. Gas phase oxygen reactivity is also greatly affected by cell temperature. Below roughly 50°C., performance of the H_2/O_2 cell is poor at other than low discharge rates. Charge retention over extended periods of time is limited because of diffusion and chemical recombination of the reactant gases at the electrodes. For practical purposes, charge retention times beyond a few weeks are not deemed suitable. Another inherent gas phase problem is the requirement for high pressure operation to reduce volume. High pressure increases leakage and diffusion problems. To date, however, operation to 500 psig has not posed any major problem.

An analysis of currently available data indicates that performance capabilities can be improved considerably. Projections are shown on Table II. The primary region for attaining improved performance is

Table II. Performance Projections of the H_2/O_2 Battery

	1966	1967
1. Watt hrs./lb.	15	25
2. Amp. hrs./lb.	18	20
3. Operation temperature (maximum)	300°F.	500°F.
4. Power level	1000 watts	2500 watts
5. Thermal sterilization capability	Sterilizable	Sterilizable
6. Radiation sensitivity	Insensitive	Insensitive
7. Cycle life	500	2000
8. Operating current density	100 ma./sq. cm.	200 ma./sq. cm.
9. Overload capability	3:1	4:1

lowering battery component weights and upping electrode performance. Current research indicates large improvements in electrode performance are achievable and can quite probably be incorporated in the regenerative fuel cell. Weight reduction analyses also indicate that by using higher strength to weight tankage and reducing component thicknesses, a large weight saving can be achieved.

Conclusions

The feasibility of the electrolytically regenerative, H_2/O_2 fuel-cell concept has been demonstrated. Engineering prototypes have been and are being developed to improve electrical performance and cycle life. The principal mode of degradation exhibited to date is the oxidation of the cathode nickel substrate used to support the platinum catalyst. Several alternative modes of cathode fabrication are being investigated.

Work reported herein was supported by the National Aeronautics and Space Administration, Contract NAS-3-2781. The assistance of Harvey Schwartz and Daniel Soltis in conducting this development program is gratefully acknowledged.

Literature Cited

(1) Findl, E., Klein, M., "Hydrogen-Oxygen Electrolytic Regenerative Fuel Cells," NASA CR-54805, NASA CR-54461, NASA CR-54380, 1965.
(2) Frank, H. A., "Electrically Regenerative Hydrogen-Oxygen Fuel Cell," Am. Rocket Soc. Paper 2563-62, September 1962.
(3) Ludwig, F. A., "Regenerative Hydrogen-Oxygen Fuel Cell," Am. Rocket Soc. Paper 1303-60, September 1960.

RECEIVED November 23, 1965.

INDEX